New Angiogenesis Research

NEW ANGIOGENESIS RESEARCH

ROBERTA V. ZUBAR
EDITOR

Nova Biomedical Books
New York

For permission to use material from this book please contact us:
Telephone 631-231-7269; Fax 631-231-8175
Web Site: http://www.novapublishers.com

Library of Congress Cataloging-in-Publication Data

New angiogenesis research / Roberta V. Zubar (editor).
p. ; cm.
Includes index.
ISBN 1-59454-239-2 (hardcover)
1. Neovascularization.
[DNLM: 1. Neovascularization, Physiologic.] I. Zubar, Roberta V.
QP106.6.N48 2004
612.1'3--dc22 2004030810

Published by Nova Science Publishers, Inc. ✣ New York

Contents

Preface

Angiogenesis (angio'gen'esis) — the growth of new blood vessels — is an important natural process occurring in the body, both for health and as related to disease. Angiogenesis occurs in the healthy body to help heal wounds and to help restore blood flow to tissues after injury or insult. In females, angiogenesis also occurs during the monthly reproductive cycle (to rebuild the uterus lining, to mature the egg during ovulation) and during pregnancy (to build the placenta, the circulation between mother and fetus). The healthy body controls angiogenesis through a series of "on" and "off" switches. The main "on" switches are known as angiogenesis-stimulating growth factors. The main "off switches" are known as angiogenesis inhibitors. When angiogenic growth factors are produced in excess of angiogenesis inhibitors the balance is tipped in favor of blood vessel growth. When inhibitors are present in excess of stimulators, angiogenesis is stopped. The normal, healthy body maintains a perfect balance of angiogenesis modulators. In general, angiogenesis is "turned off" by the production of more inhibitors than stimulators. Tumor angiogenesis is the proliferation of a network of blood vessels that penetrates into cancerous growths, supplying nutrients and oxygen and removing waste products. Tumor angiogenesis actually starts with cancerous tumor cells releasing molecules that send signals to surrounding normal host tissue. This signaling activates certain genes in the host tissue that, in turn, cause proteins to encourage growth of new blood vessels. This new book examines its angiogenesis within the context of theory and its applications to cancer treatment.

The scientific study of angiogenesis has increased exponentially over the last thirty years giving the impression that this is a new field of study. In reality, the connection between disease, such as cancer, and blood vessels was made in antiquity. As discussed in Chapter I, in 1971, Judah Folkman presented his theory that tumours were dependent upon vessel formation to the Harvard Medical School in Boston. By doing so he placed angiogenesis at the centre of tumour biology. From Dr Folkman's laboratory, angiogenesis research has exploded across the world.

The Rho GTPases comprise a subfamily of the Ras-superfamily of small GTP-binding proteins. The Rho subfamily is comprised of a group of 23 monomeric G proteins which have diverse roles in normal and malignant cells. Chapter II reviews the current understanding of the role of Rho proteins in angiogenesis. The authors will also provide evidence demonstrating that angiogenic factor expression in the MDA-231 and MDA-231-BO (bone metastatic variant) breast cancer cell lines is differentially regulated by the Rho proteins.

In the early 1980's, scientists discovered a gas molecule, nitric oxide [NO], previously considered to be merely atmospheric pollutant, is a critical signaling molecule for endothelium-dependent relaxing in blood vessel. Since then, a great scientific advance has been made to understand how and why this gas is made in the body. In Chapter III, the authors will give a general review of latest advance on the gene expression pattern of nitric oxide synthase [NOS] in tumors and its possible role in tumour angiogenesis.

Hemostasis refers to the physiological systems that maintain circulating blood fluidity under normal conditions, though primed to react rapidly to prevent blood loss following vascular injury. Four fundamental components comprise the hemostatic system: (1) the endothelium, (2) blood platelets, and the (3) coagulation and (4) fibrinolytic systems. Each of these systems has been shown to influence angiogenesis, though varied and as yet not fully understood. Chapter IV first provides an overview of hemostasis. Second, the complex relationship between hemostasis and cancer and the similarities between hemostatic and angiogenic processes are discussed. Third, the known positive and negative hemostatic regulators of angiogenesis are identified and the potential regulatory functions of the key components are highlighted. Finally, the application of anti-hemostatic agents as potential treatment strategies and future directions are discussed in the context of relevant experimental studies.

Microvessels are composed of two types of cells, endothelial cells and pericytes. Pericytes are elongated cells of the mesodermal origin, which partially surround the endothelial cells of small vessels. As pericytes contain contractile muscle filaments on their endothelial cell side, they have been regarded for a long time just as microvascular counterparts of smooth muscle cells, and implicated in the regulation of capillary tone. In Chapter V, pericyte biology and molecular mechanisms of pericyte loss or dysfunction in angiogenesis-related disorders such as diabetic angiopathy and tumor growth and expansion is discussed.

Angiogenesis involves proliferation, migration and differentiation of endothelial cells in an organized fashion and is most likely modulated by polypepetide growth factors and integrin-extracellular matrix interactions. The vascular endothelial growth factor (VEGF) family of proteins and their receptors have been shown, in extensive biological and genetic studies, to be fundamental regulators in signaling angiogenesis and lymphangiogenesis. As presented in Chapter VI, the biochemical and physiological aspects of two groups of new molecules isolated from snake venom that affect angiogenesis. As explained in Chapter VII, the proliferation and motility of vascular endothelial cells (ECs) are critical steps in angiogenesis and are strictly controlled by different extracellular signals. Among mitogens, peptides binding to tyrosine kinase receptors (i.e. VEGFs and FGFs) are well known and released by several cell types, including ECs and tumor cells. The binding of mitogens to their specific receptors triggers intracellular signalling cascades, involving a number of messengers working in a sort of network. In particular, in this chapter, the authors describe the increases of calcium levels in the cytosol, a universal, evolutionary conserved and highly versatile signal involved in the regulation of EC's proliferation and motility.

Inflammatory responses are often associated with acquisition of malignant characteristics in various human tumors. In Chapter VIII, the focus is on the idea that inflammatory angiogenesis is a critical component of tumor progression. Inflammatory angiogenesis may confer a specific microenvironment on each tumor, resulting in characteristic formation of stroma in the tumor. The chapter also discusses the anticancer therapeutic potential of molecular targets or cells appearing during the inflammatory angiogenesis. Diagnostic strategies based on imaging studies for tumor angiogenesis in lung cancer are complex. The aim of the study presented in Chapter IX was to evaluate the prevalence of VEGF-related tumor angiogenesis in lung cancer using contrast-enhanced dynamic computed tomography (CT). Increased CT measurements of tumor enhancement and arterial perfusion are predictive indicators of VEGF-related tumor angiogenesis in lung cancer that can be elicited by incorporating either CT measurement in contrast-enhanced CT into existing imaging protocols for preoperative evaluation.

As reported in Chapter X, specific expression manner of main angiogenic factors and the linked angiogenic transcription factor was studied in each gynecological cancer to create new strategies of anti-angiogenic therapy in order to avoid recruitment of alternative pathways as a form of tolerance. Chapter XI discusses how Vascular Endothelial Growth Factor (VEGF) an endothelial cell mitogen, plays a crucial role in physiological and pathological angiogenesis. The regulation of the mechanism leading to tumour angiogenesis is complex and depends on multiple and interactive factors between cells and extracellular matrix. Extracellular proteolysis has been implicated in many of these processes in particular those belonging to matrix metalloproteinases, including the 72 kDa gelatinase A/type IV collagenase (MMP-2) and the 92 kDa gelatinase B/type IV collagenase (MMP-9). In particular MMP-9 was recently discovered as a key regulator of angiogenesis.

Nitric oxide (NO) is a potent biological mediator which plays a key role in physiological as well as pathological processes including inflammation and cancer. The role of NO in tumor biology remains incompletely understood, although several studies indicate that this molecule plays an important role in neoplastic growth, being involved in tumor cell invasiveness, promotion of tumor angiogenesis and suppression of host anti-tumor defense. In Chapter XII, the authors review the clinical relevance of the NO pathway in HNSCC, focusing on its role as angiogenic factor. Our knowledge on cancerogenesis has increased dramatically. Now, we better know how it survives, grows and metastasizes. We are switching from rather crude therapies like surgery, radiotherapy and chemotherapy to finely engineered, free of side effects and specific ones in the field of oncology. Besides developing cytotoxic agents, new anti-tumoral mechanisms inspired from our knowledge on cancer cell have been engineered. New biological agents targeting some critical steps of cancer cell survival are emerging everyday and are presented in Chapter XIII.

The progression of synovitis in rheumatoid arthritis (RA) is characterized by a pronounced tumor-like expansion of the synovium. Chapter XIV will discuss the biology of these angiogenic and angiostatic factors, and their expression and regulation in the context of chronic inflammatory arthritis such as RA and experimental arthritis such as collagen-induced arthritis.

In: New Angiogenesis Research
Editor: Roberta V. Zubar, pp. 1-17

ISBN 1-59454-239-2

Chapter I

The History and Development of Angiogenesis Research

Jonathan Charles Goddard[1,*], Christopher Derek Sutton[1], Roger Clive Kockelbergh[1] and Kenneth John O'Byrne[2]
[1]University Hospitals of Leicester NHS Trust, UK
[2]St James's Hospital Dublin, Eire

Abstract

The scientific study of angiogenesis has increased exponentially over the last thirty years giving the impression that this is a new field of study. In reality, the connection between disease, such as cancer, and blood vessels was made in antiquity. A greater understanding of the microvasculature was developed during the Nineteenth Century; neovascularisation associated with tumour growth was recognized.

A body of evidence from experiments using transparent chambers, from the 1930's to the 1960's supported the theory that tumours controlled their blood supply. Subsequent work by Gimbrone et al using tumours implanted into rabbit irises confirmed this.

In 1971, Judah Folkman presented his theory that tumours were dependent upon vessel formation to the Harvard Medical School in Boston. By doing so he placed angiogenesis at the centre of tumour biology. From Dr Folkman's laboratory, angiogenesis research has exploded across the world. It is certainly fair to say that the work of Judah Folkman began the modern revolution in angiogenesis research. However, it should not be forgotten that this was based on the work of many scientists over the preceding one hundred years.

* Correspondence concerning this article should be addressed to Mr Jonathan C. Goddard, FRCS Department of Urology Leicester General Hospital dolen Road Leicester. LE5 4PW jonathan@jcgoddard.freeserve.co.uk.

Introduction

A simple online search revealed that in 2003 there were 3381 articles in the medical literature related to angiogenesis. In the first four months of 2004, 1020 have already been cited on Medline. Over the past few years there has been an explosion in the area of angiogenesis research; the upward trend beginning in the 1970's figure 1. This would suggest to many, a very modern field of research. Most authors trace its origins back to the early work of Judah Folkman in the late 1960's and early 1970's with some paying lip service to Hertig who first used the term angiogenesis in 1935 [1]. Although it is true that Folkman is responsible for this surge in angiogenesis research related to modern practice, evidence of the connection between the vasculature and health and disease can be found much earlier.

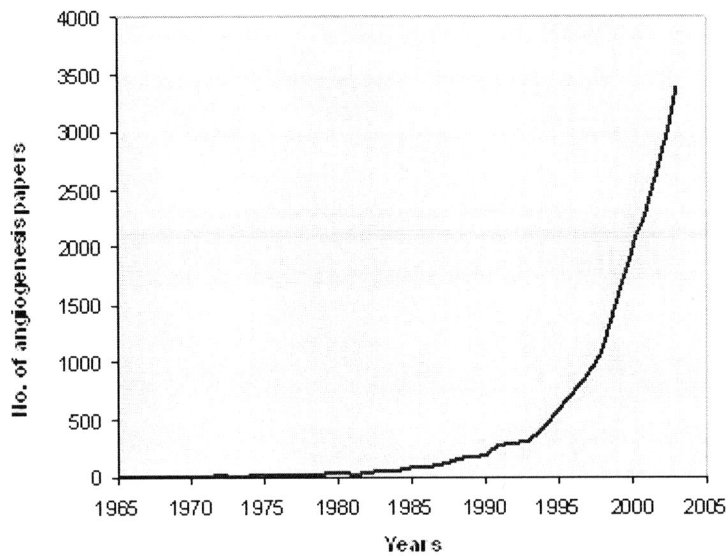

Figure 1. Plot of number of articles relating to angiogenesis cited on Medline per year from 1965 to 2003.

In this chapter we outline the progress of angiogenesis research giving both a timeline and painting a story of development. A study of this unfolding field is intended to give the modern day angiogenesis researcher a background from which to begin work. It is also intended to laud the work of early scientists who struggled to unfold the complexities of angiogenesis without the benefit of a significant canon of work to build upon.

The Association Between Vascularity and Disease

Aulus Cornelius Celsus (25 BC-40 AD), writing at the time of Christ, is credited with describing the cardinal signs of inflammation, calor (heat), rubor (redness), tumor (swelling) and dolor (pain). In ancient medicine disease was seen as an imbalance of the four humours of the body, blood, phlegm, bile and black bile. Inflammation they attributed to an excess of blood and in some respects they were quite correct. However, the circulation of the blood and the concept of the microvasculature was not elucidated until the work of William Harvey (1578-1657) in the Seventeenth Century and so in ancient Rome and Greece, no link was made between disease and the function of the blood vessels [2].

Ambroise Paré (1510-1590), the Sixteenth Century French surgeon, discussed the use of cautery in the management of disease in his book, *The Practise of Chirurgery, and the use of Three and Fifty instruments* [3]. This included the use of cautery in the management of cancer. Indeed, Paré writes, "... the *Cancer* above all Tumours hath most need of the actual Cautery...". In the English translation of 1634, the word cancer and the word crab were freely interchanged. Paré explains that, "... the fashion of a Crab doth represent the horrid forme [sic] of that Ulcer." At the end of his description he included a picture of a crab so the practitioner might know how to recognise a cancer figure 2. The derivation of the word cancer, in its medical context, stems from the similarity of this disease (particularly cancer of the breast) to the body and projecting legs of a crab. This singular appearance represents the profound and abnormal vascularity of these tumours. Thus it may be seen, the association with cancers and their peculiar blood supply has long been recognised; at least macroscopically.

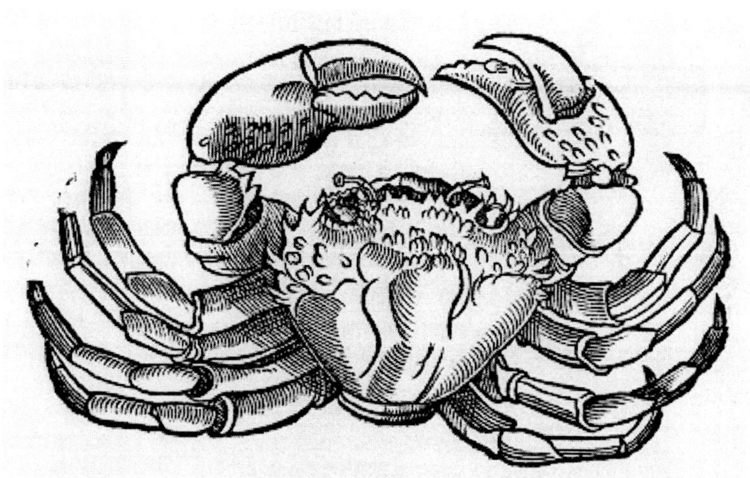

Figure 2. Cancer depicted as a crab by Paré.

John Hunter (1728-1793) the Eighteenth Century surgeon and scientist studied the seasonal growth of reindeer the antlers of the Fallow Deer (Cervus dama). He noted the associated early growth appearance of new blood vessels to supply the growing antlers, observing "a soft membranous pulp shooting out from this knob [the early sprouting antler from the deer's skull], which is extremely vascular" [4]. In general, he remarked that vessels, "would appear to have more powers of perfecting themselves, when injured, than any other part of the body; for their use is almost immediate and constant, and it is they which perform the operation of restoration on the other parts, therefore they themselves must first be perfect" [5]. This observation underpins the whole concept of angiogenesis, in that, it is a requirement for growth whether that growth be good or bad. As such John Hunter was a pioneer in the study of angiogenesis.

In the mid Nineteenth Century, Karl Thiersch (1822-1895), working in Leipzig Germany, demonstrated a vigorous formation of new vessels in the stroma of carcinomas. Using vessel injection techniques, he discovered that these new vessels originated from pre-existing capillaries [6].

Theodore Bithroth (1829-1894), the great Nineteenth Century German surgeon and scientist, noted that in the youngest parts of tumours there were numerous fine vessels and vascular networks, whereas the older areas of tumours were associated with wider, thrombosed and atrophied vessels [7].

In the early part of the Twentieth Century a series of authors performed descriptive experiments relating the presence or growth of vessels to pathological phenomena such as wound healing or tumour expansion.

On 23rd October 1907, Professor E. Goldmann of Freiburg gave a lecture to The Royal Society of Medicine in London [8]. In it he outlined his work and theories on the associations of cancers and blood vessels. He recorded the phenomenon that the normal regular distribution of blood vessels is disturbed by the invading growth of a cancer leading to chaotic irregularity. He noted the extensive new formation of vessels in the growing tumour, particularly at the periphery, this he called "Gefässunruhe".

In experiments on mice he injected Indian Ink into their vasculature which, he said, enabled him to study the number, form and width of new vessels. He described a common feature of transplanted experimental tumours. As soon as they begin to grow, "a great commotion is produced in the system of surrounding blood vessels." He also correlatedfelt the degree of this vascular reaction was related to the vascularity power of the host tissue to react against the cancer. Similar studies were carried out at about the same time by Bashford and colleagues [9].

In 1927 Warren Lewis published a descriptive study of the vascular patterns of tumours in laboratory mice models [10]. Under ether anaesthesia, 50-100ml of 3% Indian Ink in Locke solution was injected into the aorta via an incision in the heart. He used the method previously described by Goldmann [11]. Tumours were fixed in formalin and sections dehydrated and cleared in Eyclashymer fluid before being mounted in balsam. These specimens allowed Lewis to describe the vascular characteristics of a fibrosarcoma, a spindle cell sarcoma, a round cell sarcoma, a breast adenofibroma and an adenocarcinoma.

He concluded that different tumours had different vascular patterns and suggested these characteristics may be useful in diagnosis. He also noted from studies of tumour necrosis, that the blood vessels did not determine the growth of the tumour; rather the tumour determined the growth and pattern of vessels.

In 1931 Clark perfected the implantation of transparent chambers in animals allowing the study of real time vascularisation [12]. Ide, Baker and Warren, in 1939 inserted fragments of epithelioma into a rabbit ear using a Sandison-Clark chamber. They demonstrated neovascularisation of the implanted tumours and not the controls. Thus they pre-empted the elegant and much referenced experiments of Gimborne et al three decades later [13].

Lingren and Docent studied the angio-architecture of human tumours acquired at surgery or post-mortem [11]. Frozen sections, cut at 200µm, were stained with Lepehne's stain which colours erythrocytes brown-black; no counterstain was used. This achieved a map of vessels on a pale background. Adjacent sections of tissue were fixed in paraffin and stained with Haematoxylin and Eosin, Weingert's stain, Gieson-Hansen's stain or modified Mallory stain for comparison of the cyto-architecture.

The authors claimed their method gave similar results to dye injection but with less distortion of vessels due to rupture or dilatation caused by the pressure of dye injection. For study, the sections were photographed at x25 magnification with a Buschs' Citophot camera. X-ray angiography was also used to study tumour vessels; Lindgren worked together with a roentgenologist called Billing.

Lindgren and Docent concluded that tumour vessels develop from pre-existing capillaries in a process that differed from fetal vasculogenesis. They quote Goldman's theory that tumours exert an angiogenic influence and suppose that this could be due to certain substances produced by the tumours. They found that the vascular architecture "differed greatly from the normal tissue" in less differentiated tumours. They also felt that the tumour stroma affected the tumour vessel development. Although higher grade of tumour was related to decreased vascular organisation no mention is made of vessel number or density in this context.

In 1941, Harry Greene published a study on heterologous transplantation of mammalian tumours [14]. He described the transplantation of rabbit adenocarcinomas (H-31) into the anterior chambers of guinea pig eyes. A pinkish colouration was seen in the tumour after around two weeks indicating successful tumour take; this represented early neovascularisation. Visible vascularisation was usually seen by the third week. Occasionally, tumour growth was delayed (up to 110 days). Greene noted that this latent period was associated with a lack of vascularisation.

In 1945, Algire and Chalkley studied the vascular reaction of host tissue to tumour growth [15]. Vessels were studied in mice by the use of a transparent chamber implanted in a skin flap. They qualified vascularity, defining it as "the percentage of the volume measured that consists of functional vessels." The method used was based on geometric probability. They applied Chalkley's method of repeated random presentation of a point to the vascular pattern, counting the number of hits (that is when a point falls upon a vessel) [16]. The vascular level was obtained by measurement in 100 microscopic fields and represents the vascularity of the tissues.

They compared vascular growth in wounds, in implanted benign tissue and in implanted sarcomas and carcinomas. New vessel growth was seen at three days in cancers and six days in benign lesions. They concluded that the tumours produced a specific substance which induces vessel growth.

Algire and Chalkley specifically looked at the vascular reactions of benign and malignant tissue implanted into a transparent skin-flap chamber of a mouse [15]. Growth of implanted mammary gland carcinomas only began after new capillary sprouts appeared in adjacent tissue. When compared to wound healing and implantation of benign tissue they observed the tumour implants had an outstanding capacity to elicit continued growth of new capillaries from the host. Neovascularisation occurred much sooner in tumour implants (three days) than with wound healing or benign tissue implants (six days).

In his treatise Il Cancro, published in 1946, Pietro Rondoni, Professor of Pathology at the University of Milan wrote that: "a tumor acts both angioplastically and angiotactically, in other words it promotes the formation of new vessels and attracts vascular outgrowths (capillaries and pluripotent perivasal cells) so as to build up and shape a stroma of its own, a newly formed stroma. It must thus be unreservedly admitted that tumors are partly vascularized by the already existing network of vessels around them. As in other pathological processes, therefore, such neoformation as takes place is a vascular neoformation from budding of the existing capillaries" [17]. Thus Rondoni hypothesises that a cancer induces the formation of new blood vessels from those that already surround it [18].

The next step in the history of angiogenesis understanding was the realisation that the luxuriant vascularity of many solid tumours was not purely a consequence of malignant growth; it was a necessity of it for that growth. It is now accepted that a neoplasm, like the developing embryo, requires oxygen and nutrition for continued growth and survival. Tumour induction and development to a very small size (some early in-situ carcinomas contain fewer than 106 cells [19]) may proceed without a specific blood supply but once a tumour is 2 to 3mm in size it can no longer survive by diffusion alone for provision of nutrients and removal of waste products. For a tumour to continue to grow, invade locally and metastasise, a blood supply must be provided. A neoplastic cell line, therefore, must be able to induce angiogenesis in order to survive and develop into a cancer.

It was Judah Folkman in 1971 who proposed that vessels were absolutely essential for tumour growth and that angiogenesis was a fundamental requirement for the growth, progression and metastasis of cancer [20], figure 3. The evidence for this was based on animal model experiments by him and by scientistis working in this field over the preceding 30 years.

Figure 3. Judah Folkman.

In 1966 Folkman et al developed an isolated organ perfusion system to provide a vascular bed for the study of tumour growth [21]. They found that after a week and a half there was loss of endothelial cells. After this time tumour implants grew only to 2-3mm and no further but expand rapidly after transplantation onto mice [19;22].

Gimbrone et al investigated the existence of a fundamental relationship between angiogenesis and the ability of a tumour to grow malignantly. They found that prevention of neovascularisation led to tumour dormancy [22]. Brown-Pearce rabbit epithelioma was implanted into the eyes of male New Zealand rabbits. Tumour was placed either on the iris or in the avascular anterior chamber of the eye. Tumour growth and vascularity were observed.

In the iris implants, a characteristic growth pattern was seen. For the first five days there was only slow growth of tumour. At between five and eight days, vessels became visible within the tumour implant. This was associated with significant increase in size and was followed by exponential growth of the tumour to fill the entire anterior chamber. Once the eye was filled with tumour, the rate of growth deteriorated, but growth continued, if left, until rupture of the globe. This growth pattern is described by a sigmoid curve revealing the tri-phasic growth of an early pre-vascular phase, a rapid growing vascular phase and a slower late growth phase. The rate of growth of the vascular phase was ten times that of the pre-vascular phase figure 4.

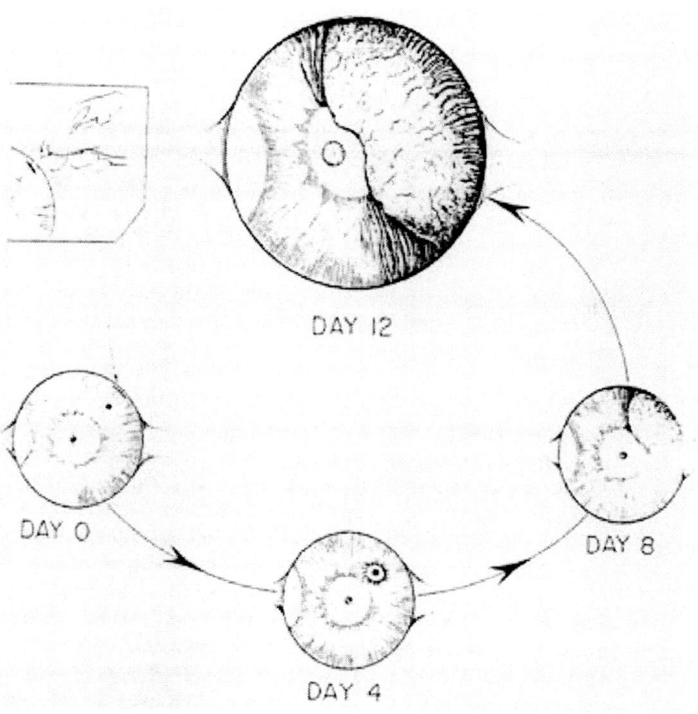

Figure 4. The Rabbit iris experiment of Gimbrone et al. From: Gimbrone MAJ, Leapman SB, Cotran RS, Folkman J: Tumor dormancy in vivo by prevention of neovascularization. *Journal of Experimental Medicine* 1972; 136: 261-276.

Tumour implants in the avascular anterior chamber failed to vascularise, remaining small pearly white masses. On careful inspection these implants underwent a biphasic growth pattern. During the first six to eight days there was slight increase in size to four times their initial volume. The final mean volume was $0.56mm^3$ (+/- 0.24SD) and none attained a volume greater than $1mm^3$. This growth corresponded to the pre-vascular phase of the iris implants.

Microscopic examination of the anterior chamber tumours at 16, 34 and 44 days confirmed their avascularity.

Reimplantation of anterior chamber tumours into the irises of fresh rabbits caused the tumours to grow in a vascularising tri-phasic pattern. Human retinoblastomas, which metastasise to the avascular anterior chamber of the eye, follow a similar pattern of avascularity and growth restriction.

Gimbrone et al then further advanced this model by implanting within the cornea as well as on the iris and in the anterior chamber [23]. Corneal implants were placed either peripherally, close to the blood supply or centrally, further from a potential blood supply. The iris and anterior chamber implants grew as before. Centrally placed corneal implants remained avascular for up to five weeks growing only slowly. At two to three weeks, neovascularisation of the iris vessels was seen. Peripherally placed corneal implants became vascularised within seven to twelve days. After that time they grew rapidly. Interestingly, vessel proliferation was also seen in the iris on the opposite side to the tumour implant.

They concluded that cellular contact was not necessary between tumour cells and host vessels for tumour neovascularisation to occur. They suggested that the tumour cells may be producing a mediator that stimulated vascularisation.

Similar results were seen in a different animal model by Knighton et al in 1977 [24]. A 1mm x 1mm x 2mm implant of Walker 256 carcinoma was injected into the chorioallantoic membrane of a chicken egg through a window in the shell. The same window was used to observe vessel growth. The tumours exhibited pre-vascular and vascular growth phases. Neovascularisation always occurred at 72 hours. Unlike the previous studies this experiment placed the tumours in an area surrounded by healthy vessels. Even so, tumour growth still did not occur until the tumour was penetrated by host vessels.

By 1971, Folkman had concluded that "The growth of solid neoplasms is always accompanied by neovascularisation" [20]. He stated that this evidence showed that tumour cells have a stimulating influence on endothelial cells, noting that capillaries grow towards tumours from the host unlike skin grafts which send out capillaries. He also importantly stated that the vessels have a modulating influence on tumours. He described an early diffusion stage (pre-vascular) of minimal tumour growth and, after vessel growth, a faster perfusion period of tumour growth. He summarised by proposing the use of anti-angiogenesis as novel cancer therapy.

Historical Studies of Angiogenesis Measurement

A vital part of angiogenesis research is quantification. Angiogenesis has been measured in living (animal) systems and in tissue. Measurement in histological tissue allows the progression from experimentation to diagnosis and prognosis. Early studies took advantage of the vessel lumen, injecting inks and X-ray contrast media. The development of immunohistochemistry allowed a less invasive method. Quantifying vessels rather than just observing them was pioneered by Algire and Chalkley using Chalkley's counting method.

The question of quantitative measurement of angiogenesis was re-addressed by Brem et al in 1972 [25]. Working with Judah Folkman, he aimed to devise a reliable method of measuring angiogenesis in histological tissue.

They expressed angiogenesis as a summation of three vascular characteristics: vasoproliferation, endothelial cell hyperplasia and endothelial cell cytology. An equation was devised to give a microscopic angiogenesis grading system (MAGS).

$$K_nN + K_eE + K_xX = MAGS$$

K_nN represents vasoproliferation, K_eE represents endothelial cell hyperplasia and K_xX represents endothelial cell cytology.

In K_nN, N is the number of vessels in a high powered (x500) field ($1.10^5 \mu m^2$). As this varies between microscopes, the constant K_n was used to correct for this. Slides were scanned at low magnification and the most vascular area was chosen for analysis. This was felt to represent the best estimate of the neovascularising potential of the tumour. An effort was also made to choose an area where the majority of vessels were cut in cross section. Each vessel (that is, a lumen with a surrounding endothelial process) was counted, although a maximum score was set at 40. This was not further explained.

The endothelial cell hyperplasia score was calculated using K_e as a constant set at three and E as the number of endothelial cells lining the cross section of the most hyperplastic capillary. Vessels with more than 20 cells were not used and the maximum value of E was 10 making a maximum K_eE of 30.

When calculating endothelial cytology, K_c was a constant, allowing the maximal cytological change of regenerating endothelium to correspond to maximal vasoproliferation and maximal hyperplasia was set at six. X stood for the cytological appearance of the most primitive group of endothelial cells with a hyperplastic zone. A score of 0-5 was given depending upon the atypia of the cells.

Although this appears complex, the authors cited its lack of complexity and its rapidity as an advantage. They stated that it took an experienced observer ten minutes to assess a section.

Once again, in 1985, Mlynek et al stated there was a lack of a reliable and readily available method for measuring vascularisation of malignant tumours, and offered one [26]. Vessels were identified by staining alkaline phosphatase present in endothelial cells. Fushin B was used which produced red staining. Some cross staining was seen with neutrophils and newly formed stroma. Only aArterioles and arterial capillaries stained but larger vessels and veins did not.

At first both total length of vessels and number of cross sectioned vessels were measured. All areas of the section were assessed (range 105 – 331). To aid vessel measurement, photomicrographs were taken and put together to form a picture of the section at x98 magnification. As good correlation was found between vessel length and number of cross sectioned vessels (no data given), it was felt sufficient to count vessels in cross section only. Only 100 areas, each being $0.09mm^2$ of tumour were counted in each section. They stated that statistically it was found that evaluation of 100 fields sufficed to obtain representative results but no details of their calculation were given.

Using this method they found that normal mucosa (4.74 +/- 1.27) was richer in vessels than corresponding colorectal carcinoma (2.06 +/- 1.43) (p=0.002).

It was Noel Weidner in 1991 who developed the most popular quantification system. It was based on both morphometery and biology. He quantified angiogenesis in 49 specimens of breast carcinoma to correlate with future metastasis [27]. Vessels were identified using a polyclonal antibody to Factor VIII (FVIIIRA). This staining technique was previously described by Pinkus et al who did not use it to perform vessel counts [28]. Weidner et al assessed a single area of one section taken from one embedded tumour block. This area was chosen by scanning the section at low magnification (x40 or x100) to detect the most dense area of vessels.

The subjective density of vessels in this area was given a grade from 1 to 4 (low to high). At higher magnification, the number of stained vessels were counted. This value was expressed as microvessel density (MVD) per high powered field (x200 or x400). Any separate area of staining was considered to be a single vessel. The presence of an obvious lumen or red blood cells was not required for confirmation. Counting was performed simultaneously by two observers using a double headed microscope. It took 5 – 10 minutes per case. For validation a third observer rescored the cases producing correlations of r=0.61 for subjective grading scores, r=0.59 for MVD at x200 magnification and r=0.62 for MVD aty x400 magnification.

Weidner's technique of counting in the most vascular area (subsequently called the hotspot) has become the most frequently used model for MVD estimation.

The Use of Microvessel Density in Cancer Prognosis

Angiogenesis as represented by a micro vessel count has been shown to be a major prognostic factor in many cancers. Brem et al after devising their MAGS system for vessel quantification suggested it may be useful to compare vascularity with other tumour properties including metastatic potential [25].

The first quantitative evidence that the intensity of angiogenesis in a human tumour may predict progression was reported by Srivastava et al in melanoma in 1986 [29]. In 20 cases, vessels were identified using Ulex europaeus agglutinin I (UEA-I). Vessel counts were performed using the IBAS-2 image analysis system in four fields in the tumour, at the tumour-dermal junction and in adjacent normal dermis. There was a positive correlation between the percentage of area occupied by vessels at the tumour-dermal junction and the thickness of melanoma ($r=0.687$, $p<0.002$). The thickness of malignant melanoma is related to prognosis. There was no direct correlation between vascularity and clinical outcome in this study.

In his 1991 paper Weidner et al measured angiogenesis in 49 cases of carcinoma of the breast; 30 patients had metastases and 19 did not [27].The number of vessels (stained with polyclonal antibody against FVIIIRA) were counted at x200 and x400 magnification and subjectively graded. The area for counting was the most vascular seen at low magnification; again subjective. They used a Cox logistic regression to look at the association of metatsatis with potential prognostic factors. Those patients with metastases were found to have 101 vessels per x200 field and 37 per x400 field. Those patients without metastases had 45 per x200 field and 17 per x400 field, $p=0.003$ (x200) and $p=0.004$ (x400) respectively. With each 10 vessel increase in MVD they found a 1.59 (1.19-2.12) increased risk of metastasis, $p=0.003$. A significant difference was also found between in cases that werethe subjectively gradeding, $p<0.001$. In the multivariate regression analysis, it was subjective microvessel grade at x200 that provided the best estimate of relative risk with MVD at 200x strongly correlating ($r=0.8$, $p<0.0001$).

The association of breast cancer outcome with angiogenesis measured by MVD was confirmed by Bosari et al and Horak et al in 1992 and in an editorial by Weidner in 1998 he was able to quote 29 articles of MVD measurement in breast cancer. In 1993 Wakui et al found that a high vascularity as measured by a blood capillary density ratio (BCDR) was related to high Gleason grade in cases of non metastatic prostate cancer [30]. In 1993 Mikami et al found that high MVD (with FVIIIRA) staining was associated with increasing nodal status and stage in head and neck cancers [31]. In the same year, Gasparini et al also looking at angiogenesis in head and neck cancers found that high MVD (measured with antibody to CD31) was associated with metastasis [32]. In the multivarient analysis, MVD along withand stage was were a predictive factors.

Macchiarini et al were the first group to find that increased MVD correlated with metastases and tumour size in a series of 87 T1N0M0 non small cell lung carcinomas [33]. Again, MVD was the only variable in the multivariate analysis to predict metastasis.

The Limitations of Microvessel Density Measurement

By the mid 1990's the techniques of angiogenesis research had been applied to the majority of human cancers. Although the majority of studies of tumour angiogenesis showed a positive relationship between MVD and tumour growth and spread, a considerable number did not. High MVD was found to be a predictor of poor outcome in many tumours but some studies failed to find a significant correlation between MVD and outcome while yet others found that high MVD correlated with a better outcome.

It was suggested that this may be due at least in part, to the difficulties in measuring angiogenesis [34-36]. There are certainly a great number of techniques which have been used to measure MVD in histopathological specimens. In a review of MVD measurement in urological tumours, 41 different methods of MVD measurement were identified in a series of 48 papers [37].

The most widely used and quoted method, was that described by Weidner previously discussed [27], which identified "hotspots" in the tumour. These hotspot were thought to correlate best with clinical outcome because of their relationship to the process of haematogenous spread [27;38]. The elegant simplicity of Weidner's hotspot method was therefore challenged and over the next few years it was reassessed.

Weidner's theories were supported by McCulloch et al who measured the shedding of malignant cells in 16 breast cancer patients and found a correlation with MVD ($p=0.024$) as measured using the hotspot method supporting an association between counts in the hotspot and metastasis [39]. Martin et al [40] compared the standard immunohistochemical technique of Weidner et al [27] with microangiography in breast tumours. A correlation was again found between the vascularity as measured by immunohistochemistry and the vascularity of the tumour as a whole as estimated by microangiography ($p<0.0003$).

As determining what is a hotspot within a section of tissue may not be obvious [36;41]. Vermeulen et al and Simpson et al suggested poor consistency may be due to lack of observer experience and could be helped by training [42;43]. Dickinson et al encountered difficulty measuring MVD in superficial bladder cancer due to the papillary nature of the tumour and were thus obliged to assess only invasive solid tumours [44]. The hotspot method however does provide a convenient area in which to perform a vessel count.

A further potential reason for inconsistency in angiogenesis research was identified as sampling errors occurring during the selection of pathological material examined. Particularly as the majority of methodologies relied on a single 5μm section to represent the angiogenic potential of the tumour as a whole. Weidner counts one area in a single hotspot [personal communication]. Several authors attempted to address this problem. De Jong et al examined 10 cases of breast cancer taking four sections 100μm apart from between two and four blocks from each tumour. MVD was assessed in two ways, firstly, a hotspot method and then counts were performed in ten high power fields in two or three systematically spread areas within the section. For the latter method, the coefficient of variation from different areas within the same section was 17.1% (range 0.7 – 52.1%), between sections from the same block was 14.7% (range 0.5 – 41.9%) and between blocks from the same tumour was 25.8% (range 9.9 – 44.6%). The hotspot method showed less variation with the coefficient of variation for sections from the same block being 11.1% (range 0.7 – 29.5%) and for different blocks from the same tumour 24.2% (5.7 – 54.9%) [45]. Van Hoef et al achieved similar results when they examined sections from two blocks of 41 cases of breast carcinoma. There was a 71-78% concordance between MVD counts between blocks [35].

Martin et al, in a series of breast carcinoma patients compared the MVD assessment of three sections from three blocks from each tumour. When the patients were divided into high or low MVD groups an 85% correlation was achieved between sections from different blocks. In addition they compared MVD with microangiography: a mixture of barium, gelatin and formalin was injected into fresh mastectomy specimens and the vascularity on subsequent mammograms was assessed subjectively by two investigators and checked by a third. A statistically significant correlation was found between the vascularity as measured by immunohistochemistry and the vascularity of the tumour as a whole as estimated by microangiography ($p<0.0003$). This suggests that despite tumour heterogenicity, the technique of selecting a single section from a block of tumour is a valid representation of the tumour as a whole in carcinoma of the breast [40].

Lissbrant et al and Offersen et al counted in both random areas and within hotspots and found a significant association between the two methods [46;47]. and Offersen found only hotspot MVD using a hotspot technique and not random areas counting was associated with crude survival. {Lissbrant, Stattin, et al. 1997 ID: 1834} {Offersen, Borre, et al. 1998 ID: 1202}

Researchers have also used a subjective estimation of the vascularisation of the tumour (eyeballing) [48]. This method is fast and has compared favourably with other techniques [49].

Vermeulen et al attempted to redress the problem of variations in counting methods by suggesting a standardised technique. They proposed the use of anti CD31 as a vessel marker, the selection of a hotspot in viable tumour tissue at x10 magnification and counting with a Chalkley graticule in a field size approximately the same as the hotspots in that tumour type. They suggest assessment by two observers with a third if the counts differ by more than 10% breast [40]. It is obvious by reviews of the literature that Vermeulen's suggestion was not taken up [37]. Weidner's method or basic variations upon it, remains the commonest technique for the assessment of angiogenesis in human tumours. It did not work well for all tumours however and it has been the advance of technology that has allowed angiogenesis research to progress further.

Use of Computer Technology in Angiogenesis Measurement

The invention of computers and the digital image has allowed image analysis to be used in angiogenesis research. A computerised image analysis system for the measurement of MVD allows more counts to be performed in a set time, allows greater objectivity and therefore greater accuracy and gives the opportunity to explore more detailed parameters of tissue vascularity. It also makes a tedious and time consuming process into something which would be more acceptable in a clinical setting.

Digital images consist of two dimensional arrays of dots. On a computer monitor these are called pixels. The colour or shade of each individual pixel determines the picture as a whole. Each pixel has a value. It is this value that determines its colour, shade or intensity; this value can be measured.

Briefly, an image analysis program must be able to recognise what is a countable vessel and then count the number of vessels in a given area. To do this the computer has to:

1. Recognise vessels,
2. Discount objects that are not vessels,
3. Recognise when a vessel is fragmented and not count its separate pieces,
4. Recognise separate vessels when they are touching and not count them as one,
5. Only count vessels in specified tissue (for example tumour),
6. Not count vessels that fall on either of two specified margins of the field
7. Express the count per unit area.

This list summarises the usual steps required for MVD measurement using image analysis. That is, the conversion of the analogue to a digital one, determining countable vessels by removing background noise and cleaning images, thresholding images into 1-bit black and white files and finally image analysis assessment.

The earliest paper describing the use of computerised image analysis in the measurement of MVD in a human cancer was that of Srivastava et al [51]. Vessels in malignant melanomas were identified using UEA-1 and analysed using an IBAS-2 semi automatic image analysis system by Kontron Ltd, West Germany. Unfortunately, no details of the image analysis system or technique used were given in the paper. Image analysis programs by Kontron have been used by other investigators although not necessarily in the same way. Smolle et al for example, used the Kontron Vidas software to assess vascularity in melanoma [52].

Techniques may vary at multiple points in the image analysis cascade. In particular, there is a spectrum of automation seen varying from a fully automated system to one requiring considerable human intervention.

Summary

The scientific study of angiogenesis has increased exponentially over the last thirty years giving the impression that this is a new field of study. In reality, the connection between disease, such as cancer, and blood vessels was made in antiquity. A greater understanding of the microvasculature was developed during the Nineteenth Century; neovascularisation associated with tumour growth was recognised. In the 1920's Lindgren and Docent postulated that substances produced by the tumours affected their blood supply.

A body of evidence from experiments using transparent chambers, from the 1930's to the 1960's supported the theory that tumours controlled their blood supply. Subsequent work by Gimbrone et al using tumours implanted into rabbit irises confirmed this.

In 1971, Judah Folkman presented his theory that tumours were dependent upon vessel formation to the Harvard Medical School in Boston. By doing so he placed angiogenesis at the centre of tumour biology. From Dr Folkman's laboratory, angiogenesis research has exploded across the world. It is certainly fair to say that the work of Judah Folkman began the modern revolution in angiogenesis research. However, it should not be forgotten that this was based on the work of many scientists over the preceding one hundred years.

References

[1] Hertig A: Angiogenesis in the early human chorion and in the primary placenta of the Macque monkey. *Contributions to Embryology 1935*; 25: 37

[2] Aulus Cornelius Celsus, *Spencer WGtr: De Medicina*. London: Harvard Medical Press, 1938;

[3] Paré A: *The practise of chirurgery, and the use of three and fifty instruments. By artificiall figures representing the members, and fit termes expressing the same. Set forth either to pleasure or to profit those who are addicted to this study*. London: Tho. Cotes, 1634.

[4] Hunter J: *The works of John Hunter. Volume II. Observations in Comparative Anatomy*. London: John van Voorst, 1861; 137

[5] Hunter J: *The works of John Hunter. Volume I. Essays and Observations on Natural History*. London: John van Voorst, 1861; 127

[6] Thiersch K: *Der Epithelialkrebs, namenthlich der Haut mit Atlas*. Leipzig: 1865.

[7] Bilroth T: *General Surgery, Pathology and Therapeutics*. New York: Appleton, 1871;

[8] Goldmann E: The growth of malignant disease in man and the lower animals. *Lancet* 1907; -1236

[9] Bashford E, Murray J, Cramer W: *The growth of cancer under natural and experimental conditions. Imperial Cancer Research Fund Scientific Reports* 1904; 2: 24-29.

[10] Lewis WH: *The Vascular Patterns of Tumors. Bulletin of the Johns Hopkins Hospital* 1927; 41: 156-170.

[11] Lindgren AGH, Docent MD: The Vascular Supply of Tumours with special reference to the capillary angioarchitekture. *Acta Pathol Microbiol Scand* 1945; 22: 493-522.

[12] Clark ER, Hitschler WJ, Kirby-Smith HT, Rex RO, Smith JH: *General observations on the ingrowth of new blood vessels into standardized chambers in the rabbit's ear, and the subsequent changes in the newly grown vessels over a period of months. Anatomy Records* 1931; 50: 129-167.

[13] Ide H, Baker N, Warren S: Vascularisation of the Brown-Pierce rabbit epithelioma transplant as seen in the rabbit ear chamber. *American Journal of Roentgenological Radium Therapy* 1939; 42: 891-899.

[14] Greene HSN: Heterologous transplantation of mammalian tumors. *Journal of Experimental Medicine* 1941; 73: 461-473.

[15] Algire GH, Chalkley HW, Legallais FY: Vascular Reactions of normal and malignant tumours in vivo. I. Vascular reactions of mice to wounds and to normal and neoplastic transplants. *Journal of the National Cancer Institute* 1945; 6: 72-85.

[16] Chalkley HW: Method for the quantitative morphological analysis of tissues. *Journal of the National Cancer Institute* 1943; 4: 47

[17] Rondoni P: *Il Cancro*. Milan: 1946;

[18] Ribatti D, Vacca A, Presta M: An Italian pioneer in the study of tumor angiogenesis. *Haematologica* 2001; 12: 1234-1235.

[19] Folkman J: What is the evidence that tumors are angiogenesis dependent? [editorial]. *Journal of the National Cancer Institute* 1990; 82: 4-6.

[20] Folkman J: Tumor angiogenesis: therapeutic implications. [Review] [21 refs]. *New England Journal of Medicine* 1971; 285: 1182-1186.

[21] Folkman J, Cole P, Zimmerman S: Tumor behavior in isolated perfused organs: in vitro growth and metastases of biopsy material in rabbit thyroid and canine intestinal segment. *Annals of Surgery* 1966; 164: 491-502.

[22] Gimbrone MAJ, Leapman SB, Cotran RS, Folkman J: Tumor dormancy in vivo by prevention of neovascularization. *Journal of Experimental Medicine* 1972; 136: 261-276.

[23] Gimbrone MAJ, Leapman SB, Cotran RS, Folkman J: Tumor angiogenesis: iris neovascularization at a distance from experimental intraocular tumors. *Journal of the National Cancer Institute* 1973; 50: 219-228.

[24] Knighton D, Ausprunk D, Tapper D, Folkman J: Avascular and vascular phases of tumour growth in the chick embryo. *British Journal of Cancer* 1977; 35: 347-356.

[25] Brem S, Cotran R, Folkman J: Tumor angiogenesis: a quantitative method for histologic grading. *Journal of the National Cancer Institute* 1972; 48: 347-356.

[26] Mlynek ML, van Beunigen D, Leder LD, Streffer C: Measurement of the grade of vascularisation in histological tumour tissue sections. *British Journal of Cancer* 1985; 52: 945-948.

[27] Weidner N, Semple JP, Welch WR, Folkman J: Tumor angiogenesis and metastasis--correlation in invasive breast carcinoma. *New England Journal of Medicine* 1991; 324: 1-8.

[28] Pinkus GS, Etheridge CL, O'Conner EM: Are keratin proteins a better tumor marker than epithelial membrane antigen? *American Journal of Clinical Pathology* 1986; 85: 269-277.

[29] Srivastava A, Laidler P, Hughes LE, Woodcock J, Shedden EJ: Neovascularization in human cutaneous melanoma: a quantitative morphological and Doppler ultrasound study. *European Journal of Cancer & Clinical Oncology* 1986; 22: 1205-1209.

[30] Wakui S, Furusato M, Itoh T, et al: Tumour angiogenesis in prostatic carcinoma with and without bone marrow metastasis: a morphometric study. *Journal of Pathology* 1992; 168: 257-262.

[31] Mikami Y, Tsukuda M, Mochimatsu I, Kokatsu T, Yago T, Sawaki S: [Angiogenesis in head and neck tumor]. [Japanese]. *Nippon Jibiinkoka Gakkai Kaiho [Journal of the Oto-Rhino-Laryngological Society of Japan]* 1993; 96: 645-650.

[32] Gasparini G, Weidner N, Maluta S, et al: Intratumoral microvessel density and p53 protein: correlation with metastasis in head-and-neck squamous-cell carcinoma. *International Journal of Cancer* 1993; 55: 739-744.

[33] Macchiarini P, Fontanini G, Hardin MJ, Squartini F, Angeletti CA: Relation of neovascularisation to metastasis of non-small-cell lung cancer. *Lancet* 1992; 340: 145-146.

[34] Hall NR, Fish DE, Hunt N, Goldin RD, Guillou PJ, Monson JR: Is the relationship between angiogenesis and metastasis in breast cancer real? *Surgical Oncology* 1992; 1: 223-229.

[35] Van Hoef ME, Knox WF, Dhesi SS, Howell A, Schor AM: Assessment of tumour vascularity as a prognostic factor in lymph node negative invasive breast cancer. *European Journal of Cancer* 1993; 29A: 1141-1145.

[36] Axelsson K, Ljung BM, Moore DH, et al: Tumor angiogenesis as a prognostic assay for invasive ductal breast carcinoma [see comments]. Journal of the National Cancer Institute 1995; 87: 997-1008.

[37] Goddard JC, Sutton CD, Berry DP, O'Byrne K, Kockelbergh RC: The use of Microvessel Density Assessment in Human Urological Tumours. *BJU International* 2001; 87: 866-876.

[38] Weidner N, Folkman J, Pozza F, et al: Tumor angiogenesis: a new significant and independent prognostic indicator *in early-stage breast carcinoma [see comments]. Journal* of the National Cancer Institute 1992; 84: 1875-1887.

[39] McCulloch P, Choy A, Martin L: Association between tumour angiogenesis and tumour cell shedding into effluent venous blood during breast cancer surgery [see comments]. *Lancet* 1995; 346: 1334-1335.

[40] Martin L, Green B, Renshaw C, et al: Examining the technique of angiogenesis assessment in invasive breast cancer. *British Journal of Cancer* 1997; 76: 1046-1054.

[41] Bosari S, Lee AK, DeLellis RA, Wiley BD, Heatley GJ, Silverman ML: Microvessel quantitation and prognosis in invasive breast carcinoma. *Human Pathology* 1992; 23: 755-761.

[42] Vermeulen PB, Verhoeven D, Hubens G, et al: Microvessel density, endothelial cell proliferation and tumour cell proliferation in human colorectal adenocarcinomas. *Annals of Oncology* 1995; 6: 59-64.

[43] Simpson JF, Ahn C, Battifora H, Esteban JM: Endothelial area as a prognostic indicator for invasive breast carcinoma. *Cancer* 1996; 77: 2077-2085.

[44] Dickinson AJ, Fox SB, Persad RA, Hollyer J, Sibley GN, Harris AL: Quantification of angiogenesis as an independent predictor of prognosis in invasive bladder carcinomas. *British Journal of Urology* 1994; 74: 762-766.

[45] de Jong JS, van Diest PJ, Baak JP: Heterogeneity and reproducibility of microvessel counts in breast cancer [see comments]. *Laboratory Investigation* 1995; 73: 922-926.

[46] Lissbrant IF, Stattin P, Damber JE, Bergh A: Vascular density is a predictor of cancer-specific survival in prostatic carcinoma. *Prostate* 1997; 33: 38-45.
[47] Offersen BV, Borre M, Overgaard J: Immunohistochemical determination of tumor angiogenesis measured by the maximal microvessel density in human prostate cancer. *APMIS* 1998; 106: 463-469.
[48] Mooteri S, Rubin D, Leurgans S, Jakate S, Drab E, Saclarides T: Tumor angiogenesis in primary and metastatic colorectal cancers. *Diseases of the Colon & Rectum* 1996; 39: 1073-1080.
[49] Fox SB, Leek RD, Weekes MP, Whitehouse RM, Gatter KC, Harris AL: Quantitation and prognostic value of breast cancer angiogenesis: comparison of microvessel density, Chalkley count, and computer image analysis. *Journal of Pathology* 1995; 177: 275-283.
[50] Vermeulen PB, Gasparini G, Fox SB, et al: Quantification of angiogenesis in solid human tumours: an international consensus on the methodology and criteria of evaluation. [Review] [78 refs]. *European Journal of Cancer* 1996; 32A: 2474-2484.
[51] Srivastava A, Laidler P, Davies RP, rgan K, Hughes LE: The prognostic significanceof tumour vascularity in intermediate thickness skin melanoma: a quantitative histological study. *American Journal of Pathology* 1988; 133: 419-423.
[52] Smolle J, Soyer H-P, Hofmann-Wellenhof R, Smolle-Juettner F-M, Kerl H: Vascular architecture of melanocytic skin tumours. *Pathology, Research & Practice* 1989; 185: 740-745.

In: New Angiogenesis Research
Editor: Roberta V. Zubar, pp. 19-42

ISBN 1-59454-239-2

Chapter II

The Rho GTPases and Angiogenesis

Kate Groh[1], Min Lin[1], Cynthia M. van Golen[2] and Kenneth L. van Golen[1,*]

[1] Department of Internal Medicine, Division of Hematology/Oncology, The University of Michigan Comprehensive Cancer Center

[2]Department of Neurology, The University of Michigan Medical School. Ann Arbor, MI

Abstract

The Rho GTPases comprise a subfamily of the Ras-superfamily of small GTP-binding proteins. The Rho subfamily is comprised of a group of 23 monomeric G proteins which have diverse roles in normal and malignant cells. Traditionally, the Rho GTPases are thought to control cellular motility and invasion through rearrangement of the actin cytoskeleton. However, it is becoming increasingly evident that the Rho proteins control other cellular events such as transformation, growth, survival, intracellular transport, production of extracellular matrix-degrading proteases and angiogenic factors. Recent evidence from an increasing number of laboratories, including our own, has demonstrated the role of the Rho GTPases in mediating the production of active angiogenic factors in breast and other types of tumor cells. This report will review the current understanding of the role of Rho proteins in angiogenesis. We will also provide evidence demonstrating that angiogenic factor expression in the MDA-231 and MDA-231-BO (bone metastatic variant) breast cancer cell lines is differentially regulated by the Rho proteins.

Key words: Rho GTPases, Angiogenic Factors, C3 exotransferase, protein tyrosine kinase receptors, cell motility.

Abbreviations

Rho	Ras homology

* Correspondence concerning this article should be addressed to Kenneth L. van Golen, Ph.D. R4048A Kresge II 200 Zina Pitcher Drive Ann Arbor, MI 48109-0548; kgolen@umich.edu. Telephone: (734) 615-6887.

GAP	GTPase activating protein
GEF	guanine nucleotide exchange factor
GDI	guanine nucleotide dissociation inhibitor
VEGF	vascular endothelial growth factor
VEGFR	vascular endothelial growth factor receptor
PDGF	platelet derived growth factor
TGF	transforming growth factor
bFGF	basic fibroblast growth factor
IGF	insulin-like growth factor
EGF	epidermal growth factor
IL	interleukin
MAPK	mitogen activated protein kinase
Erk	extracellular regulated kinase
PKC	protein kinase C
PLC	phospholipase C
PI3K	phosphatidyl inositol 3-kinase
FAK	focal adhesion kinase
Ig	immunoglobulin.

Overview of Angiogenesis

The term "angiogenesis" was initially coined to describe the formation of new blood vessels in the placenta [1] [2]. Angiogenic factors are molecules such as peptides and lipids that function to promote the formation of new blood vessels, and fall into two categories; the first group acts directly on vascular endothelial tissue to promote locomotion or mitosis, and the second acts indirectly by signaling cells to release endothelial growth factors. Angiogenic factors are found in all types of cells, whether undergoing neovascularization or not. This suggests that the actions of these growth factors are highly regulated.

Early investigations into the importance of angiogenesis in tumor growth lead to the hypothesis that in order for a tumor to grow beyond a threshold size, neovascularization had to precede the growth (reviewed in [1] [2] [3]). Experiments demonstrated that if angiogenesis is inhibited surrounding a developing tumor, the tumor will not exceed 1 to 2 mm^3 in size, tumor cells will not be shed into the circulation and the tumor will remain dormant. This hypothesis is further supported by histological evidence that tumors tend to cluster around capillaries, and tumor cells that are not in close proximity to a capillary tend to undergo less mitosis.

In the early 1980's complete angiogenic factors were first identified as endothelial cell growth factors, the first of which was basic fibroblast growth factor (bFGF) [4]. Since then angiogenic factors have been purified from extracts of tumor cells, cultured vascular endothelial cells and wound fluid (reviewed in [2]). Their functions began to be elucidated using *in vivo* mouse and rabbit models such as ocular vascularization. Soon after came the identification of specific inhibitory molecules which act to inhibit angiogenesis and thus regulate the angiogenic process maintaining endothelial cells in a quiescent state [2] [3]. Perturbation of the balance between pro-angiogenic and anti-angiogenic molecules leads to an ordered series of events in the formation of new vessels. New capillaries arise from sprouting small venules, followed by degradation of the basement membrane of the parent venule. Endothelial cells migrate toward the angiogenic stimulus, and align with each other to form a solid sprout. As the endothelial cells elongate and proliferate, they curve to form a lumen. Two hollow sprouts join to form a loop and blood begins to flow through the lumen, at which point pericytes align with the apex of the loop to create a new sprout which continues neovascularization.

Angiogenic Factors and Signal Transduction

Angiogenic Factor Receptors Signal Transduction

A number of angiogenic factors have been identified over the years and include: Fibroblast Growth Factor (FGF), Vascular Endothelial Growth Factor (VEGF), Angiogenin, Transforming Growth Factors (TGF-α and TGF-β), and platelet derived growth factor (PDGF). These factors act to increase angiogenesis by stimulating endothelial cell locomotion, and/or proliferation via protein tyrosine kinase receptors such as vascular endothelial growth factor receptor (VEGFR), Tie2, Eph, and platelet derived growth factor receptor (PDGFR). By and large these protein tyrosine kinase receptors signal in a similar manner; ligand binding initiates receptor dimerization and activation, followed by autophosphorylation of the intracellular domain. This initiates an intracellular signaling cascade by associating with and activating a host of intracellular proteins, most of which contain SH2 and PTB domains that allow for binding to phosphorylated tyrosine residues, and SH3 domains that confer protein-protein binding specificity to proline-rich regions. These associated proteins include enzymatic proteins (phosphatidyl inositol 3-kinase (PI3K), phospholipase C (PLC), the Src family kinases, and tyrosine phosphatases), non-enzymatic adaptor proteins (Grb-2, Shc, and Nck), cytoskeleton-associated proteins (Rho GTPase family), and transcription factors (STATS).

The prototypical angiogenic factor, VEGF, utilizes protein tyrosine kinase receptors to activate the cell signaling cascade. VEGF signaling is initiated by the binding and activation of one of three receptor tyrosine kinases; VEGFR-1/Flt-1, VEGFR-2/KDR/Flk-2, and VEGFR-3/Flt-4, all which contain seven immunoglobulin (Ig) domains. Ig domains 1 through 3 mediate ligand binding, with 2 conferring specificity, and Ig domain 4 responsible for receptor dimerization. Five different ligands bind to these three receptors: VEGF-A, -B, -C, -D, and placental growth factor (PlGF). VEGFR-1 binds VEGF-A, -B, and PlGF, VEGFR-2 binds VEGF-A, -C, and -D, and VEGFR-3 has highest affinity for VEGF-C and -D. VEGFs are recognized as disulfide-linked dimers by their respective receptors and receptor dimerization is required for binding to VEGF and activation of the receptor. Although VEGFRs usually function as homodimers, there is evidence that VEGFR-1 and VEGFR-2 can function as a heterodimer when binding VEGF-A. Signaling proteins such as PLC, Ras GTPase activating protein (RasGAP), PI3K, and focal adhesion kinase (FAK) have been implicated in VEGFR signaling. Evidence suggests that VEGFR-2 is the primary receptor involved in VEGF signaling in endothelial cells, and functions in the development of embryo vasculature. Endo et. al. recently studied the role of VEGFR-2 by treating human aortic endothelial cells, which express VEGFR-1 and VEGFR-2, with a highly selective anilinoquinazoline inhibitor of VEGFR-2 [5]. The inhibitor, ZM323881, inhibited activation of VEGFR-2 but not of VEGFR-1, PDGFR, epidermal growth factor receptor (EGFR) or hepatocyte growth factor receptor (HGFR). Inhibition of VEGFR-2 blocked activation of Akt and the extracellular regulated kinase (Erk) and p38 arms of the mitogen activated protein kinase (MAPK) pathway. Furthermore, endothelial cell migration was inhibited through inactivation of CrkII and p130Cas, molecules known to be involved activated by Rho GTPases and intricately involved in cell migration. PIGF, a ligand specific for VEGFR-1 was still able to activate the p38 MAPK pathway. VEGFR-1 may function to negatively regulate VEGFR-2 in endothelial cells. This suggests that different signaling mechanisms exist between these classes of receptors.

The MAPK pathway is the most prominent signaling pathway induced by VEGF. Activation of MAPK regulates vascular development through the expression of mitogens, inactivation of apoptosis, and chemotaxis. MAPK activation begins with receptor dimerization and autophosphorylation that recruits receptor associated proteins such as Grb2, Shc, Nck, or SHP-2. This is followed by the association of Sos (guanine nucleotide exchange factor) with the plasma membrane, resulting in the conversion of GDP-bound Ras to active Ras-GTP. GTP-bound Ras phosphorylates Raf-1 which leads to the activation of MEK-1 and MAPK. RasGAP converts Ras GTP back into an inactive GDP-bound state, hence acting as a negative regulator of this pathway. Deletion of genes involved in regulation or relay of this signaling pathway leads to defective vasculature development during embryogenesis. Also, activation of the PLC/Protein kinase C (PKC) pathway may lead to VEGF-induced endothelial cell proliferation [6].

VEGF-C and –D, which bind and activate their receptor VEGFR-3, were the first molecules shown to promote lymphangiogenesis, the formation of neo-lymphatic vessels. Expression of VEGF-C and –D has been shown to be upregulated in only certain cancers (reviewed in [7] and [8]). By and large VEGF-C and –D expression correlates with increased lymphatic invasion and metastasis. In addition, since VEGF-C also has affinity for the VEGFR-2 receptor, it may cooperate with VEGF-A in regulating embryonic vasculogenesis [9] [4]. Further studies into the role of VEGF-C have utilized transgenic mice either overexpressing VEGF-C or VEGF-C on a keratin-14 promoter [10] [11]. These mice produce hyperplastic cutaneous lymphatic vessels, while the growth of the blood vasculature remains unaffected. Similarly, VEGF-C null mice die before the formation of lymphatic vessels prior to birth [12]. Mice heterozygous for VEGF-C are viable; however they develop lymphedema and chylous fluid in their abdomen, suggesting insufficient formation of lymphatic vessels. Similarly, VEGFR-3 null mice also die prior to lymphatic vessel formation well before birth [13]. A transgenic model utilizing a VEGFR-Ig fusion protein that acts as an antagonist of VEGFR-3 by binding VEGF-C and –D has demonstrated the role of VEGFR-3 during lymphangiogenesis [14]. VEGFR-3 is found expressed primarily on lymphatic endothelial cells [15] [16]. The VEGF-R-Ig fusion protein was expressed under a keratin-14 promoter, thus inducing apoptosis of lymphatic endothelial cells in the skin and causing a regression of previously formed dermal lymphatic vessels and vessels in the internal organs. At 3 weeks after birth, the lymphatics in the internal organs, but not in the skin, began to grow back suggesting differential regulation of lymphangiogenesis in the skin versus the internal organs. The absence of dermal lymphatics in these mice also resulted in lymphedema.

Similar defects are seen in mice that are deficient in angiopoietin 2 (Ang2). Whereas, VEGF-C knockout or VEGFR-3-Ig mice lack peripheral dermal lymphatics, Ang2 deficient mice have a developed lymphatic vasculature, this system lacks organization [17].

Angiopoietins are the ligands for the protein tyrosine kinase receptors Tie1 and Tie2 receptors. These receptors contain cytosolic domains similar to members of the VEGFR and PDGFR family. Tie2 activation is regulated by opposing actions of agonistic and antagonistic binding of the angiopoietins [18]. Tie1 is believed not to bind ligands, but functions as a co-receptor that increases the affinity for ligands binding to Tie2. Mice lacking Tie1 die due to a loss of microvasculature which leads to fatal hemorrhages, and Tie2 mutants die from a decrease in vascular integrity and a reduction in the amount of endothelial cells [19] [20]. Activation of Tie2 has been implicated in vascular maturation and remodeling, by means of cell-cell and cell-matrix interactions [21] [22]. Tie2 directly binds and activates PI3K, leading to the activation of Rac GTPase, which functions to regulate and reorganize the actin cytoskeleton. Tie2 also binds a novel protein, Dok-R, which then interacts with Nck, an adaptor protein that is involved in growth-factor mediated cytoskeletal remodeling [23]. Lastly, Tie2 functions by directly signaling transcription factors in the nucleus through the activation of STAT 3 and 5 [24].

Another receptor tyrosine kinase that promotes morphogenesis, capillary sprouting and enhances cellular responses to chemoattractants is the Eph receptor. Unlike the afore mentioned receptors, the Eph receptor does not induce mitogenesis, rather it functions to control cell localization [18]. Ephrins, which are ligands for the Eph receptors, are membrane bound, and cell surface expression is required to cluster and activate the Eph receptors [25]. The fact that ephrins are membrane bound allows for the possibility of bi-directional signaling between the cells expressing the ephrin to the cell expressing the Eph receptor. The primary role of Eph signaling is to promote cell positioning that enhances vascular development and does so by activating specific molecules [25]. Evidence suggests that PI3K may be activated by Eph receptors and then affects cytoskeletal rearrangement. Another group of enzymes that are activated by Eph receptors is the src family kinases (SFK) that regulate cellular functions like mitogenesis and cytoskeleton organization. Another possible target for Eph signaling effector molecules are RasGAPs and RhoGAPs, which are negative regulators of cytoskeletal rearrangement (the function of these molecules will be described later).

Finally, PDGF receptors function to regulate smooth muscle cell development [4]. There are two types of PDGF receptors, α and β, that bind both ligands PDGF-A and -B (α) or just PDGF-B (β) with high affinity and can homo or heterodimerize [26]. Mutations in PDGFRβ result in compromised microvasculature, leading to hemorrhaging and edema [4] [26]. Under normal physiological conditions, the receptors function to promote vasculature development and maintenance. The role of PDGFRα is less understood and is believed not to play as significant of a role in angiogenesis. PDGFRβ signals through molecules similar to VEGF receptors, Tie2, and Eph receptors, including PI3K, SFK, RasGAP, phospholipase C, and Grb2 and induce cellular responses such as chemotaxis, proliferation, and gene induction. Ras signaling has been shown to play an important role in post-vasculogenesis events such as maintenance of vasculature integrity.

Growth Factor Stimulation of Angiogenic Factor Expression

Growth factors play a large role in tumor survival and proliferation. One other role that growth factors play is in the regulation of production of tumor-derived angiogenic factors.

Specific activating point mutations of the tumor suppressor, p53, have been shown to regulate genes associated with angiogenesis, growth and metastasis [27] [28]. Using a murine melanoma model transfected with a human p53, it was demonstrated that point mutations at codons 143, 175, 249 or 273 of the p53 gene increased expression of the IGF-I receptor (IGF-IR) by 2.6- to 4.5-fold over wild type control. Similarly, autocrine production of IGF-I increased 1.5- to 2.5-fold in those same cells. VEGF production also increased 1.4- to 6-fold suggesting that specific, activating p53 point mutations regulate expression of genes involved in tumor angiogenesis and growth. Further, coupled with evidence from other laboratories, these data suggest that increased IGF-IR and IGF-I expression may account for the increase in VEGF expression.

The role of IGF-I in the regulation of VEGF expression has been demonstrated for both hepatocellular carcinoma and endometrial adenocarcinoma [29] [29] [30] [31]. Human colon cancer cells treated with IGF-I demonstrate increased VEGF mRNA and protein levels within 2 h after IGF-I treatment. Furthermore, stimulation of the cells with des-(1,3)-IGF-I, an active derivative that does not interact with the IGF-binding proteins, had similar effects on VEGF production [29]. Thus, suggesting that IGF-I regulation of VEGF expression is not further regulated by the IGF-binding proteins.

Similarly, treatment of HEC-1A endometrial adenocarcinoma cells with IGF-I resulted in an increase of VEGF mRNA expression 48 h later [32]. At the 48 h time point, the expression of the 165 isoform was found to be more prominent than the 121 isoform. However, Northern blot analysis demonstrated that the 121 isoform was more stable than the 165 isoform. This study did fail to demonstrate that VEGF promoter activity was increased after IGF-I treatment. Rather, the results suggest that IGF-I regulates VEGF at the posttranscriptional level by enhancing stabilization of the transcripts. Subsequently, the same group demonstrated that insulin treatment of HEC-1A cells had similar results as IGF-I treatment [30]. VEGF mRNA levels were increased and the stability of the message was prolonged 24 h after insulin treatment.

The molecular mechanisms of insulin and IGF-I regulation of VEGF expression has been studied using NIH3T3 cells transfected with and expressing either the insulin receptor (NIH3T3-IR) or the IGF-IR (NIH3T3-IGFR) [33]. A significant increase in VEGF mRNA expression was detected after treatment of these cells with either insulin or IGF-I, respectively. Furthermore, pre-treatment with the PI3K inhibitor wortmannin inhibited insulin-induced VEGF expression in the NIH3T3-IR cells but not IGF-I-induced expression in the NIH3T3-IGFR cells. Similarly, treatment of the cells with PD98059, a pharmacologic inhibitor of the MAPK pathway abolished IGF-I-induced VEGF expression in the NIH3T3-IGFR cells but not insulin-induction in the NIH3T3-IR cells. Therefore, induction of VEGF either by insulin or IGF-I appears to occur through different signal transduction pathways.

A Brief Introduction to the Rho GTPases

Many of the diverse components of the metastatic phenotype are controlled by members of the Ras-superfamily of small GTP-binding proteins. The Ras-superfamily currently boasts in excess of 130 members, which fall into the Ras, Rho, Arf/Sar1 and Rab/Ran-subfamilies (reviewed in [34]) and nearly all cellular functions can be attributed to one or more of these molecules.

All aspects of cell motility and invasion, including cellular polarity, cytoskeletal organization, and transduction of signals from the outside environment are controlled through an interplay between the Rho-GTPases [35] [36] [37] [38] [39] [40] [41] [42] [43] [44] [45]. The Rho-GTPases subfamily consists of small, 20-30 kDa monomeric GTP-binding proteins that are highly conserved throughout evolution in a variety of organisms [46]. Like Ras, Rho proteins are able to bind GDP/GTP and hydrolyze GTP leading to activation of downstream effector molecules subsequently leading to a cellular response [46] [47]. While in their GDP-bound state the GTPases are inactive; conversely when GTP-bound they are active [48] [47] [46].

Rho was first isolated in 1985 due to its homology to Ras (Rho stands for Ras homology) from the sea slug, *Aplysia Californica [46]*. Identification of three closely related human Rho homologues, RhoA, RhoB and RhoC, soon followed [46]. Other members of the Rho-subfamily were later identified in the early 1990's. Human Cdc42 (a homolog of yeast Cdc42), Rac1, Rac2 and Rac3 were found to be distinct in function from the other Rho proteins [48] [49] [50] [51].

In the time since *Aplysia Californica* Rho was first described, 21 Rho-family genes encoding 23 signaling molecules have been identified in humans [45]. These proteins, although related, are distinct from one another and are organized on the Rho "family-tree" by virtue of their structural, biochemical and functional features (reviewed in [52], [45] and [53]). Interestingly, some Rho-family members such as Rnd and RhoH appear to lack intrinsic GTPase activity [54] [55] [56]. Similar to Ras, Rho proteins are localized to the inner plasma membrane by a C-terminal lipid modification. Localization to the plasma membrane is necessary for activation [57].

Out of the nearly two dozen Rho genes that have been identified, four members of the Rho-family, RhoA, RhoB, Rac1 and Cdc42, have been studied extensively. A series of elegant experiments were performed early on to determine the functions of the RhoA, Rac1 and Cdc42 proteins. At nearly the same time that RhoA was identified, C3 exotransferase, a toxin derived from *Clostridium botulinum* was found to effectively target Rho (A, B and C) proteins and later found to have little or no effect on Rac1 or Cdc42 [58] [59] [60] [61]. C3 exotransferase inhibits Rho protein activity by promoting ADP-ribosylation of asparagine 41and thereby inhibiting the interaction between GTP-bound Rho and downstream effector molecules [59]. Although the active state of Rho is unaffected, the GTPase is rendered ineffectual. Using a combination of C3 exotransferase treatment and transfection of cells with man-made, constituatively-active forms of RhoA, the Hall and Ridley groups demonstrated the role of Rho in organizing the actin cytoskeleton, specifically forming bundles of actin stress fibers [62] [47]. Other experiments utilizing either constituatively-active or dominant-negative forms of Rac1 and Cdc42 established those proteins role in forming actin-rich lamellipodia and filopodia, respectively [48] [49] [50]. Thus, the individual role of each of these GTPases in cellular motility was established. Rac1 forms the leading lamellipodial edge of the cell. Cdc42 forms the "ruffles" or "microspikes" known as filopodia, which redistribute the cell membrane to lamellipodium extension as the cell migrates. And RhoA redistributes the actin stress fibers contracting the cell body in the direction of cell movement. Additional roles of Rho proteins have been demonstrated including control of vesicular trafficking, apoptosis, cellular transformation, cell adhesion, angiogenesis and growth control apoptosis [63] [64] [65] [66] [67] [68] [69] [70] [71].

A great deal of excitement ensued over the discovery of Rho-GTPases, as many investigators assumed that due to their homology to Ras, the Rho proteins would also be oncogenes in human cancer. The three isoforms of Ras, Ha-Ras, Ki-Ras and N-Ras, were identified early in the 1980's as oncogenes mutated in a variety of human cancers [72] [73] [74] [75] [76] [77]. Approximately, 30% of human tumors carry an identifiable Ras mutation, which render the GTPase incapable of hydrolyzing bound GTP, thus remaining constitutively active [78]. Breast cancer is the exception, where approximately 5% tumors harbor an activating Ras mutation [79]. However, in contrast to Ras, no mutation in any of the Rho proteins has been identified in human tumors. Rather, overexpression of Rho proteins, particularly RhoA and RhoC, appears to be the rule in human cancers [80] [81] [82] [83] [84] [85] [38] [86] [87].

Rho proteins, like other members of the Ras superfamily, are active when bound to GTP and inactive when bound to GDP. The cycling and exchange between GDP and GTP is controlled by a class of proteins called GEFs (Guanine Nucleotide Exchange Factors) and GAPs (GTPase Activating Proteins), the former being responsible for exchanging GDP for GTP and the latter for catalyzing the hydrolysis of GTP to GDP [67] [88] [89] [89]. In order for Rho GTPases to be active and interact with downstream molecules, they need to be prenylated with the addition of either a farnesyl or geranylgeranyl moiety. Farnesyl and geranyl moieties are cholesterol derivatives associated with the plasma membrane, and their addition to proteins is catalyzed by farnesyltransferase or geranylgeranyltransferase, respectively [90] [91] [92].

The major role of the Rho GTPases is controlling cytoskeletal rearrangement, and hence motility and invasion. They are activated by a variety of signals such as growth factors (IGF, EGF, PDGF, VEGF), interleukins, hormones and steroids (reviewed in [93]). Activation of the GTPases can also be modulated through interaction of the cell with the extracellular environment. Binding of cells to various extracellular matrix proteins via the integrin cell surface receptors can lead to Rho activation and refinement of Rho signaling.

The Rho GTPases and Angiogenic Factors

Nearly every process within a cell is controlled by one or more members of the Rho GTPase family (reviewed in [34] [36]). Without exception so is the process of angiogenesis. Rho proteins play two key roles in this process; 1) control of angiogenic factor production and 2) regulation of endothelial cell motility and migration during the formation of new blood vessels. The next few paragraphs will examine these processes in detail.

Control of Angiogenic Factor Production by Rho GTPases

The concept that the Rho GTPase could affect production of angiogenic factors first originated with experiments demonstrating that activation of the Ras GTPases could lead to expression of pro-angiogenic and inflammatory cytokines [6]. Evidence from Kerbel's group demonstrated that introduction of mutant, constitutatively active Ras could upregulate VEGF-A production in epithelial cells and fibroblasts [94]. Cell lines expressing activated Ki-Ras or H-Ras typically display increased levels of VEGF-A expression but not VEGF-B or –C.

Under normal and hypoxic conditions, control of VEGF transcription by active Ras is thought to occur on multiple levels [95] [96]. Ras signal transduction pathways activate several transcription factors such as AP-2, Spl/3and HIF-1. In addition, overexpression of the translation initiation factor, eIF-4E upregulates VEGF protein levels. The 4E-binding protein 1 (4E-BP1) negatively regulates eIF-4E, and phosphorylation of 4E-BP1 by the Ras Raf Erk cascaded results in increased eIF-4E translation initiation [97] [98].

Because of the distinct homology between the Rho proteins and Ras, and due to the predominance of their expression in human cancers, investigators began to demonstrate that activation of these potent molecular switches could induce pro-angiogenic and inflammatory cytokines. Several of the inflammatory cytokines also have a dual role in stimulating the production of angiogenic factors through either autocrine or paracrine fashion [6]. Transcriptional regulation of acidic FGF has been shown to be controlled by Ras, Rac1 and Cdc42, the latter two are well-characterized members of the Rho family [99]. Ras and Rac1 are able to activate the bFGF promoter *in* vitro; however, it has yet to be shown that these GTPases can transcriptionally regulate bFGF expression *in vivo.*

In a variety of tumor cells, activation of Rac1 by oncogenic Ras, signaling through the stress-activated c-Jun Kinase (JNK) pathway, leads to repression of thromobspondin-1 and -2 (Tsp-1 and Tsp-2) [6] [99]. The thrombospondins are extracellular matrix proteins that act as negative regulators of angiogenesis [99]. Tsp-1 and Tsp-2 interact with various extracellular matrix components, growth factors, and cytokines and have direct effects on endothelial cell viability (reviewed in [99]). Therefore, their negative regulation of angiogenesis is thought to be complex. Regardless, activation of the JNK pathway, leading to phosphorylation of the transcription factor c-Jun leads by activated Ras, leads to repression of Tsp-1. Often, downregulation of Tsp-1 is accompanied by increased VEGF production. Activation of c-Jun alone also represses Tsp-1 transcription.

Evidence demonstrated that RhoA GTPase could induce prostate cancer angiogenesis and interleukin-8 (IL-8) expression in LPS-stimulated human endothelial cells [100]. LPS-stimulation led to activation of the p38-MAPK pathway resulting in expression of VEGF and IL-8. Our laboratory was one of the first to demonstrate that expression and activation of RhoC GTPase, a close homologue of RhoA and RhoB GTPase, induced production of VEGF, basic FGF, IL-8 and IL-6 in mammary epithelial cells that could be detected in cell conditioned medium [89]. We had previously demonstrated that RhoC was predominantly overexpressed in inflammatory breast cancer tumors compared with stage-matched, locally advanced breast cancers [83] [82]. Inflammatory breast cancer is a highly aggressive, angiogenic and lymphogenic form of locally advanced breast cancer [101] [102] [103]. Ectopic overexpression of RhoC in immortalized human mammary epithelial cells leads to transformation and near recapitulation of the inflammatory breast cancer phenotype, including the production of angiogenic factors [82.] Although production of anti-angiogenic factors was not tested, conditioned medium from the RhoC transfected human mammary epithelial cells and from the SUM149 inflammatory breast cancer cell line lead to growth of vessels in a rat aortic ring assay [42,89]. In comparison, conditioned medium from untransfected or control transfected human mammary epithelial cells contained significantly less VEGF, bFGF, IL-8 and IL-6 and did not induce vessel formation in the rat aortic ring assay. Also, inhibition of Rho activity by introducing either active C3 exotransferase or a plasmid coding for C3 exotransferase, significantly inhibited angiogenic factor production and angiogenic factor activity. Through the use of pharmacologic inhibitors of the PI3K and the MAPK pathways, it was demonstrated that similar to what has been observed for RhoA, the p38 arm of the MAPK pathway was responsible for RhoC induced expression of angiogenic factors, in particular VEGF. Both the p38 and extracellular regulated kinase (Erk) arms controlled RhoC-mediated breast cell motility and invasion. Finally, the PI3K pathway was responsible for RhoC-transformation as measured by anchorage independent growth [42]. Recently, Van Den Eynden et. al. presented at the 95th annual meeting of the American Association for Cancer Research tissue microarray analysis and real time PCR to demonstrate a role for RhoC and E-cadherin in increased lymphogenesis and angiogenesis in inflammatory breast cancers compared with stage-matched, non-inflammatory breast cancer cells. Of particular note; they demonstrated a significant increase in VEGF-D production in the inflammatory breast cancer cells, but expression of VEGF-C did not differ between the two types of breast cancers.

Rho GTPase Mediated Endothelial Cell Motility

New blood vessel formation requires the migration of endothelial cells into the area through chemotaxis, largely controlled by the angiogenic factors discussed above. The Rho GTPases regulate motility and migration in virtually every cell studied. These processes within cells are dependent upon internal actin cytoskeletal reorganization, changes in adhesion to the extracellular matrix (ECM), and the link between the two through transmembrane proteins. For any cell to become motile, several steps occur: 1) a protrusion, either a lamellipodia or filipodia, must be extended away from the cell in one direction, 2) new attachments to the ECM must be formed and stabilized, 3) contractile forces must pull the cell forward, usually through the action of myosin-based motors, and 4) the adhesions at the rear of the cell must be released [104].

Lamellipodial and filipodial formation occurs due to an organization of actin filaments into a meshwork at the cell membrane, forming a protrusion [105]. Rac is primarily thought to control lamellipodial formation; in most cases, introduction of dominant negative N17Rac into cells completely prevents lamellipodial formation, while constitutively active V12rac produces broad lamellipodia even in the absence of an exogenous motility factor [48]. A similar observation is made for Cdc42 in filipodial formation [64]. In endothelial cells specifically, Rac activity must be highly controlled for proper migration, as N17Rac prevents lamellipodial formation altogether, while V12rac produces lamellipodia in all directions, preventing proper migration [106]. The two processes that occur for membrane protrusion, actin reorganization and attachment formation, are regulated by different downstream effectors of Rac and Cdc42. Actin reorganization occurs due to GTPase control of actin-associated proteins, such as ARP and cofilin [64] [107]. In contrast, control of attachment formation occurs through Rac and Cdc42 regulation of focal adhesion proteins, such as FAK and PAK, and integrins [64] [108]. Formation of a third type of actin-based structure, the actin stress fiber, is also regulated by Rho GTPases. Actin stress fibers are long actin polymers which stretch throughout the body of the cell and are anchored to the ECM through focal adhesions. These structures may lead to contraction of the cell and stabilization of cell attachments. As motility is critically dependent upon alternating extension/contraction and adhesion/release cycles, the cycling of the Rho GTPases between an active GTP bound state and an inactive GDP bound state is ideal for regulation of this process [104]. Unlike membrane protrusion, stress fiber formation is controlled by the Rho proteins [105]. Retroviral transfer of constitutively active V14RhoA into endothelial cells induces stress fiber formation and cell contractility, whereas dominant negative N19RhoA reduces stress fibers and contractility [96]. Finally, Rho proteins are also implicated in the release of the rear of the cell, allowing forward motility, through regulation of adhesion [104].

Endothelial cell motility and migration are largely controlled by VEGF signaling through the tyrosine kinase receptor VEGFR-2/KDR/Flk-1. VEGF enhances endothelial cell migration; this action is inhibited by either adenoviral transfection of dominant negative RhoA or the Rho kinase inhibitor Y-27632 [109]. VEGFR-2 signaling through the heterotrimeric G protein Gq/11 stimulates endothelial cell migration, which completely requires RhoA activation and partially requires Rac1 activation [110]. This activation of RhoA is also partially inhibited by dominant negative Rac1 [110]. Interestingly, in human foreskin dermal endothelial cells, Rho activation did not occur during VEGF-stimulated chemotaxis; rather Rac mediates chemotaxis in this model [111] [112]. Recent evidence also suggests that Cdc42 downstream from VEGFR-2 is necessary for stress fiber formation and endothelial cells migration, and this occurs in a SAPK2/p38 dependent fashion [113]. Therefore, all of these proteins are likely required for endothelial cell migration in different models and under different conditions.

Control of adhesion proteins, particularly the integrins responsible for cell-ECM adhesion, is critical for proper migration. The αVβ3 integrin heterodimer is essential for neovascularization, both during development and during tumor angiogenesis [114]. The αVβ3 integrin mediates endothelial cell migration through activation of Rac [115]. In addition, VEGF-induced endothelial cell migration requires αVβ3 integrin [116] [114]. Interestingly, not only does αVβ3 regulate Rho GTPases during outside-in signaling, but the GTPases also modulate cell-surface integrin expression in an inside-out fashion. Rac induces clustering of an αVβ3 integrin with high affinity for ECM at the lamellipodia during endothelial cell migration [117]. There are currently multiple drugs either in or near clinical trials that target the αVβ3 integrin to prevent tumor angiogenesis, most notably the humanized form of the αVβ3 integrin antibody LM609, known as Vitaxin [118]. Given the dual role for Rho GTPases in integrin regulation, therapies targeted against the GTPases will also likely be efficacious against angiogenesis.

Angiogenic Factor Expression in Breast Cancer Cells

Background

As evidenced within this chapter, several studies have been completed which demonstrate that expression and activation of the Rho GTPases can affect production of angiogenic factors within tumor cells. The signal transduction pathways leading to expression and activation of angiogenic factors have been explored to a relatively modest extent. The impact of growth factor stimulation on cells, particularly tumor cells, leading to changes in pro-angiogenic and anti-angiogenic factors has also been explored. Finally, the impact of activation of individual Rho GTPases on expression of angiogenic factors has begun to be explored.

To determine whether a metastatic variant of a cell line markedly differed in its Rho GTPase expression and activation profile, and whether this difference has a bearing on expression of angiogenic factors, we compared the MDA MB 231 breast cancer cell line with the MDA 231 BO, metastatic bone variant. The MDA MB 231 cell line was derived from a pleural effusion of a 51-year old Caucasian female in 1973 (cancer cell line database: www.mdanderson.org/departments/cancerbiology/). This cell line is estrogen and progestrone receptor and E-cadherin negative and is highly invasive in an *in vitro* Boyden chamber assay. *In vivo* this cell line is tumorigenic when grown orthotopically in the mammary fat pad. The MDA MB 231 BO cell line was derived from an osseous metastasis formed after intracardiac injection into athymic nude mice and is highly metastatic to bone [119]. Both cell lines are responsive to IGF-I activation.

Methods

Cell Lines and Cell Culture

Both the MDA MB 231 and MDA MB 231 BO cell lines were gifts from Dr. Doug Yee, University of Minnesota. Cells were maintained in 95% and 90% DMEM (Life Technologies, Gaithersburg, MD), respectively, supplemented with 5 μg/ml insulin (Sigma Chemical Co., St. Louis, MO) at 37°C in a 10% CO_2 atmosphere. Prior to stimulation with IGF-I, cells were serum starved for 24 h in IMEM zinc option (Life Technologies). Inhibition of Rho GTPases was carried out by treatment of the cells with 5 μg C3 exotransferase (Cytoskeleton, Denver, CO) as previously described [89] [42]. Briefly, active recombinant C3 exotransferase was introduced into MDA MB 231 and MDA MB 231 BO cells grown in 100 mm dishes, using FuGene6 transfection reagent (Roche, Indianapolis, IN) per the manufactures instructions.

Rho GTPase Expression and Activation

Rho activation assays were performed as previously described [89] [120]. Briefly, the breast cancer cells grown to 70% confluence, serum starved as indicated above, stimulated with 5 nM IGF-I (Adelaide, Australia) and lysed with ice-cold GST-FISH buffer (10% glycerol, 50 mM Tris-HCl, pH 7.4, 100 mM NaCl, 2 mM MgC12, 1% NP-40) at 0, 1, 3, 10 and 30 minutes. Cell lysates, 900 μl of 1 μg/μl, were precleared with gluthione-sepharose 4B (Amersham, Uppsala, Sweden) for 1 h at room temperature. GST-Rhotekin and GST-PAK (a gift from Dr. John Collard of the Netherlands Cancer Institute) was prepared fresh from a 50 ml overnight bacterial culture, stimulated for 2 h with 0.1 mM IPTG (Sigma) to induce GST-fusion protein production. GST-Rhotekin and GST-PAK were bound to 50% slurry of gluthione-sepharose 4B. The cleared lysates were incubated with the GST-Rhotekin-sepharose or GST-PAK-sepharose conjugate at 4°C for 30 min, washed 3 times with GST-FISH buffer, collected by centrifugation, resuspended in Laemelli buffer, separated by SDS-PAGE on an 8-20% Tris-HCl gradient (BioRad, Hercules, CA), transferred to nitrocellulose and probed for either RhoA, RhoB, RhoG, Rac1, Cdc42 (Santa Cruz Biotechnology, Santa Cruz, CA) or RhoC (antibody developed in our laboratory). Total Rho GTPase levels (GTP- and GDP-bound levels) were measured at each time point by Western blot analysis. Aliquots of 30 μg total protein lysate were separated by SDS-PAGE, transferred to nitrocellulose and probed with the corresponding antibodies. Each analysis was performed in triplicate.

Semi-Quantitative PCR

Total RNA was isolated from the MDA-MB-231 and MDA-MB-231 BO cell lines at 0, 1, 3, 10, 30 and 120 minutes after IGF-I stimulation using Trizol reagent (Invitrogen, Carlsbad, CA) according to the manufactures specifications. A 1 μg aliquot of total RNA was then reverse transcribed to form cDNA using the Wizard AMV reverse transcriptase kit (Promega Corp., Madison, WI). PCR reactions were carried out using 5 μg cDNA to probe for expression of angiogenic factors. Primers specific for VEGF-A (5'-GCAGAATCATCACGAAGTGG-3', 5'-GCATGGTGATGTTGGACTCC-3'), VEGF-C (5'-AGACTCAATGCATGCCACG-3', 5'-TTGAGTCATCTCCAGCATCC-3'), basic FGF (5'-AGCGGCTGTACTGCAAAAC-3', 5'-TGTGGCCATTAAAATCAGCTC-3'), And the anti-angiogenic factor thrombospondin-1 (Tsp-1; 5'-GTTCGTCGGAAGGATTTGTTA-3', 5'-TCTATTCCAATGGCAACGAG-3') were used. Primers for GAPDH were used as a loading control.

Results

Rho GTPase Expression and Activation

MDA MB 231 and MDA MB 231 BO cells were grown to 70% confluence, serum starved for 24 h and then stimulated with 5 nM IGF-I. Total protein lysates and active GTPases were harvested at 0, 1, 3, 10 and 30 min. Figure 1. demonstrates that in the MDA MB 231 B0 cells, levels of both total and active RhoA and RhoC increased over time, while RhoB decreased. Rac1, Cdc42 and RhoG remained relatively unchanged. Expression of total Rho GTPase levels appeared to mirror the activation state of the GTPase proteins. In contrast, IGF-I treatment of the MDA 231 cells resulted in an increased in active RhoB and RhoC levels, while the levels of RhoA, Rac1 and Cdc42 levels remained constant over the time course. RhoG activity appeared to decrease in the parental line as well. The total levels of Rho proteins appear to remain relatively constant in these cells over the time course of activation. These data demonstrate a marked difference in IGF-I-induced expression and activation of Rho GTPases in the MDA 231 metastatic variant compared with the parental cell line. Further, these data suggest that increased RhoA and RhoC, along with decreased RhoB, activity resulting from IGF-I stimulation, result in cellular responses that vary between the MDA MB 231 and MDA MB 231 BO lines.

Expression of Angiogenic Factors

To determine whether differences exist in the expression of angiogenic factors, total RNA was isolated from the parental and metastatic MDA 231 cell lines after IGF-I treatment at the time points indicated previously. In addition, to determine whether long-term expression of any angiogenic factor occurred, we included a 120 minute time point. Semi-quantitative RT-PCR was performed for pro-angiogenic factors VEGF-A, VEGF-C, bFGF and the anti-angiogenic factor thrombospondin-1 (Tsp-1). To determine relative expression a GAPDH control RT-PCR was also performed. As shown in Figure 2, expression of angiogenic factors differed between the two cell lines. Expression of Tsp-1 decreased in both cell lines up to 120 min after IGF-I stimulation. VEGF-A and VEGF-C were expressed by the MDA 231 at the 0 min time point and increased 1 min after IGF-I stimulation and lasted up to 120 min. VEGF-A and VEGF-C were expressed in very low levels at the 0 min time point in the MDA 231 BO cell line and similar to the parental cell line increased dramatically at 1 min after stimulation which last up to 120 min. Expression of bFGF in the MDA 231 cell line peaked at 10 min after stimulation and deceased steadily in the longer time points. In the bone metastatic MDA 231 BO cell line bFGF expression decreased over the 120 min time course.

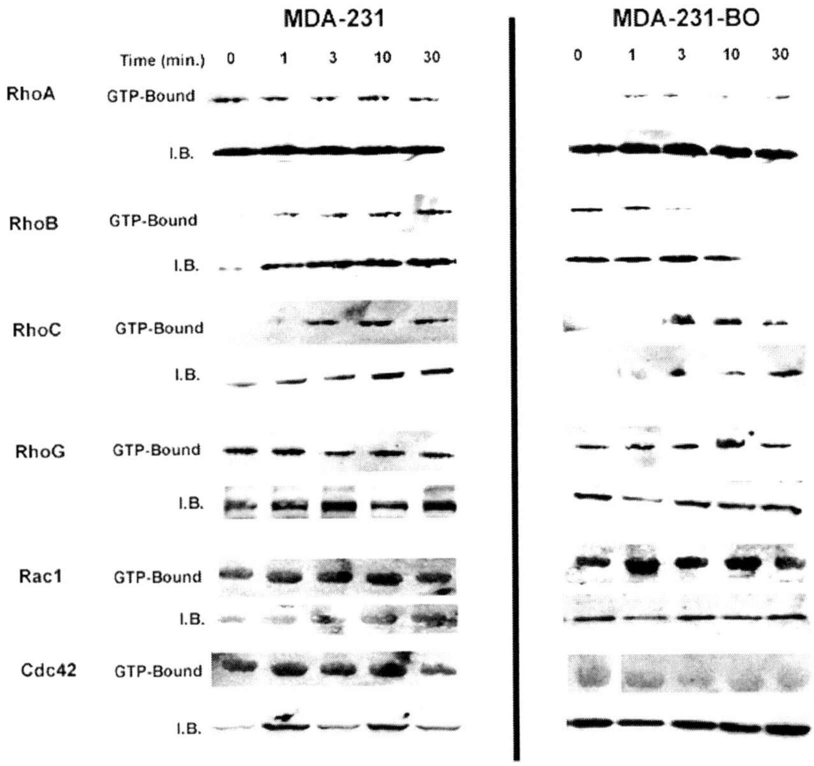

Figure 1. Time course comparison of Rho GTPase expression and activation in the MDA 231 and MDA 231 BO cell lines after IGF-I stimulation. Cells were grown in 100 mm dishes to 70% confluence, serum starved for 24 h and then stimulated with 5 nM IGF-I. Cell lysates were collected at the indicated time points. Either an activation assay determining levels of active, GTP-bound Rho proteins or Western blot analysis for total GTP and GDP-bound Rho proteins was performed. Levels of active RhoB and RhoC increased in the MDA 231 cells, while RhoA, RhoG, Rac1 and Cdc42 essentially remained unchanged. In contrast, active RhoA and RhoC levels increased while RhoB decreased in the MDA 231 BO metastatic variant. Results are representative of three separate analyses.

Because expression of VEGF-A, VEGF-C, bFGF and Tsp-1 has been suggested to be controlled by the Rho GTPases, we set out to determine whether the difference in IGF-I-induced Rho activation and expression between the parental and metastatic MDA 231 cell lines accounted for the differences seen in angiogenic factor expression. Since Rac1 and Cdc42 expression and activation did not change in either cell line due to IGF-I activation, we chose to use C3 exotransferase to inhibit RhoA, RhoB and RhoC. C3 exotransferase is a potent inhibitor of RhoC>RhoA>>RhoB and has been used extensively for studies determining the role of Rho expression and activation in cells [59] [61]. Cells were grown as previously described and serum starved for 24 h. In addition, 5 μg C3 exotransferase was introduced into the cells using a lipoporation method [89]. Total RNA was isolated at the indicated time points and expression of angiogenic factors analyzed by semi-quantitative RT-PCR as before.

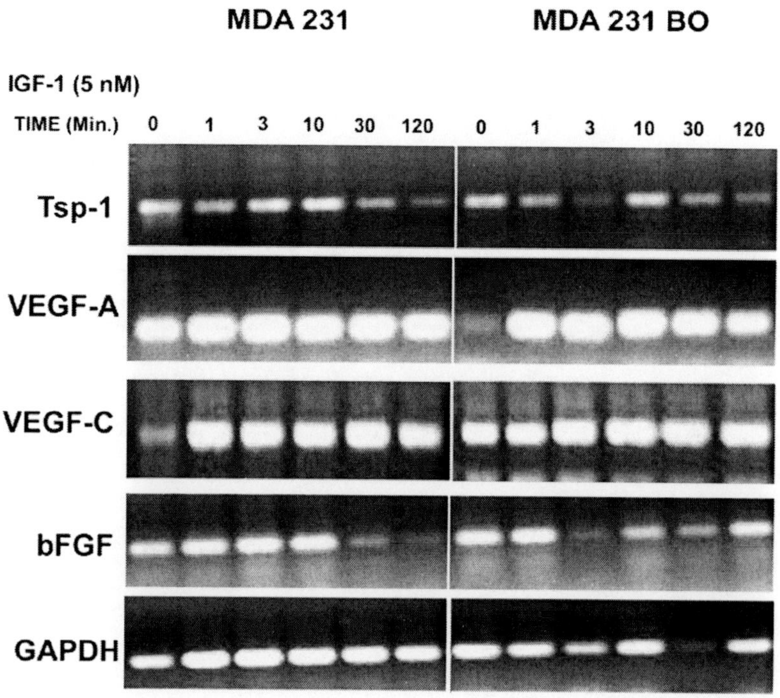

Figure 2. Semi-quantitative RT-PCR for expression of angiogenic factors after IGF-I stimulation. The MDA 231 and MDA 231 BO cells were serum starved and stimulated with IGF-I as previously descried for the Rho GTPase activation assay. Total RNA was harvested at the indicated time points, reverse transcribed to cDNA and then PCR performed using primers specific for thrombospondin-1 (Tsp-1), VEGF-A, VEGF-C and bFGF. PCR for GAPDH was performed as a loading control. Tsp-1 expression decreased over the 2 hour time course in MDA 231 cells, while VEGF-A levels increased slightly. VEGF-C levels increased dramatically 1 minute after stimulation but remained unchanged for the duration of the 2 hour time course. Finally, bFGF levels increased and peaked at 10 minutes after IGF-I stimulation and then decreased dramatically at 30 and 120 minutes. In the MDA 231 BO cells, Tsp-1 levels decreased over the 2 hour time course similar to the parental MDA 231 cell line. Both VEGF-A and –C levels increased and bFGF started higher and decreased over the time course. Levels of expression were normalized against the GAPDH expression. Each experiment was repeated at least three separate times.

Figure 3 demonstrates that overall expression of the angiogenic factors were decreased in both cell lines. More importantly, the IGF-I-induced changes were abrogated by C3 treatment. Of particular interest, Tsp-1 and bFGF expression was nearly non-existent in the C3 treated cells. Whereas, VEGF-A and –C levels were significantly reduced compared to the non-treated cell lines. Thus, these data suggest a difference in angiogenic factor expression which can be attributed to differences in Rho GTPase expression in the MDA 231 and MDA 231 BO breast cancer cell lines.

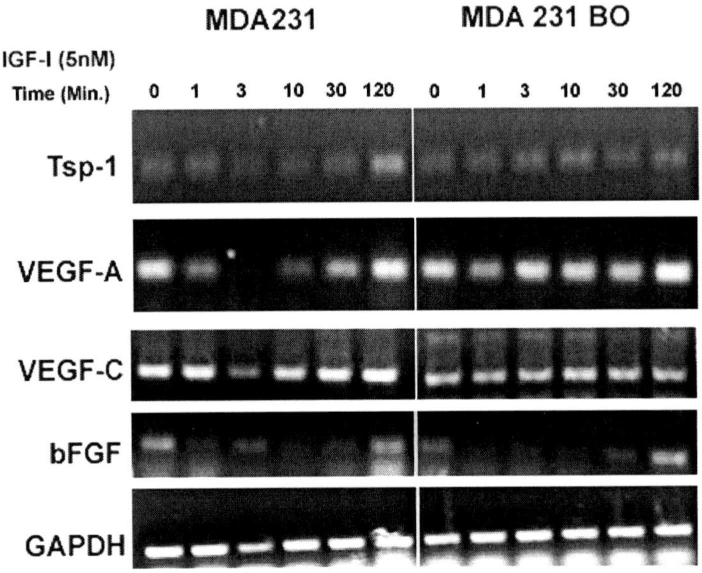

Figure 3. Comparison of angiogenic factor expression in breast cancer cell lines treated with C3 exotransferase. In order to block activity of RhoA, RhoB and RhoC, the MDA 231 and MDA 231 BO cell lines were treated 24 h prior to IGF-I stimulation with C3 exotransferase using a lipoporation method. Expression of angiogenic factors was carried out by semi-quantitative RT-PCR. Aside from the 0 and 120 minute time points, expression of Tsp-1 and bFGF was barely detectable in both cell lines treated with C3 exotransferase. Both VEGF-A and VEGF-C expression levels were also significantly lower in both C3 treated cell lines. The increase in expression after stimulation was altered and significantly less for all angiogenic factors in both cell lines after C3 treatment. Expression was normalized against GAPDH expression. Each experiment was repeated at least three separate times.

Conclusions

It is becoming increasingly evident that the Rho GTPases play a major role in nearly every cellular process, including angiogenesis. Our laboratory, as well as others, has demonstrated that active Rho GTPases can control expression and activation of anti- and pro-angiogenic factors. Thus, anomalous Rho activation can lead to perturbation between these factors, favoring the pro-angiogenic factors, leading to new blood and lymph vessel growth. In addition, the Rho proteins are also intimately involved in endothelial cell proliferation and migration. Without doubt, given the intimate roles of the Rho GTPases in the formation of new blood vessels, therapies targeting Rho proteins will prove efficacious for inhibiting aberrant angiogenesis.

References

[1] Folkman, J. and Klagsbrun, M. Angiogenic factors. *Science, 235*: 442-447, 1987.
[2] Folkman, J. and Shing, Y. Angiogenesis. *J.Biol.Chem., 267*: 10931-10934, 1992.
[3] Folkman, J. Angiogenesis and apoptosis. *Semin.Cancer Biol., 13*: 159-167, 2003.

[4] Tallquist, M. D., Soriano, P., and Klinghoffer, R. A. Growth factor signaling pathways in vascular development. *Oncogene, 18*: 7917-7932, 1999.

[5] Endo, A., Fukuhara, S., Masuda, M., Ohmori, T., and Mochizuki, N. Selective inhibition of vascular endothelial growth factor receptor-2 (VEGFR-2) identifies a central role for VEGFR-2 in human aortic endothelial cell responses to VEGF. *J.Recept.Signal.Transduct.Res., 23*: 239-254, 2003.

[6] Kranenburg, O., Gebbink, M. F., and Voest, E. E. Stimulation of angiogenesis by Ras proteins. Biochim.Biophys.*Acta, 1654*: 23-37, 2004.

[7] Scavelli, C., Vacca, A., Di Pietro, G., Dammacco, F., and Ribatti, D. Crosstalk between angiogenesis and lymphangiogenesis in tumor progression. *Leukemia, 18*: 1054-1058, 2004.

[8] He, Y., Karpanen, T., and Alitalo, K. Role of lymphangiogenic factors in tumor metastasis. *Biochim.Biophys.Acta, 1654*: 3-12, 2004.

[9] Gospodarowicz, D., Brown, K. D., Birdwell, C. R., and Zetter, B. R. Control of proliferation of human vascular endothelial cells. Characterization of the response of human umbilical vein endothelial cells to fibroblast growth factor, epidermal growth factor, and thrombin. *J.Cell Biol., 77*: 774-788, 1978.

[10] Jeltsch, M., Kaipainen, A., Joukov, V., Meng, X., Lakso, M., Rauvala, H., Swartz, M., Fukumura, D., Jain, R. K., and Alitalo, K. Hyperplasia of lymphatic vessels in VEGF-C transgenic mice. *Science, 276*: 1423-1425, 1997.

[11] Vassar, R., Rosenberg, M., Ross, S., Tyner, A., and Fuchs, E. Tissue-specific and differentiation-specific expression of a human K14 keratin gene in transgenic mice. *Proc.Natl.Acad.Sci.U.S.A, 86*: 1563-1567, 1989.

[12] Karkkainen, M. J., Haiko, P., Sainio, K., Partanen, J., Taipale, J., Petrova, T. V., Jeltsch, M., Jackson, D. G., Talikka, M., Rauvala, H., Betsholtz, C., and Alitalo, K. Vascular endothelial growth factor C is required for sprouting of the first lymphatic vessels from embryonic veins. *Nat.Immunol., 5*: 74-80, 2004.

[13] Dumont, D. J., Jussila, L., Taipale, J., Lymboussaki, A., Mustonen, T., Pajusola, K., Breitman, M., and Alitalo, K. Cardiovascular failure in mouse embryos deficient in VEGF receptor-3. *Science, 282*: 946-949, 1998.

[14] He, Y., Kozaki, K. i., Karpanen, T., Koshikawa, K., Yla-Herttuala, S., Takahashi, T., and Alitalo, K. Suppression of Tumor Lymphangiogenesis and Lymph Node Metastasis by Blocking Vascular Endothelial Growth Factor Receptor 3 Signaling. *J Natl Cancer Inst, 94*: 819-825, 2002.

[15] Joukov, V., Pajusola, K., Kaipainen, A., Chilov, D., Lahtinen, I., Kukk, E., Saksela, O., Kalkkinen, N., and Alitalo, K. A novel vascular endothelial growth factor, VEGF-C, is a ligand for the Flt4 (VEGFR-3) and KDR (VEGFR-2) receptor tyrosine kinases. *EMBO J., 15*: 290-298, 1996.

[16] Achen, M. G., Jeltsch, M., Kukk, E., Makinen, T., Vitali, A., Wilks, A. F., Alitalo, K., and Stacker, S. A. Vascular endothelial growth factor D (VEGF-D) is a ligand for the tyrosine kinases VEGF receptor 2 (Flk1) and VEGF receptor 3 (Flt4). *Proc.Natl.Acad.Sci.U.S.A, 95*: 548-553, 1998.

[17] Gale, N. W., Thurston, G., Hackett, S. F., Renard, R., Wang, Q., McClain, J., Martin, C., Witte, C., Witte, M. H., Jackson, D., Suri, C., Campochiaro, P. A., Wiegand, S. J., and Yancopoulos, G. D. Angiopoietin-2 is required for postnatal angiogenesis and

lymphatic patterning, and only the latter role is rescued by Angiopoietin-1. *Dev.Cell, 3*: 411-423, 2002.

[18] Patan, S. Vasculogenesis and angiogenesis. *Cancer Treat. Res.,* 117: 3-32, 2004.

[19] Patan, S. TIE1 and TIE2 receptor tyrosine kinases inversely regulate embryonic angiogenesis by the mechanism of intussusceptive microvascular growth. *Microvasc.Res., 56*: 1-21, 1998.

[20] Dumont, D. J., Gradwohl, G., Fong, G. H., Puri, M. C., Gertsenstein, M., Auerbach, A., and Breitman, M. L. Dominant-negative and targeted null mutations in the endothelial receptor tyrosine kinase, tek, reveal a critical role in vasculogenesis of the embryo. *Genes Dev., 8*: 1897-1909, 1994.

[21] Suri, C., Jones, P. F., Patan, S., Bartunkova, S., Maisonpierre, P. C., Davis, S., Sato, T. N., and Yancopoulos, G. D. Requisite role of angiopoietin-1, a ligand for the TIE2 receptor, during embryonic angiogenesis. *Cell, 87*: 1171-1180, 1996.

[22] Puri, M. C. and Bernstein, A. Requirement for the TIE family of receptor tyrosine kinases in adult but not fetal hematopoiesis. *Proc.Natl.Acad.Sci.U.S.A, 100*: 12753-12758, 2003.

[23] Jones, N. and Dumont, D. J. The Tek/Tie2 receptor signals through a novel Dok-related docking protein, Dok-R. *Oncogene, 17*: 1097-1108, 1998.

[24] Korpelainen, E. I., Karkkainen, M., Gunji, Y., Vikkula, M., and Alitalo, K. Endothelial receptor tyrosine kinases activate the STAT signaling pathway: mutant Tie-2 causing venous malformations signals a distinct STAT activation response. *Oncogene, 18*: 1-8, 1999.

[25] Himanen, J. P. and Nikolov, D. B. Eph receptors and ephrins. *Int.J.Biochem.Cell Biol., 35*: 130-134, 2003.

[26] Yu, J., Ustach, C., and Kim, H. R. Platelet-derived growth factor signaling and human cancer. *J.Biochem.Mol.Biol., 36*: 49-59, 2003.

[27] Koura, A. N., van Golen, K. L., Tsan, R., Radinsky, R., Price, J. E., and Ellis, L. M. Regulation of genes associated with angiogenesis, growth and metastasis by specific p53 point mutations in a murine melanoma cell line. *Oncology Reports., 4*: 475-479, 1997.

[28] Koura, A. N., van Golen, K. L., Price, J. E., Tsan, R., Radinsky, R., and Ellis, L. M. Regulation of Angiogenesis, Growth, and Metastasis-Related Genes by Specific p53 Point Mutations in a Transfected Melanoma Cell Line. XL VII. 1996. American College of Surgeons.

[29] Akagi, Y., Liu, W., Zebrowski, B., Xie, K., and Ellis, L. M. Regulation of vascular endothelial growth factor expression in human colon cancer by insulin-like growth factor-I. *Cancer Res., 58*: 4008-4014, 1998.

[30] Bermont, L., Lamielle, F., Lorchel, F., Fauconnet, S., Esumi, H., Weisz, A., and Adessi, G. L. Insulin up-regulates vascular endothelial growth factor and stabilizes its messengers in endometrial adenocarcinoma cells. *J.Clin.Endocrinol. Metab, 86*: 363-368, 2001.

[31] Wang, D. S., Yamazaki, K., Nohtomi, K., Shizume, K., Ohsumi, K., Shibuya, M., Demura, H., and Sato, K. Increase of vascular endothelial growth factor mRNA expression by 1,25-dihydroxyvitamin D3 in human osteoblast-like cells. *J.Bone Miner.Res., 11*: 472-479, 1996.

[32] Bermont, L., Lamielle, F., Fauconnet, S., Esumi, H., Weisz, A., and Adessi, G. L. Regulation of vascular endothelial growth factor expression by insulin-like growth factor-I in endometrial adenocarcinoma cells. *Int. J. Cancer, 85*: 117-123, 2000.

[33] Miele, C., Rochford, J. J., Filippa, N., Giorgetti-Peraldi, S., and Van Obberghen, E. Insulin and insulin-like growth factor-I induce vascular endothelial growth factor mRNA expression via different signaling pathways. *J. Biol. Chem., 275*: 21695-21702, 2000.

[34] Takai, Y., Sasaki, T., and Matozaki, T. Small GTP-binding proteins. *Physiol Rev, 81*: 153-208, 2001.

[35] Kjoller, L. and Hall, A. Signaling to Rho GTPases. *Exp. Cell Res*, 253: 166-179, 1999.

[36] Sahai, E. and Marshall, C. J. RHO-GTPases and Cancer. Nature Reviews - *Cancer, 2*: 133-142, 2002.

[37] Sander, E. E., ten Klooster, J. P., van Delft, S., van der Kammen, R. A., and Collard, J. G. Rac downregulates Rho activity: reciprocal balance between both GTPases determines cellular morphology and migratory behavior. *J Cell Biol, 147*: 1009-1022, 1999.

[38] del Peso, L., Hernandez-Alcoceba, R., Embade, N., Carnero, A., Esteve, P., Paje, C., and Lacal, J. C. Rho proteins induce metastatic properties in vivo. *Oncogene, 15*: 3047-3057, 1997.

[39] Zondag, G. C., Evers, E. E., ten Klooster, J. P., Janssen, L., van der Kammen, R. A., and Collard, J. G. Oncogenic Ras downregulates Rac activity, which leads to increased Rho activity and epithelial-mesenchymal transition. *J Cell Biol, 149*: 775-782, 2000.

[40] Frost, J. A., Steen, H., Shapiro, P., Lewis, T., Ahn, N., Shaw, P. E., and Cobb, M. H. Cross-cascade activation of ERKs and ternary complex factors by Rho family proteins. *EMBO J, 16*: 6426-6438, 1997.

[41] Li, W., Chong, H., and Guan, K. L. Function of the Rho family GTPases in Ras-stimulated Raf activation. *J Biol Chem, 276*: 34728-34737, 2001.

[42] van Golen, K. L., Bao, L. W., Pan, Q., Miller, F. R., Wu, Z. F., and Merajver, S. D. Mitogen activated protein kinase pathway is involved in RhoC GTPase induced motility, invasion and angiogenesis in inflammatory breast cancer. *Clin.Exp.Metastasis, 19*: 301-311, 2002.

[43] Danen, E. H., Sonneveld, P., Sonnenberg, A., and Yamada, K. M. Dual stimulation of Ras/mitogen-activated protein kinase and RhoA by cell adhesion to fibronectin supports growth factor-stimulated cell cycle progression. *J Cell Biol, 151*: 1413-1422, 2000.

[44] Wittmann, T. and Waterman-Storer, C. M. Cell motility: can Rho GTPases and microtubules point the way? *J Cell Sci, 114*: 3795-3803, 2001.

[45] Ridley, A. J. Rho family proteins: coordinating cell responses. *Trends Cell Biol, 11*: 471-477, 2001.

[46] Madaule, P. and Axel, R. A novel ras-related gene family. *Cell*, 41: 31-40, 1985.

[47] Ridley, A. J. and Hall, A. The small GTP-binding protein rho regulates the assembly of focal adhesions and actin stress fibers in response to growth factors. *Cell, 70*: 389-399, 1992.

[48] Ridley, A. J., Paterson, H. F., Johnston, C. L., Diekmann, D., and Hall, A. The small GTP-binding protein rac regulates growth factor-induced membrane ruffling. *Cell, 70*: 401-410, 1992.

[49] Nobes, C. D. and Hall, A. Rho, rac, and cdc42 GTPases regulate the assembly of multimolecular focal complexes associated with actin stress fibers, lamellipodia, and filopodia. *Cell, 81*: 53-62, 1995.
[50] Ridley, A. J. and Hall, A. Distinct patterns of actin organization regulated by the small GTP- binding proteins Rac and Rho. *Cold Spring Harb.Symp.Quant.Biol, 57*: 661-671, 1992.
[51] Kozma, R., Ahmed, S., Best, A., and Lim, L. The Ras-related protein Cdc42Hs and bradykinin promote formation of peripheral actin microspikes and filopodia in Swiss 3T3 fibroblasts. *Mol.Cell Biol, 15*: 1942-1952, 1995.
[52] Wherlock, M. and Mellor, H. The Rho GTPase family: a Racs to Wrchs story. *J Cell Sci, 115*: 239-240, 2002.
[53] Lin, M. and van Golen, K. L. Rho-regulatory proteins in breast cancer cell motility and invasion. *Breast Cancer Res Treat.*, 2003.
[54] Dallery, E., Galiegue-Zouitina, S., Collyn-d'Hooghe, M., Quief, S., Denis, C., Hildebrand, M. P., Lantoine, D., Deweindt, C., Tilly, H., Bastard, C., and TTF, a gene encoding a novel small G protein, fuses to the lymphoma- associated LAZ3 gene by t(3;4) chromosomal translocation. *Oncogene, 10*: 2171-2178, 1995.
[55] Nobes, C. D., Lauritzen, I., Mattei, M. G., Paris, S., Hall, A., and Chardin, P. A new member of the Rho family, Rnd1, promotes disassembly of actin filament structures and loss of cell adhesion. *J Cell Biol, 141*: 187-197, 1998.
[56] Dallery-Prudhomme, E., Roumier, C., Denis, C., Preudhomme, C., Kerckaert, J. P., and Galiegue-Zouitina, S. Genomic structure and assignment of the RhoH/TTF small GTPase gene (ARHH) to 4p13 by in situ hybridization. *Genomics, 43*: 89-94, 1997.
[57] Hori, Y., Kikuchi, A., Isomura, M., Katayama, M., Miura, Y., Fujioka, H., Kaibuchi, K., and Takai, Y. Post-translational modifications of the C-terminal region of the rho protein are important for its interaction with membranes and the stimulatory and inhibitory GDP/GTP exchange proteins. *Oncogene, 6*: 515-522, 1991.
[58] Fritz, G., Kaina, B., and Aktories, K. The ras-related small GTP-binding protein RhoB is immediate-early inducible by DNA damaging treatments. *J Biol Chem, 270*: 25172-25177, 1995.
[59] Aktories, K. Rho proteins: targets for bacterial toxins. *Trends Microbiol., 5*: 282-288, 1997.
[60] Aktories, K. and Hall, A. Botulinum ADP-ribosyltransferase C3: a new tool to study low molecular weight GTP-binding proteins. *Trends Pharmacol.Sci, 10*: 415-418, 1989.
[61] Aktories, K., Braun, U., Rosener, S., Just, I., and Hall, A. The rho gene product expressed in E. coli is a substrate of botulinum ADP-ribosyltransferase C3. Biochem.*Biophys.Res Commun., 158*: 209-213, 1989.
[62] Paterson, H. F., Self, A. J., Garrett, M. D., Just, I., Aktories, K., and Hall, A. Microinjection of recombinant p21rho induces rapid changes in cell morphology. *J Cell Biol, 111*: 1001-1007, 1990.
[63] Hall, A. The cellular functions of small GTP-binding proteins. Science, 249: 635-640, 1990.
[64] Hall, A. Rho GTPases and the actin cytoskeleton. *Science, 279*: 509-514, 1998.
[65] Ridley, A. J. Membrane ruffling and signal transduction. *Bioessays, 16*: 321-327, 1994.
[66] Price, L. S. and Collard, J. G. Regulation of the cytoskeleton by Rho-family GTPases: implications for tumour cell invasion. Semin.*Cancer Biol, 11*: 167-173, 2001.

[67] Evers, E. E., van der Kammen, R. A., ten Klooster, J. P., and Collard, J. G. Rho-like GTPases in tumor cell invasion. *Methods Enzymol., 325*: 403-415, 2000.

[68] Gampel, A., Parker, P. J., and Mellor, H. Regulation of epidermal growth factor receptor traffic by the small GTPase rhoB. *Curr.Biol, 9*: 955-958, 1999.

[69] Esteve, P., Embade, N., Perona, R., Jimenez, B., del Peso, L., Leon, J., Arends, M., Miki, T., and Lacal, J. C. Rho-regulated signals induce apoptosis in vitro and in vivo by a p53- independent, but Bcl2 dependent pathway. *Oncogene, 17*: 1855-1869, 1998.

[70] Coleman, M. L. and Olson, M. F. Rho GTPase signalling pathways in the morphological changes associated with apoptosis. *Cell Death.Differ., 9*: 493-504, 2002.

[71] Cussac, D., Leblanc, P., L'Heritier, A., Bertoglio, J., Lang, P., Kordon, C., Enjalbert, A., and Saltarelli, D. Rho proteins are localized with different membrane compartments involved in vesicular trafficking in anterior pituitary cells. Mol.*Cell Endocrinol., 119*: 195-206, 1996.

[72] Hall, A., Marshall, C. J., Spurr, N. K., and Weiss, R. A. Identification of transforming gene in two human sarcoma cell lines as a new member of the ras gene family located on chromosome 1. *Nature, 303*: 396-400, 1983.

[73] Brown, R., Marshall, C. J., Pennie, S. G., and Hall, A. Mechanism of activation of an N-ras gene in the human fibrosarcoma cell line HT1080. *EMBO J, 3*: 1321-1326, 1984.

[74] McGrath, J. P., Capon, D. J., Smith, D. H., Chen, E. Y., Seeburg, P. H., Goeddel, D. V., and Levinson, A. D. Structure and organization of the human Ki-ras proto-oncogene and a related processed pseudogene. *Nature, 304*: 501-506, 1983.

[75] Capon, D. J., Seeburg, P. H., McGrath, J. P., Hayflick, J. S., Edman, U., Levinson, A. D., and Goeddel, D. V. Activation of Ki-ras2 gene in human colon and lung carcinomas by two different point mutations. *Nature, 304*: 507-513, 1983.

[76] Feramisco, J. R., Gross, M., Kamata, T., Rosenberg, M., and Sweet, R. W. Microinjection of the oncogene form of the human H-ras (T-24) protein results in rapid proliferation of quiescent cells. *Cell, 38*: 109-117, 1984.

[77] Stacey, D. W. and Kung, H. F. Transformation of NIH 3T3 cells by microinjection of Ha-ras p21 protein. *Nature, 310*: 508-511, 1984.

[78] Rodenhuis, S. ras and human tumors. Semin. *Cancer Biol, 3*: 241-247, 1992.

[79] Rochlitz, C. F., Scott, G. K., Dodson, J. M., Liu, E., Dollbaum, C., Smith, H. S., and Benz, C. C. Incidence of activating ras oncogene mutations associated with primary and metastatic human breast cancer. *Cancer Res, 49*: 357-360, 1989.

[80] Fritz, G., Just, I., and Kaina, B. Rho GTPases are over-expressed in human tumors. Int. *J Cancer, 81*: 682-687, 1999.

[81] Moscow, J. A., He, R., Gnarra, J. R., Knutsen, T., Weng, Y., Zhao, W. P., Whang-Peng, J., Linehan, W. M., and Cowan, K. H. Examination of human tumors for rhoA mutations. *Oncogene, 9:* 189-194, 1994.

[82] van Golen, K. L., Wu, Z. F., Qiao, X. T., Bao, L. W., and Merajver, S. D. RhoC GTPase, a novel transforming oncogene for human mammary epithelial cells that partially recapitulates the inflammatory breast cancer phenotype. *Cancer Res, 60*: 5832-5838, 2000.

[83] van Golen, K. L., Davies, S., Wu, Z. F., Wang, Y., Bucana, C. D., Root, H., Chandrasekharappa, S., Strawderman, M., Ethier, S. P., and Merajver, S. D. A novel putative low-affinity insulin-like growth factor-binding protein, LIBC (lost in

inflammatory breast cancer), and RhoC GTPase correlate with the inflammatory breast cancer phenotype. *Clin. Cancer Res, 5*: 2511-2519, 1999.

[84] Imamura, F., Mukai, M., Ayaki, M., Takemura, K., Horai, T., Shinkai, K., Nakamura, H., and Akedo, H. Involvement of small GTPases Rho and Rac in the invasion of rat ascites hepatoma cells. *Clin. Exp. Metastasis, 17*: 141-148, 1999.

[85] Clark, E. A., Golub, T. R., Lander, E. S., and Hynes, R. O. Genomic analysis of metastasis reveals an essential role for RhoC. *Nature, 406*: 532-535, 2000.

[86] Cheng, J. C., Frackelton, A. R., Jr., Bearer, E. L., Kumar, P. S., Kannan, B., Santos-Moore, A., Rifai, A., Settleman, J., and Clark, J. W. Changes in tyrosine-phosphorylated p190 and its association with p120 type I and p100 type II rasGAPs during myelomonocytic differentiation of human leukemic cells. *Cell Growth Differ., 6*: 139-148, 1995.

[87] Avraham, H. rho gene amplification and malignant transformation. Biochem.Biophys.*Res Commun., 168*: 114-124, 1990.

[88] Diekmann, D. and Hall, A. In vitro binding assay for interactions of Rho and Rac with GTPase- activating proteins and effectors. *Methods Enzymol., 256*: 207-215, 1995.

[89] van Golen, K. L., Wu, Z. F., Qiao, X. T., Bao, L., and Merajver, S. D. RhoC GTPase overexpression modulates induction of angiogenic factors in breast cells. *Neoplasia., 2:* 418-425, 2000.

[90] Hancock, J. F., Cadwallader, K., Paterson, H., and Marshall, C. J. A CAAX or a CAAL motif and a second signal are sufficient for plasma membrane targeting of ras proteins. *EMBO J, 10*: 4033-4039, 1991.

[91] Kirschmeier, P. T., Whyte, D., Wilson, O., Bishop, W. R., and Pai, J. K. In vivo prenylation analysis of Ras and Rho proteins. *Methods Enzymol., 332*: 115-127, 2001.

[92] Lebowitz, P. F. and Prendergast, G. C. Non-Ras targets of farnesyltransferase inhibitors: focus on Rho. *Oncogene, 17*: 1439-1445, 1998.

[93] van Golen, K. L. Inflammatory Breast Cancer: Relationship between growth factor signaling and motility in aggressive cancers. *Breast Cancer Research, 5*: 174, 2003.

[94] Rak, J., Mitsuhashi, Y., Bayko, L., Filmus, J., Shirasawa, S., Sasazuki, T., and Kerbel, R. S. Mutant ras oncogenes upregulate VEGF/VPF expression: implications for induction and inhibition of tumor angiogenesis. *Cancer Res., 55*: 4575-4580, 1995.

[95] Feldkamp, M. M., Lau, N., Rak, J., Kerbel, R. S., and Guha, A. Normoxic and hypoxic regulation of vascular endothelial growth factor (VEGF) by astrocytoma cells is mediated by Ras. *Int.J.Cancer, 81*: 118-124, 1999.

[96] Okada, F., Rak, J. W., Croix, B. S., Lieubeau, B., Kaya, M., Roncari, L., Shirasawa, S., Sasazuki, T., and Kerbel, R. S. Impact of oncogenes in tumor angiogenesis: mutant K-ras up-regulation of vascular endothelial growth factor/vascular permeability factor is necessary, but not sufficient for tumorigenicity of human colorectal carcinoma cells. *Proc.Natl.Acad.Sci.U.S.A, 95*: 3609-3614, 1998.

[97] Kevil, C. G., De Benedetti, A., Payne, D. K., Coe, L. L., Laroux, F. S., and Alexander, J. S. Translational regulation of vascular permeability factor by eukaryotic initiation factor 4E: implications for tumor angiogenesis. *Int. J. Cancer, 65:* 785-790, 1996.

[98] Herbert, T. P., Tee, A. R., and Proud, C. G. The extracellular signal-regulated kinase pathway regulates the phosphorylation of 4E-BP1 at multiple sites. *J. Biol. Chem., 277*: 11591-11596, 2002.

[99] Wojciak-Stothard, B. and Ridley, A. J. Rho GTPases and the regulation of endothelial permeability. *Vascul. Pharmacol., 39*: 187-199, 2002.

[100] Hippenstiel, S., Soeth, S., Kellas, B., Fuhrmann, O., Seybold, J., Krull, M., Eichel-Streiber, C., Goebeler, M., Ludwig, S., and Suttorp, N. Rho proteins and the p38-MAPK pathway are important mediators for LPS-induced interleukin-8 expression in human endothelial cells. *Blood, 95*: 3044-3051, 2000.

[101] American Cancer Society. Cancer Facts & Figures 2003. 2003. Ref Type: Pamphlet.

[102] Kleer, C. G., van Golen, K. L., and Merajver, S. D. Molecular biology of breast cancer metastasis. Inflammatory breast cancer: clinical syndrome and molecular determinants. *Breast Cancer Res, 2:* 423-429, 2000.

[103] Jaiyesimi, I. A., Buzdar, A. U., and Hortobagyi, G. Inflammatory breast cancer: a review. *J Clin.Oncol., 10*: 1014-1024, 1992.

[104] Lauffenburger, D. A. and Horwitz, A. F. Cell migration: a physically integrated molecular process. *Cell, 84*: 359-369, 1996.

[105] Nobes, C. D. and Hall, A. Rho, rac and cdc42 GTPases: regulators of actin structures, cell adhesion and motility. *Biochem.Soc.Trans., 23*: 456-459, 1995.

[106] Hu, Y. L., Li, S., Miao, H., Tsou, T. C., del Pozo, M. A., and Chien, S. Roles of microtubule dynamics and small GTPase Rac in endothelial cell migration and lamellipodium formation under flow. *J.Vasc.Res., 39*: 465-476, 2002.

[107] Meyer, G. and Feldman, E. L. Signaling mechanisms that regulate actin-based motility processes in the nervous system. *J.Neurochem., 83*: 490-503, 2002.

[108] Huttenlocher, A., Sandborg, R. R., and Horwitz, A. F. Adhesion in cell migration. Curr.*Opin.Cell Biol., 7*: 697-706, 1995.

[109] Nieuw Amerongen, G. P., Koolwijk, P., Versteilen, A., and van Hinsbergh, V. W. Involvement of RhoA/Rho kinase signaling in VEGF-induced endothelial cell migration and angiogenesis in vitro. Arterioscler.*Thromb.Vasc.Biol., 23*: 211-217, 2003.

[110] Zeng, H., Zhao, D., and Mukhopadhyay, D. KDR stimulates endothelial cell migration through heterotrimeric G protein Gq/11-mediated activation of a small GTPase RhoA. *J.Biol.Chem., 277*: 46791-46798, 2002.

[111] Soga, N., Namba, N., McAllister, S., Cornelius, L., Teitelbaum, S. L., Dowdy, S. F., Kawamura, J., and Hruska, K. A. Rho family GTPases regulate VEGF-stimulated endothelial cell motility. *Exp.Cell Res., 269*: 73-87, 2001.

[112] Soga, N., Connolly, J. O., Chellaiah, M., Kawamura, J., and Hruska, K. A. Rac regulates vascular endothelial growth factor stimulated motility. *Cell Commun. Adhes., 8*: 1-13, 2001.

[113] Lamalice, L., Houle, F., Jourdan, G., and Huot, J. Phosphorylation of tyrosine 1214 on VEGFR2 is required for VEGF-induced activation of Cdc42 upstream of SAPK2/p38. *Oncogene, 23*: 434-445, 2004.

[114] Hutchings, H., Ortega, N., and Plouet, J. Extracellular matrix-bound vascular endothelial growth factor promotes endothelial cell adhesion, migration, and survival through integrin ligation. *FASEB J., 17*: 1520-1522, 2003.

[115] Ruegg, C., Dormond, O., and Mariotti, A. Endothelial cell integrins and COX-2: mediators and therapeutic targets of tumor angiogenesis. *Biochim. Biophys. Acta*, 1654: 51-67, 2004.

[116] Masson-Gadais, B., Houle, F., Laferriere, J., and Huot, J. Integrin alphavbeta3, requirement for VEGFR2-mediated activation of SAPK2/p38 and for Hsp90-dependent phosphorylation of focal adhesion kinase in endothelial cells activated by VEGF. Cell Stress. *Chaperones., 8*: 37-52, 2003.

[117] Kiosses, W. B., Shattil, S. J., Pampori, N., and Schwartz, M. A. Rac recruits high-affinity integrin alphavbeta3 to lamellipodia in endothelial cell migration. *Nat.Cell Biol., 3:* 316-320, 2001.

[118] Jin, H. and Varner, J. Integrins: roles in cancer development and as treatment targets. *Br.J.Cancer, 90*: 561-565, 2004.

[119] Jackson, J. G., Zhang, X., Yoneda, T., and Yee, D. Regulation of breast cancer cell motility by insulin receptor substrate- 2 (IRS-2) in metastatic variants of human breast cancer cell lines. *Oncogene, 20*: 7318-7325, 2001.

[120] Pan, Q., Kleer, C. G., van Golen, K. L., Irani, J., Bottema, K., Bias, C., De Carvello, M., Mesri, E. A., Robins, D. M., Dick, R. D., Brewer, G. J., and Merajver, S. D. Copper Defiiency Induced by Tetrathiomolybdate Suppresses Tumor Growth and Angiogenesis. *Molecular Cancer Therapeutics, 62*: 4854-4859, 2002.

In: New Angiogenesis Research
Editor: Roberta V. Zubar, pp. 43-62
ISBN 1-59454-239-2

Chapter III

Nitric Oxide and Angiogenesis

Weiming Xu**, Mohamed Ahmed and Gang Xu
Wolfson Institute for Biomedical Research. University College London
University of Leicester, Leicester Medical School, UK

Abstract

In the early 1980's, scientists discovered a gas molecule, nitric oxide [NO], previously considered to be merely atmospheric pollutant, is a critical signaling molecule for endothelium-dependent relaxing in blood vessel. Since then, a great scientific advance has been made to understand how and why this gas is made in the body. We know NO is formed in the body by a family of isoenzymes, called nitric oxide synthase [NOS], which use L-arginine and molecular oxygen to produce nitric oxide and its by product, citrillune. In this article, we will give a general review of latest advance on the gene expression pattern of nitric oxide synthase [NOS] in tumors and its possible role in tumour angiogenesis. Especially, we will present an immunohistochemical study on the abnormal eNOS expression pattern in *in situ* breast cancer carcinoma and its relation with other angiogenesis factor, such as CD31. The finding may provide a support for the balance hypothesis for the angiogenic switch in tumor formation. Furthermore, the role of NOS family in human disease is described and possible molecular intervention, including gene therapy will be discussed to give reader a relative overview on nitric oxide and angiogenesis.

Introduction: Discovery of Magic Gas- Nitric Oxide [NO] in the Endothium of Blood Vessel

Scientific breakthrough often comes from unexpected results, and pursuing adventurous research. In the early 80's at the New York Laboratory of Suny health centre, Dr. Robert

* Correspondence concerning this article should be addressed to Dr. Weiming Xu, Wolfson Institute for Biomedical Research. University College London, Cruciform Building, Gower Street, London WC1E 6AU.UK. Email: w.xu@ucl.ac.uk.

Furchgott was presented contradicting results by his two technicians. One technician always found the acetylcholine relaxed the blood vessel. Where as the other, found it always caused contraction. Furchgott noticed that one technician handled the vessels roughly, and inadvertently rubbed off the thin layer of endothelium from the surface of the vessel, whilst the other was careful, and kept the endothelium intact. He then realized that an intact endothelium is a prerequisite for the relaxant effect of acetylcholine [1]. By separating the endothelium from the smooth muscle, he showed that a labile factor is released from the endothelium; he named it the "endothelium-dependent relaxing factor"(EDRF). This discovery is so important, that three prominent scientists, pursing this line of research, won the Nobel Prize for physiology/medicine in 1998. They are pharmacologists Robert Furchgott, of the state University of New York; Louis Ignarro [2], of the University of California, Los Angeles; and Ferid Murad, of University of Texas Medical School in Houston [3]. Although many scientists feel that a fourth name should also been recognized-that of Salvador Moncada, currently director of the Wolfson Institute for biomedical Research at University College London for his contribution to conclude that EDRF, and nitric oxide was identical [4] [5].

NO Regulates Vasodilatation, Neurotransmission and Immunological Process

In late 80's these pioneer scientists, discovered a gas, Nitric Oxide (NO), previously considered to be merely atmospheric pollutant, is a critical signaling molecule for endothelium-dependent relaxing occurs in response to a wide variety of stimuli, including acetylcholine, bradykinin, substance P, thrombin, adenine nucleotide, calcium ionosphere A23187. NO increases in the blood flow through arteries, microvessles and some veins. It is now clear that the endothelium-dependent relaxation, described by Furchgott and the others, is just one of the myriad mediator functions of NO. NO also carries important information in the nervous system: In the brain, NO have been shown to be a neurotransmitter, and play an important role in learning and memory [6]. In male, it is message that translates sexual excitement into an erect penis. Pfizer's blockbuster drug Viagra reverses impotence by enhancing an No stimulated pathway. At a time when vascular pharmacologists were pursuing the identity of EDRF, immunologists were independently exploring the cytotoxic properties of macrophages that appeared to be dependent on the generation of large amounts of NO in response to infection [7] [8]. The immune system uses NO in fighting virus, bacteria, parasites, and tumors. By early 1990's, scientists in distinct disciplines-immunology, cardiovascular physiology, and neuroscience- sudden realized they were studying the same molecule, NO [9].

Nitric Oxide is Synthesized Endogenously from a NOS Isoenzyme Gene Family

NO is a highly labile gas, and a very small compound that is not stored, but diffuses from its site of formation to its site of action [since it is both water/lipid soluble, it diffuses freely within tissues]. Because it contains an unpaired electron, it is extremely active. It binds to the haem moiety of guanylate cyclase, and cause a greater than 400-fold activation of the enzyme. NO is formed directly from the guanidino nitrogen of the L-arginine by nitric oxide synthase [NOS] through a process that consumes five electrons and results in the formation of L-citrulline (Fig.1.). NOS is an unusual oxidative enzyme, in that most other enzymes consume one or two electrons for a similar function.

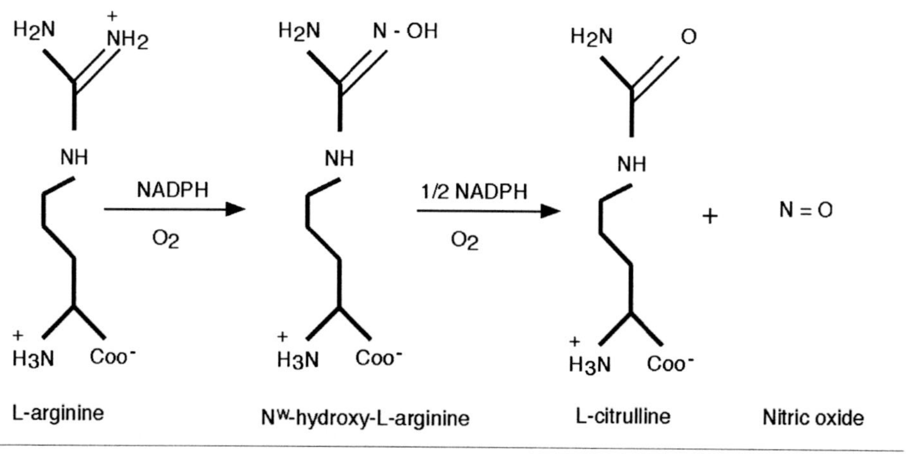

Fig.1. Biosynthesis of NO. L-arginine is converted to NO in two successive steps of which a two-electron oxidation of L-arginine to N-ω-hydroxy-L-argninie is the first, then converted to NO and citrulline, utilizing one and half NADPH and O_2. Both steps require Ca^{2+} and calmodulin as activators and are accelerated by tetrahydrobiopterin.

NOS's structure, and function have been clarified by molecular cloning of the cDNA from the brain (NOS1) [10], endothelial (NOS3) [11], macrophages, and other type of Inducible cells (NOS2) [12] (Fig.2). Three forms of the NO synthase enzyme are known: NOS3 being initially isolated from the endothelium, NOS1 being initially isolated from brain cerebellum, and NOS2 is initially isolated from murine macrophage and human hepatocytes and chondrocytes. The molecular cloning, functional analysis, and crystal structure study data revealed the NOS gene family shares similar compositions with each other: All have two domains: N-terminal half of Heme-oxygenase dome, with tetrahydrobiopterin, heme and arginnine binding sites and C-terminal half of P-450 reductase domain with the positions of recognition sites for NADPH, as well as for flavin mononucleotide [FMN] and flavin adenosine dinucleotide (FAD). Cytochrome P-450 reductase is the only other mammalian enzyme known to contain these recognition sites (Fig.2).

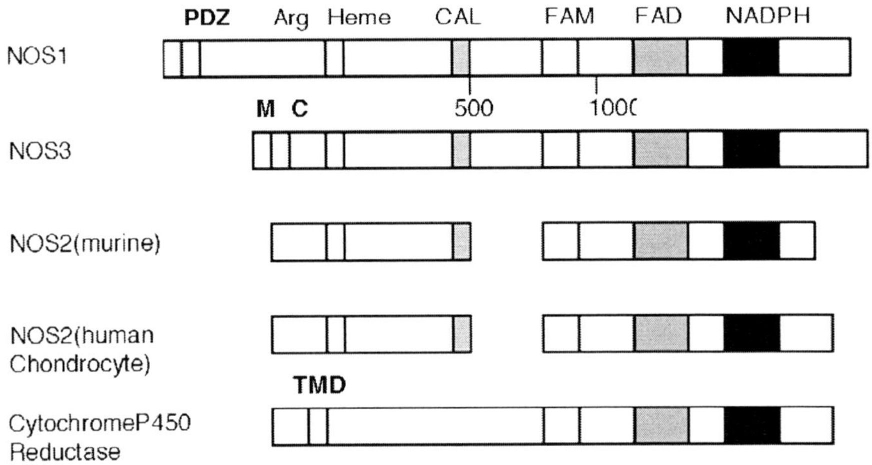

Fig.2. Sequence homologies of molecular isoforms of NOS. All NOS enzymes have consensus-binding sites for Arginine [Arg], Heme, FAD, FMN, NADPH and calmodulin [Cal]. NOS1 has PDZ binding domain. NOS3 has myristoylation [M] and Caveolin [C] binding sites and Cytochrome P450 reductase has transmembrane domain [TMD].

Both NOS3, and NOS1 enzymes are constitute in the sense that their activation does not required new enzymes protein synthesis. For instance, the NOS1 is activated by glutamate - induced increase in intracellulular Ca^{2+} levels activates NOS via calmodulin. NOS3 is also a constitute, being activated by the increase in intracellular Ca^{2+} level. Agonists such as acetylcholine, bradykinin activating at muscarininc or bradykinin receptor on the endothelial cells active the phosphinosititide cycle to generated Ca^{2+} which then stimulates NOS by biding calmadulin. Constitute NOS enzymes account for the role of NO in mediating rapidly events, such as neurotransmission, and blood vessel dilatation. In constrast, the inducible nitric oxide, NOS2, which mediated produce large amount of NO, followed by endotoxin, microbacteria, and cytokines induction. Soon after the first NOS has been cloned in 1991, we have mapped this gene on the human chromosome 12q12-q24 in 1992 [13]. In 1993, the fluorescence –situ hybridization has been used to pinpoint the gene on 12q24.3 [14]. The NOS3 have been mapped to 7q35-q36 and NOS2 has been 17q11.2 [15]. We have discovered the NOS gene family is a dispersed gene family. Although NOS1, and NOS3 genes shows only a single chromosomal localization, we have found multiple copies of inducible nitric oxide synthase gene-like sequences in the human genome. They have been called NOS2A, NOS2B and NOS2C (Table 1) [16].

Nitric oxide is a diatomic free radical molecule, and is a gas at room temperature. Within mammalian cells L-arginine catalysed by nitric oxide synthase (NOS) is required to generate NO. The reaction that yields NO requires L-arginine, NADPH and oxygen as substrates. Additional cystolic factors that enable the NOS enzyme to express and maintain its activity are also required. These factors are tetrahydrobiopterin (BH4), thiol, flavin adenine dinucleotide (FAD) and flavin mononucleotide (FMN). nNOS and eNOS are constitutively expressed in endothelium, platelets, and some neurons and at a lesser extent within an array of other cells. They are activated as a result of calmodulin binding after a rise in intracellular calcium. They may also be activated and inhibited by phosphorylation via various protein kinases. This enables eNOS and nNOS activity to be tightly regulated and be part of effective physiological responses. Unlike nNOS and eNOS, iNOS displays a high affinity for calmodulin and is tightly bound to it within physiological concentrations of calcium. Hence the activation of iNOS is not calcium dependent. However, the expression of iNOS is induced by factors such as cytokines e.g. interferon-γ, IL-1β,TNF-α and endotoxin (LPS) and oxidative stress e.g. hypoxia. Hence, once iNOS is expressed it is continuously active, thereby potentially producing higher levels of NO for a longer duration in comparison to eNOS and nNOS, which are activated transiently. iNOS is found to be expressed during inflammation as part of host-defence mechanisms against invading pathogens. As a result iNOS is often expressed in macrophages and neutrophils, as well as hepatocytes cardiac myocytes, chondrocytes and many other cell types. It has been shown that iNOS knockout mice have increased susceptibility to infections, thereby substantiating the role of iNOS within host defence mechanisms [17].

Table 1. Chromosomal localization of NOS1, NOS3, NOS2 and NOS2-like sequences onto different regions of human chromosomes.

Name	Other Name	Type	Regulated by	Present in	Human chromossome
NOS1	Neuronal NOS nNOS	constitute	Ca^{2+}/ calmodulin	Brain, cerebellum other neuronal tissues	12q24.1-12q24.31
NOS3	Endothelium NOS eNOS	constitute	Ca^{2+}/ calmodulin	Endothelial cells	7q35-7q36
NOS2A	Inducible NOS iNOS	inducible	endotoxin cytokines	Macrophages Neutrophiles Chondrocytes Hepatocytes	17q11.2
NOS2B		Unknown		Unknown	17p11.2-17q11.2
NOS2C		Unknown		Unknown	17p11.2-17q11.2

In order to assess the function of NO in mammalian physiology one must initially examine its chemical properties. NO is a gas at room and body temperature, making it highly diffusible within the vasculature. Consequently in vivo measurement of NO concentration is difficult to quantify. As NO is a free radical, it is a highly reactive molecule within biological systems, reacting with other free radicals, molecular oxygen and heavy metals. Biological effects of NO are mainly mediated by the products of different NO metabolites. NO rapidly reacts intracellular to form nitrite and nitrate, S-nitroso-thiols or peroxynitrate. These metabolites play a key role in mediating many of the key genotoxic effects, such as DNA damage, that are associated with NO and may have feedback mechanisms for DNA repair, such as upregulating p53, poly(ADP-ribose) polymerase (PARP) and the DNA-dependent protein kinase (DNA-PK) [18,19].

The fact that NO binds rapidly and with high affinity to ferrous iron [Fe^{2+}] are regarded as one of its most important properties. It enables NO to bind easily to free iron, iron within iron-sulphur centres and iron within haemproteins [especially when the heam contains a free ligand position). The majority of the physiological actions mentioned [e.g. smooth muscle relaxation, neurotransmission, and inhibition of platelet aggregation and adhesion] are due to NO binding to the ferrous haem iron of soluble guanylate cyclase (sGC)(Fig.3), which converts Guanosine triphosphate (GTP) to Cyclic guanosine monophophate(cGMP). The increase in the concerntration of intracellular cyclic GMP affects the activity of protein kinases and cyclic nucleotide phophsdiesterases in a complex manner not yet fully understood, finally resulting the decreases intracellular free calcium concentration. As the degree of concentration of vascular smooth mucle dependent directly on the concentration of free calcium, a decrease in its concentration result in relaxation. The cGMP is converted by the enzyme, called phosphodiesterase to GMP. Viagra works by blocking this PDE enzyme, leading the sustained cGMP, which in turn mediating the penile erection (Fig.3).

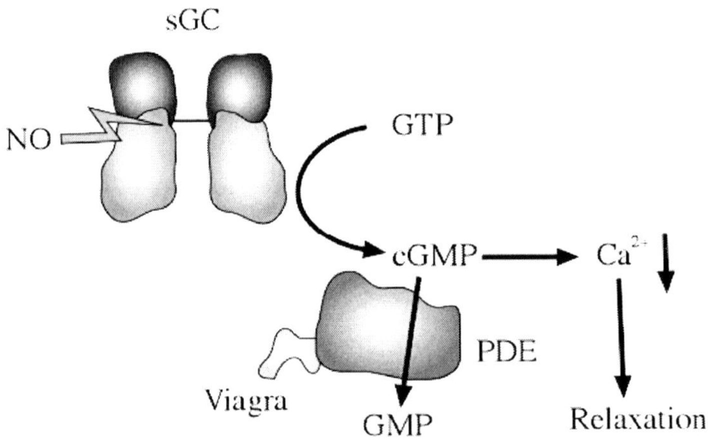

Figure 3. Representation of NO-cGMP pathway.

Due to NO association with haem centres it is not surprising that the binding of NO to haemoglobin is regarded as the main route by which NO is broken down in the body (Fig.4). Therefore the haemoglobin of circulating erythrocytes represents a significant 'sink' for NO. The rate constant for NO uptake by human red blood cells was reported to be 167 $mM^{-1}\ s^{-1}$. However the orientation of membrane molecules and the intracellular concentration are critical determinants of the rate of NO uptake by red blood cells.

Its charge neutrality, thus facilitating its free diffusability in aqueous solution and across cell membranes, also affects bioactivity of NO. Therefore, NO can travel substantial distances to reach target cells, which neighbour the NO producing cell, with little consumption or direct reaction. However, this is dependent upon the concentration of surrounding bioreactants that may significantly alter the concentration of available NO. It has been demonstrated that the reaction of NO with oxygen molecules within hydrophobic membrane regions is approximately three hundred times more rapid than in surrounding aqueous medium. This suggests that biological membranes can account for failure of NO to travel from the cell that has generated it to the target cell and could be a key mediating factor in NO interactions within cells. In short, as a result of the diversity of NO interactions the metabolic pathway of NO is dependent on its site of administration and its site of formation.

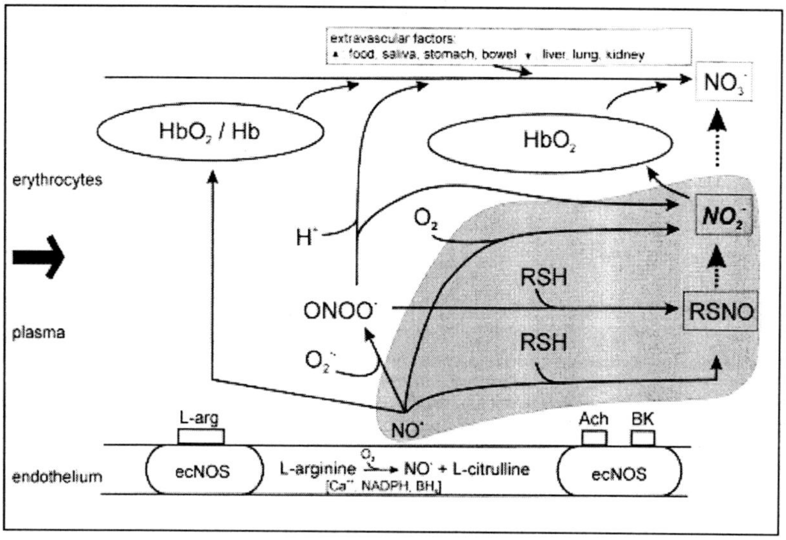

Figure 4. Representation of NO metabolism in the body.

The diversity of roles that NO encompasses can either be of a beneficial or harmful nature. Beneficial effects include acting as an essential mediator of vascular relaxation, neurotransmission in the brain, cytotoxic defence against invading pathogens, a signalling molecule [NO/ cGMP signalling pathway] within many other biological processes and possibly a mediator of mitochondrial respiration.

NO is a very reactive molecule and therefore it has the potential to interact with a variety of different biological components. NO can cause effects such as DNA damage towards host tissue, which can be initiated by nitrosative deamination, DNA strand breakage or DNA modification. Alternatively it has the ability to repair tumour DNA. Importantly NO has also been shown to play a pivotal role in the process of apoptosis by having the ability to both induce and protect against it. In addition NO reacts at the diffusion limited rate with superoxide [O_2^-] to form peroxynitrite, which is a strong oxidant that is thought to be responsible for a lot of the cytotoxicity attributed with NO. The concoction of different biological effects is very much dependent upon many factors, such as formation and metabolism of NO, the type of NOS enzymes that are present, the interaction between NO utilising processes, and crucially the concentration of NO that is present.

Nitric Oxide Synthase Expression in Many Different Type of Tumors

The iNOS isoform has been mostly studied for its role in immuno-mediated processes; for example, iNOS knockout mice have been generated and shown to have increased susceptibility to infections [17]. The first NOS isoform implicated in the macrophage-mediated tumour killing process was also iNOS, and as a consequence this isoform has been at the center of attention for study of its expression in cancer. In normal [non-tumourogenic] cells, iNOS has been detected in macrophages and neutrophils, as well as in hepatocytes, cardiac myocytes, chondrocytes and many other cell types. Recently, lack of iNOS in knockout mice has been found to promote intestinal tumorigenesis in the Apc [Min/+] colon cancer mouse model, thereby substantiating the role of iNOS within host defence mechanisms [20].

An initial study on iNOS expression in human breast cancer suggested that iNOS activity was higher in less differentiated tumours in a panel of 15 invasive breast carcinomas [21]. iNOS expression could be detected predominantly in peritumoural and intratumoural macrophages. NO biosynthesis was significantly greater for grade III tumours as compared with grade II in specimens from 10 breast cancer tissues. Recently, three relatively large-scale studies [22, 23, 24], suggested that iNOS is not only expressed in stromal cells and macrophages in the tumor, but also in tumor cells themselves. Reveneau et al reported NOS activity in 27 of 40 tumours studied [24]. Vakkala et al showed that carcinomas with both iNOS positive tumour and stromal cells had a higher apoptotic index and a higher calculated microvessel density index [22]. Loibl et al further demonstrated that while none of the benign lesions were positive for iNOS, 67% *in situ* carcinomas and 61% invasive lesions showed iNOS tumour cell staining. eNOS expression was found in 33 invasive lesions (61%) [23]. Both iNOS expressing lesions and eNOS expressing lesions showed strong co-expression (p=0.0008) [23]. ENOS expression has also been associated with tumor grade, proliferation rate, and expression of the oestrogen and progesterone receptor status in invasive breast cancers [25,26].

Tumor Angiogenesis

Angiogenesis is a natural process in the body that involves the growth of new blood vessels. Blood vessels are composed of endothelial cells. They are among the longest-lived cells in the body outside the central nervous system; in adult vessel, only 1 in every 10,000-endothelial cells is undergoing cell division. In contrast, about 14% of normal intestinal epithelial cells are in the cell cycle division. Therefore, the turnover time to replace the cells of the gut is measured in days and that of the endothelium in years. Despite this, upon an appropriate stimulus, the quiescent vascular can become activated through degrading surrounding base membrane and new formed the capillaries. This process is called angiogenesis. It is largely controlled by pathological conditions, such as wound healing and tumor growth. It can also occur during coronary artery disease; peripheral artery disease and stroke when there's insufficient blood supply and oxygen to the tissues, a condition known as ischemia.

The importance of angiogenesis for the growth of solid tumours was first put forward by Hanahan D. & Folkman J. [27, 28]. They put forward an angiogenesis switch hypothesis that there are angiogenic inducers and angiogenic inhibitors during tumorigenesis formation periods. The changes in the relative balance of inducers and inhibitors activates the switch. Among the angiogenic inducers, there is basic fibroblast growth factor (bFGF, or FGF2), acidic FGF (aFGF, or FGF-1). They are characterized by high affinity binding to heparin. and luck of a traditional signal sequences for secretion. Almost at the same time, a secreted protein was identified its ability to elicit vascular permeability, called vascular endothelial growth factor (VEGF). Both FGF and VEGF are binding to the receptors on the endothelial cells. These are transmembrane tyrosine kinases and thus are coupled through transduction cascade to the cellular network. The first clue about the existence of endogenous angiogenesis inhibitors come from the observations that an interferon and platelet factor-4 could inhibit endothelial cells cell chemotaxis and proliferation, respectively. More recently, angiostatin and endostatin have been identified as potent inhibitors of angiogenesis.

NO and Tumour Cell Angiogenesis

Since Hibbs first described that NO's role in macrophage-mediated tumor killing process [7], the following lists the anti-tumor effects of NO that have been suggested:

- Loss of a large fraction of the iron pool.
- Inhibition of DNA synthase and its rate limiting enzyme ribonucleotide reductase.
- Reduced activity of cis-aconitase
- Reduction of oxygen consumption by reversible inhibition of complex IV activity in mitochondria
- Damage to complex I and complex II in the mitochondrial electron chain.
- Induction of apoptosis by upregulating both Fas/Fas ligand system [29].

In contrast the tumor promoting properties of NO are summarised as:

- To protect cells against apoptosis, by upregulating the cyto-protective genes, such as HIF-1, hemo oxygenase-1, p53 and DNA-dependent protein kinase [18].
- To be unregulated by tumor angiogenesis agents such as of vascular endothelial growth factor (VEGF)
- To up regulate the angiogenic factors, such as FGF-2, MMP-9 and VEGF.

Jenkins et al [30] [1995] first reported the surprising finding that human carcinoma cells transfected with a murine iNOS cDNA cassette (DLD-1 cells generating 20 pmol min-1 mg-1 NOS activity) showed increased tumour growth, rather than decreased growth. Using a nude mouse/xanograft model it was shown that growth of these NO-generating tumours was accompanied by increased neovascularization. These results were supported by Ambs et al, who used recombinant iNOS expressing Calu-6 and HT-29 human carcinoma cell lines containing mutant p53 [31] to look at tumour growth. The authors demonstrated that an NO-mediated up-regulation of VEGF corresponded with increased vascularisation in the xenograft tumours. Therefore it is possible that NO generated by NOS (located either within the tumour or in the surrounding stroma) may promote new blood vessel formation by up-regulating VEGF. This neovasculaturization not only enhances the ability of the tumour to grow, but also increases its invasiveness and metastasis ability.

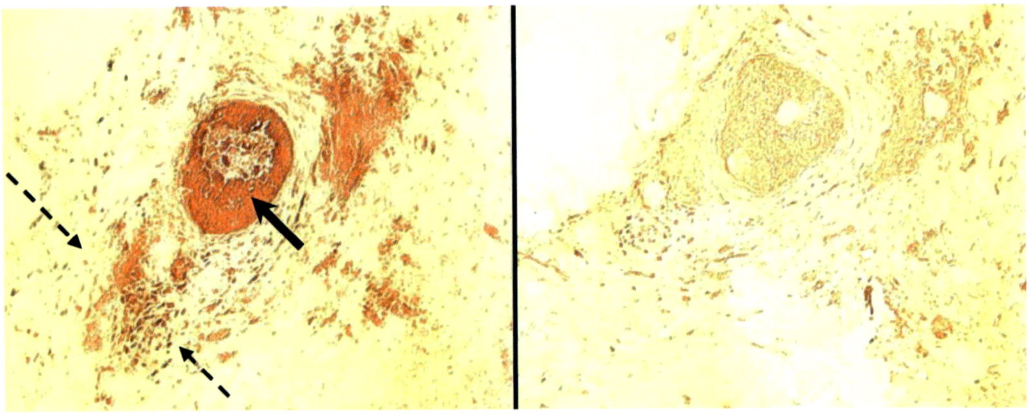

iNOS immunoperoxidase staining [a] Preimmune rabbit serum staining [b]

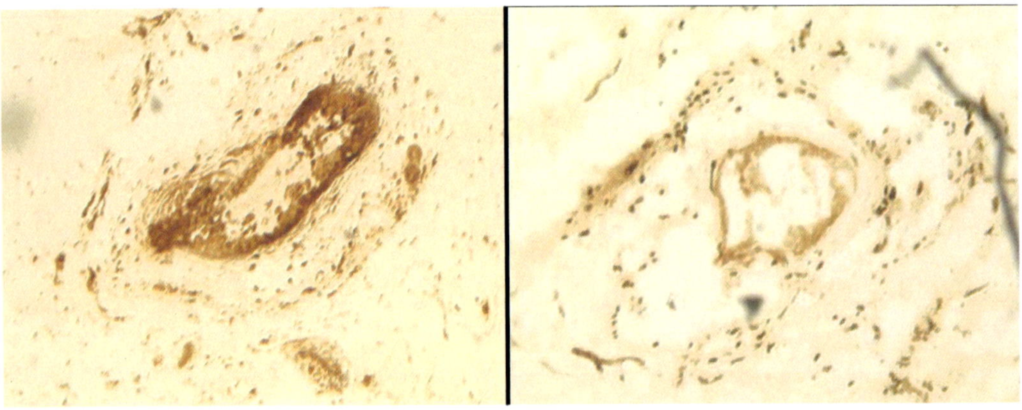

eNOS immunoperoxidase staining [c] **CD31** immunoperoxidase staining [d]

Fig 5. (a) A representative immunohistochemical analysis of in situ ductal carcinomas (frozen sections) for human iNOS C-terminal peptide antibody [18]. (b) is a control, which has been stained using preimmune rabbit serum. (c) eNOS using rabbit anti-serum to eNOS.(aa.1179-1194) Slides (c) CD31 using purified mouse anti-human monoclonal antibody(PharMinge). There is a distinct expression of iNOS in the stroma. Solid arrow indicates in situ carcinoma. Dashed arrow indicates surrounding stroma cells. All the slides were taken at x150 magnification. All the antibodies were used as 1:200 dilution.

An Immunohistochemical Study of iNOS, eNOS and CD31 in Breast In Situ Ductal Carcinomas

In our recent studies, we have also found strong co expression of iNOS and eNOS in *in situ* ductal carcinomas [32]. Using an antibody raised against a C-terminal peptide of iNOS [18] we demonstrated that there was considerable iNOS expression, not only in the surrounding stroma, but also within the *in situ* ductal carcinoma itself (Fig 5a) as compared with preimmune rabbit serum control (Fig 4b). Interestingly, in consecutive sections, strong immune positive staining can also be detected with an-eNOS antibody [rabbit antibody raised against synthetic peptide SLQERQLRGAVPWAFD corresponding to amino acids 1179-1194 of human eNOS protein], mainly in the stromal cells, but also in some tumor cells (Fig.5c). eNOS is primarily found in endothelial cells (form blood vessels) and platelets (found in blood stream), so therefore its presence is usually attributed with the presence of blood vessels. The other marker, CD31 is widely used in breast pathology as a marker of angiogenesis [33]. Therefore localization of CD31 is used as a marker for blood vessels. Staining for CD31monoclone antibody [PharMingen] (5d) highlights the presence of blood vessels surrounding the duct (dashed arrows), but not actually within the duct itself.

The localisation of eNOS within in situ ductal carcinomas without overlap by CD31 is a major finding of this study. As there is no overlap with CD31 it is unlikely that the eNOS expressed within the carcinoma is marking for blood vessels. This suggests the presence of endothelial cells, expressing eNOS, in abnormal capillaries. Alternatively, tumor cell itself could be mutated to express eNOS, or another type of cell with altered morphology. If this abnormal eNOS represent the abnormal endothelial cells, this may indicate the formation of initial structures of the carcinoma neovasculature. The results from this and other studies have suggested that local production of NO by NOS in breast carcinoma cells is able to mediate angiogenesis. This not only enhances the tumors' growth, but also increases its invasiveness and metastasis ability. Therefore the presence of eNOS within in situ ductal carcinomas could be a useful prognosis tool in determining the metastatic potential of the tumor [25]. The presence of eNOS, like iNOS promotes blood flow, increases VEGF, protects tumor cells from DNA damage and anti-tumor agents, and selects for mutant p53 gene. These combined effects contribute greatly towards the growth of the tumor.

The vascularisation of tumor masses can ultimately determine extent to which cancers can proliferate and grow. An increase in tumor cells needs to coincide with an increase in blood flow to accommodate the energy requirements of these cells. NO is able to mediate an increase in blood supply to tumor cells by inducing angiogenesis and the formation of neovasculature.

The additional sections(Fig.6) clearly show the manifestation of the carcinoma within a duct. From Fig.6 [a], it can be seen that there is CD31 expression surrounding the duct. Therefore this indicates the presence of blood vessels that surround the duct. Blood vessels surrounding ducts is characteristic with any ducts within the breasts that have not been affected by tumor growth. Therefore it can be suggested that although there is tumor growth within the duct itself, there is still no breach into the blood supply surrounding the duct [periductal blood vessels]. Upon staining for eNOS localization (Fig.6b) it can be seen that apart from staining outside the duct, there is a substantial amount of eNOS immunity within the duct.

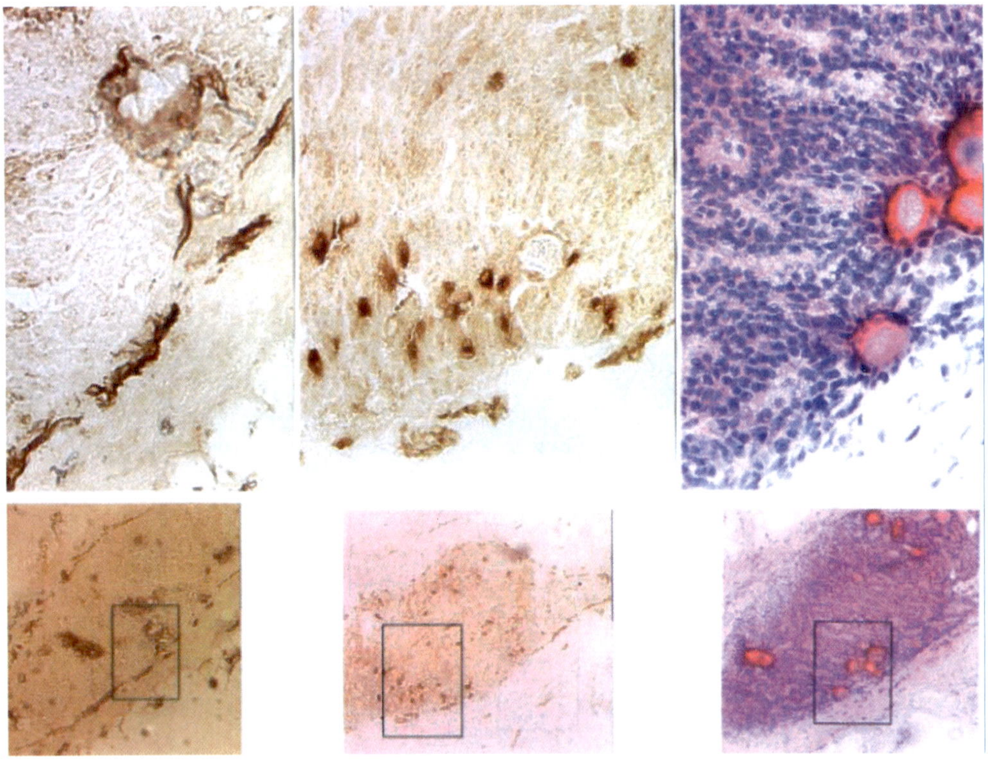

CD31(a) eNOS(b) Haematoxylin and Eosin staining (c)

Fig.6. A representative .immunohistochemical analysis of the *in situ* ductal carcinomas.. Slide a stained for CD31. Slides (b) for eNOS and (e) for H/E staining. The lower panel were taken at x20 and upper panel were taken at x150 magnification.

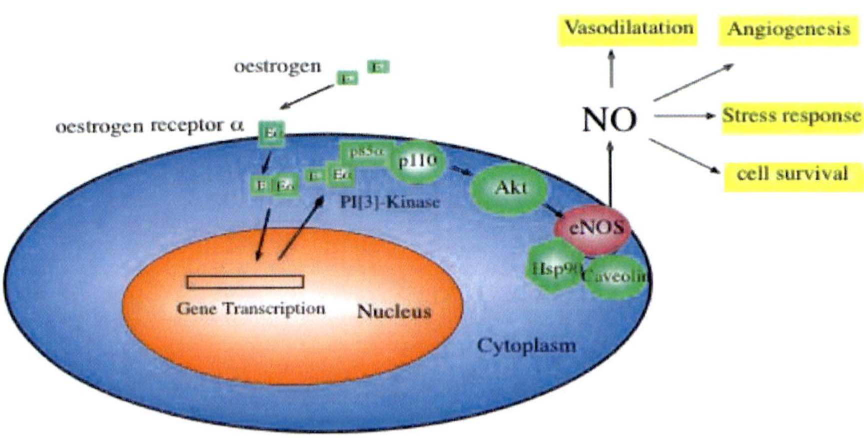

Fig. 7. Schematic presentation of pathway mediating indirect activation of eNOS by oestrogen.

It has been suggested that oestrogen acting on the oestrogen receptor (ER) located on the surface of tumor cell membranes is able to indirectly activate the release of NO from membrane bound eNOS. Recently several studies have shown that the oestrogen/oestrogen receptor complex binds to the p85α regulatory subunit of phosphatidylinositol-3-OH kinase (PI- [3]K), which leads to activation of protein kinase B/Akt [34], [35]. It is known that the catalytic activity of eNOS is augmented by phosphorylation of a C-terminal serine residue [Ser-1177 of human eNOS] through the PI- [3]K/Akt pathway [36,37]. Therefore, it is possible that oestrogen acting on the oestrogen receptor [ERα] located on the surface of cell membranes, could indirectly activate the release of NO from membrane bound eNOS (Fig 7). It is possible that the NO generated from this activation of eNOS may contribute significantly to tumour cell survival under hypoxia and other stress conditions. It should be noted that there are complicated signalling network [s] in endothelial cells capable of regulating eNOS activity. For example, the Akt-mediated phosphorylation activity can be enhanced by binding to heat shock protein-90 [38] and inhibited by binding to Caveolin-1 [39](Fig 7). Hence, the activity of eNOS located within in situ ductal carcinomas may be regulated by oestrogen. The activation of eNOS by ER may constitute a clinically important process, which could be targeted by therapeutic drugs, thereby reducing NO-mediated tumor growth promotion.

Recombinant NOS as a Therapeutic Agent

NO-based therapeutics can be traced back from a century when William Murell proposed the sublingual application of nitroglycerin as a remedy for angina pectoris. From the time of discovery of the vasodilatory properties of the organic nitrates and nitrites, it took more than one hundred years to elucidate their mode of action at the molecular level. For example, it was not until 1980s' that NO gas was identified both as the endogenous endothelium-derived relaxing factor and as being involved as a primary defense mechanism against tumor cells and intracellular microorganisms.

Several laboratories have demonstrated that NO-releasing agents can kill tumor cells, and as a consequence there have been attempts deliver NO to cells. While NO-releasing drugs are under development, an attractive alternative mechanism for delivery would be to transfer NOS- encoding cDNA sequences into cancer cells for gene therapy purposes. Several studies have shown that this approach may work. For example, using a mouse model it was demonstrated that transfection of K-1735 melanoma cells with an iNOS cDNA expression cassette suppressed tumourogenicity and abrogated metastasis [40]. Transfection of human renal carcinoma cells with a retroviral iNOS cassette showed similar results [41]. But using retroviral and adenoviral vector maybe hazardous to the host and pose a major health and safety risk [42]. A potential strategy to overcome the problems associated with gene therapy is to use a cell-based approach. Cell-based approaches utilize the delivery of recombinant cells [rather than genes] to the target site, with the advantage that the expression of the gene of interest can be optimized prior to delivery [43]. For example, we have recently shown the utility of two novel iNOS-expressing human cell lines that can generate high concentrations of NO following treatment with analogues of either the insect hormone ecdysone or tetracycline [18, 29]. In order to make the NO- generating cells suitable for therapeutic delivery they have been encapsulated within a semipermeable alginate-poly-L-lysine membrane. Encapsulated cells are protected from environmental stresses encountered in the host (such as the host immune response) and can be delivered to tumor site [s] in a nude mouse model [29]. Following delivery, high concentrations of NO and reactive nitrogen species can be generated by administration of the appropriate inducer. This approach has been very successful, and we have used it in a tumor model showing 100% killing of SKOV-3 tumors and 54% killing of DLD-1 tumors [29]. Importantly, this strategy allowed the mechanism of tumor killing to be determined as it was shown that tumor killing was associated with concomitant up-regulation of the Fas/FasL proteins. Overall we believe that the cell-delivery approach addresses some of the shortcomings of competing strategies and has the potential to inhibit or kill many different types of tumors from various histological origins [29].

Experimental gene transfer using iNOS or eNOS cDNA for cardiovascular diseases have also been attempted. Transfections of iNOS cDNA have been tested for treatment of coronary artery restenosis after balloon angioplasty [44]. A wide variety of vascular diseases [eg, atherosclerosis, hypertension, vasospasm, diabetic vascular disease, impotence] have been tested for potential therapeutic value in animal models of vascular diseases [45]. For eNOS based gene therapy, a study has shown that blood flow in ischemic limb was almost normalized in rats treated with recombinant eNOS although further experiments need to be carried out to exclusive other possibilities [45]. Recent experiments using the eNOS knockout mice suggested that VEGF enhanced angiogenesis and vascular permeability were reduced in eNOS –deficient mouse [46]. However, gene therapy still needs many improvements before it becomes routine treatment for cardiovascular disease.

Hypothesis and Conclusion

The discovery of the generation of NO by mammalian tissues and the elucidation of some of its biological roles in cancer has thrown new light onto many areas of tumor biology research. Although initial findings suggested that the immune-cell generated NO is cytostatic or cytotoxicity for tumor cells, later findings have shown that NO can also possess apparently contradictory activity leading to increased tumor growth regulating VEGF pathway.

Hanahan D. & Folkman J has first put forward the balance hypothesis for the angiogenic switch in tumor formation. Among the angiogenic inducers, there is basic fibroblast growth factor (bFGF, or FGF2), acidic FGF (aFGF, or FGF-1). Among the angiogenic inhibitors, there are platelet factor-4, angiostatin and endostatin. NO may be placed among the angiogenic inducers. This occurs primarily as a result of NO increasing blood flow to the tumor and inducing angiogenesis, thereby encouraging the formation of neovasculature. Other tumor promoting qualities of NO include the selection for mutant p53, increasing release of angiogenic factors (e.g. VEGF) and are induced by these factors. The other important consideration will be that NO-mediated hypoxia may be related with local angiogenesis as hypoxia and angiogenesis are intricately associated. A good example is that in solid tumor, where oxygen and nutrition are lucking, that stabilizing HIF-1α, a key factor for hypoxia regulation , which then upregulating the VEGF. It is well known that VEGF increases eNOS, therefore can adjust tumor cells to adapt the hypoxia and forming the new blood vessel to promote tumor growth and metastasis (Fig.8).

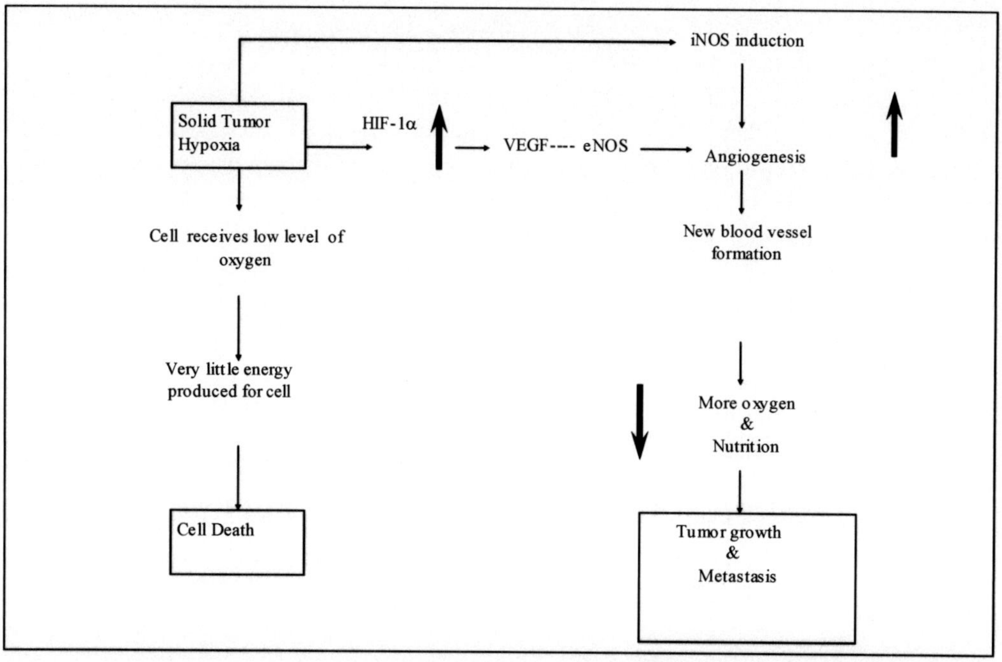

Fig 8. Representation of a possible physiological mechanism by which production of NO enables cell survival under hypoxic conditions through both hypoxia and angiogenesis pathway.

We present evidence first time here that there are abnormal expressing pattern for eNOS in *in situ* breast cancer carcinoma. Although there is overlapping expression between CD31 and eNOS in myoepithelal cells as both are endothelial markers, only eNOS present within in situ ductal carcinomas. It is likely that abnormal eNOS expression may indicate the formation of initial structures of the carcinoma neovasculature. If that is the case, eNOS may represent at a stage 4(Fig.9 d), there is an initial angiogenic CIS formation, as proposed by Hanahan D. & Folkman J in 1996. In their proposal, that the breast cancer arises from the ductal epithelium of the breast; ductal lesions that are presumptive progenitors can begin with hyperplasia and progressing to dysplasia and Carcinoma *In Situ* (CIS). Of these, a subset of CIS lesion has switched on angiogenesis, eNOS immunoreactivity indicating new capillaries, and then progressed into invasive cancer(Fig.9). The results from this and other studies have suggested that local production of NO by NOS in breast carcinoma cells may be able to mediate angiogenesis. This not only enhances the tumors' growth, but also increases its invasiveness and metastasis ability.

There is considerable iNOS expression in *in situ* ductal carcinoma , not only in the surrounding stroma, but also within the in situ carcinoma itself. Vakkala et al reported that carcinomas with both iNOS positive tumor and stromal cells had a higher apoptotic index and a higher calculated microvessel densities index [22]. This is a possible example of a double-edged sword effect of NO in breast cancer. It can therefore be proposed that iNOS, which is located in the stroma forms part of a host defence against tumor growth and is primarily located within macrophages. iNOS expressed as a result of induction by factors, such as cytokines and hypoxia [factors that are abundant in the presence of tumor manifestation and proliferation], increases local NO concentrations to levels that can cause tumor cell death [e.g.

by apoptosis or suppression of tumor cell respiration]. This may help the explain the presence of a higher apoptotic index observed by Vakkala et al [22].

The opposite edge of the sword looks at the tumor promoting qualities of NO. It can therefore be suggested that iNOS located within the in situ ductal carcinoma is expressed by the tumor cells in order to promote growth. This occurs primarily as a result of NO increasing blood flow to the tumor and inducing angiogenesis, thereby encouraging the formation of neovasculature. Other tumor promoting qualities of NO include the selection for mutant p53, increasing release of angiogenic factors [e.g. VEGF], and protection against DNA stranded breaks. As we have shown previously, that NO mediated increasing DNA dependent protein kinase catalytic subunit(DNA-PKcs), which in turn protect tumor cells against the DNA-damage agents, such as X-ray irradiation, bleomycin, adriamycin and cisplatin [18]. The work supported by recent finding, that in human melanoma, depleting of endogenous nitric oxide enhances cisplatine-induced apoptosis [47]. In fact, expression of the inducible nitric oxide synthase in human melanoma tumor cells correlated strongly with poor patient survival after combination biochemotherapy [P<0.001] [47]. Nitric oxide may be the key link between hypoxia and drug resistance, as necrosis region in solid tumor, theregion of angiogenesis and both condition, may contribute the drug-resistance in cancer.

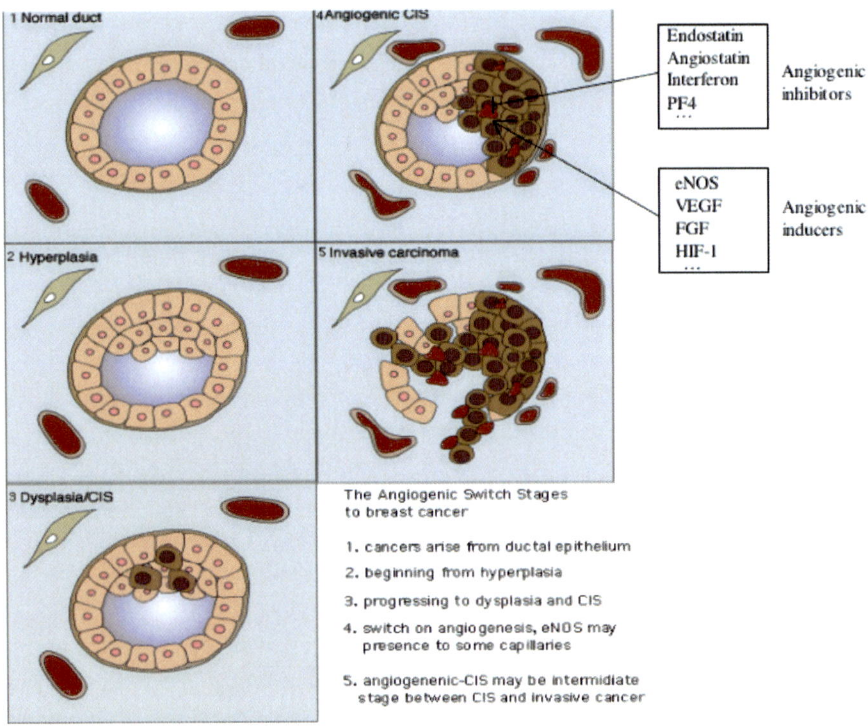

Fig.9. Proposed angiogenic progenitor stages to breast cancer from ductal epithelium of the breast to invasive cancer. Histopathological evaluation of biopsies taken carcinoma breasts has revealed distinctive preneoplastic lesions, including hyperplasic duct [2], dysplastic ducts [3], and CIS [Carcinoma *In Situ*] [4] at this stage, the abnormal expression of eNOS and or other angiogenic inducers, such as VGF,FGF and HIF-1 α may play a role in angiogenic CIS. Alternatively, the angiogenic inhibitors, such as endostatin, angiostatin,interferon and platelet factor-4 [PH4] may inhibit this precarcinoma stage. The balance of these two force can finally decide the foci develop to invasive cancer or not.

The vascularisation of tumor masses can ultimately determine extent to which cancers can proliferate and grow. An increase in tumor cells needs to coincide with an increase in blood flow to accommodate the energy requirements of these cells. In the angiogenesis-free period, tumor cell growth mainly dependent on adjacent tissue diffusion in order to acquired oxygen and nutrition. Its growth rate is severally limited, not exceeding to $1mm^3$-$2mm^3$. Only in the angiogenesis period, that tumor is able to growth rapidly through newly formed blood vessel and transfer to blood stream to metastasis. NO is able to mediate an increase in blood supply to tumor cells by inducing angiogenesis and the formation of neovasculature. Therefore the presence of eNOS within in situ ductal carcinomas could be a useful prognosis tool in determining the metastatic potential of the tumor. Although, many of the direct actions of NO have been well documented, it is evident that there are many parts of the jigsaw, which are yet to be pieced together. Further study is needed to explore of the role of nitric oxide in cancer in order to develop new therapeutic tools in cancer treatment.

Acknowledgements

We would like to thank the Medical Research Council [UK] for their support.

References

[1] Furchgott RF, Zawadzki JV. The obligatory role of endothelial cells in the relaxation of arterial smooth muscle by acetylcholine. *Nature* 1980; 288:373-6.

[2] Ignarro LJ, Buga GM, Wood KS, Byrns RE, Chaudhuri G. Endothelium-derived relaxing factor produced and released from the artery and vein is nitric oxide. *Proc Natl Acad Sci USA* 1987; 84:9265-9.

[3] Katsuki S, Arnold W, Mittal C, Murad F. Stimulation of guanylate cyclase by sodium nitroprusside, nitroglycerin and nitric oxide in various tissue preparations and comparison to the effects of sodium and hydroxylamine. *J Cyclic Nucleotides Res* 1977; 3:23-5.

[4] Palmer RM, Ferrige AG, Moncada S. Nitric oxide release accounts for the biological activity of endothelium-derived relaxing factor. *Nature* 1987; 327:524-6.

[5] Howlett R Nobel award stirs up debate on nitric oxide breakthrough. Nature 1998; 395:625-626

[6] Garthwaite J. Garthwaite, nitric oxide and cell-cell signaling in the nervous system. *Trends Neurosci* 1991;14:60-7

[7] Hibbs JB Jr, Taintor RR,Vavrin Z. Macrophage cytotoxicity: role for L-arginine deiminase and imino nitrogen oxidation to nitrite. *Science* 1987; 235:473-6.

[8] Marlett MA. Nitric oxide: biosynthesis and biological significance. Trends Biochem Sci 1989;14:488-92

[9] Xu W, Liu L. Nitric Oxide: from a mysterious labile factor to the molecule of the Nobel Prize. Recent progress in nitric oxide research. *Cell Res* 1998; 8:251-8.

[10] Bredt DS, Hwang PH, Lowenstein C, Reed RR, Snyder SH Cloned and expressed nitric oxide synthase structurally resemble cytochromeP-450 reductase. *Nature* 351;714-718

[11] Busconi L, Michel T [1993] Endothelial nitric oxide synthase. N-terminal myristolation determines subcellular localzation. *J Bio Chem* 268:8410-8413.
[12] Charles IG Palmer MJ Hickery MS Baylisa MT Chubb AP Hall VS Moss DW Moncada S Cloning, characterization and expression of cDNA encoding an inducible NO synthase from the human chondrocyte *Proc.Natl Acad Sci USA* 1993; 90:11419-11423.
[13] Kishimoto J, Spurr N, Liao M, Liu L, Emson PC, Xu W. Localization of brain nitric oxide synthase [NOS] to human chromosome12. *Genomics* 1992.14,,02-804.
[14] Xu W, Gorman P, Sheer D, Bates G, Kishimoto J, Liu L., and Emson PC. Regional localization of the gene coding for human brain nitric oxide synthase [NOS1] to 12q24.2-24.31 by fluorescent in situ hybridization. *Cytogenet Cell Genet.*1993; 64: 62-63.
[15] Xu W, Charles I, Moncada S, Gorman P, Sheer D, Liu L., and Emson, PC.. Mapping of the genes encoding human inducible and endothelial nitric oxide synthase [NOS2 and NOS3] to the pericentric region of chromosome 17 and to chromosome 7, respectively. *Genomics* 1994; 21, 419-422.
[16] Xu W, Charles I, Liu L, Koni P, Moncada S, Emson PC. Molecular genetic analysis of the duplication of human inducible nitric oxide synthase [NOS2] sequences. *Biochem.Biophy.Res.Commun.* 1995; 212: 466-472
[17] Nathan C. Inducible nitric oxide synthase: what difference does it make? *J Clin Invest.*1997; 15 :2417-23.
[18] Xu W, Liu L, Smith GC, Charles IG. Nitric oxide upregulates expression of DNA-PKcs to protect cells from DNA-damaging anti-tumour agents. *Nat Cell Biol* 2000; 2:339- 45.
[19] Xu W, Liu L, Loizidou M, Ahmed M & Charles IG. The role of nitric oxide in cancer. *Cell Res.* 2002;12, 311-320.
[20] Scott DJ, Hull MA, Cartwright EJ, et al. Lack of inducible nitric oxide synthase promotes intestinal tumorigenesis in the Apc [Min/+] mouse. *Gastroenterology* 2001; 121:889-99.
[21] Thomsen LL, Miles DW, Happerfield L, Bobrow LG, Knowles RG, Moncada S. Nitric oxide synthase activity in human breast cancer. *Br J Cancer* 1995; 72:41-4.
[22] Vakkala M, Kahlos K, Lakari E, Paakko P, Kinnula V, Soini Y. Inducible nitric oxide synthase expression, apoptosis, and angiogenesis in in situ and invasive breast carcinomas. *Clin Cancer Res* 2000; 6:2408-16.
[23] Loibl S, von Minckwitz G, Weber S, et al. Expression of endothelial and inducible nitric oxide synthase in benign and malignant lesions of the breast and measurement of nitric oxide using electron paramagnetic resonance spectroscopy. *Cancer* 2002; 95:1191-8.
[24] Reveneau S, Arnould L, Jolimoy G, et al. Nitric oxide synthase in human breast cancer is associated with tumor grade, proliferation rate, and expression of progesterone receptors. *Lab Invest* 1999; 79:1215-25.
[25] Vakkala M, Paakko P, Soini Y. eNOS expression is associated with the estrogen and progesterone receptor status in invasive breast carcinoma. *Int J Oncol* 2000; 17:667-71.
[26] Martin JH, Begum S, Alalami O, Harrison A, Scott KW. Endothelial nitric oxide synthase: correlation with histologic grade, lymph node status and estrogen receptor expression in human breast cancer. *Tumour Biol* 2000; 21:90-7.

[27] Folkman J, Watson K, Ingber D, Hanahan D. Induction of angiogenesis during the transition from hyperplasia to neoplasia. *Nature.* 1989;339:58-61.

[28] Hanahan D, & Folkman J. Patterns and emerging mechanisms of the angiogenic switch during tumorigenesis. *Cell.* 1996,86:353-64.

[29] Xu W, Liu L, Charles IG. Microencapsulated iNOS-expressing cells cause tumour suppression in mice. *FASEB J* 2002; 16:213-5.

[30] Jenkins DC, Charles IG, Thomsen LL, et al. Roles of nitric oxide in tumour growth. *Proc Natl Acad Sci USA* 1995; 92:4392-6.

[31] Ambs S, Merriam WG, Ogunfusika MO, et al. p53 and vascular endothelial growth factor regulate tumor growth of NOS2-expressing human carcinoma cells. *Nat Med* 1998; 4:1371-6.

[32] Xu W, Lizhi L, Loizidou M, Ahmed M, Taylor I, Moncada S, Charles IG. Nitric Oxide Synthase in Human Breast Cancer, A Doubled-Edged Sword? *Nitric Oxide* 2002; 6:490.

[33] Righi L, Deaglio S, Pecchioni C, Gregorini A, Horenstein AL, Bussolati G, Sapino A, Malavasi F. Role of CD31/platelet endothelial cell adhesion molecule-1 expression in in vitro and in vivo growth and differentiation of human breast cancer cells. *Am J Pathol.* 2003;162:1163-74.

[34] Simoncini T, Hafezi-Moghadam A, Brazil DP, Ley K, Chin WW, Liao JK. Interaction of oestrogen receptor with the regulatory subunit of phosphatidylinositol-3-OH kinase. Nature 2000; 407:538-41.

[35] Haynes MP, Sinha D, Russell KS, et al. Membrane estrogen receptor engagement activates endothelial nitric oxide synthase via the PI3-kinase-Akt pathway in human endothelial cells. *Circ Res* 2000; 87:677-82.

[36] Dimmeler S, Fleming I, Fisslthaler B, Hermann C, Busse R, Zeiher AM. Activation of nitric oxide synthase in endothelial cells by Akt-dependent phosphorylation. *Nature* 1999; 399:601-5.

[37] Fulton D, Gratton JP, McCabe TJ et al. Regulation of endothelium-derived nitric oxide production by the protein kinase Akt. *Nature* 1999; 399:597-601.

[38] Garcia-Cardena G, Fan R, Shah V, Sorrentino R, Cirino G, Papapetropoulos A, Sessa WC. Dynamic activation of endothelial nitric oxide synthase by Hsp90. *Nature* 1998; 392:821-4.

[39] Goligorsky MS, Li H, Brodsky S, Chen J. Relationships between caveolae and eNOS: everything in proximity and the proximity of everything. *Am J Physiol Renal Physiol* 2002; 283:F1-10.

[40] Xie K, Huang S, Dong Z. et al. Transfection with the inducible nitric oxide synthase gene suppresses tumorigenicity and abrogates metastasis by K-1735 murine melanoma cells. J Exp Med 1995; 181:1333-43.

[41] Juang SH, Xie K, Xu L, et al. Suppression of tumorigenicity and metastasis of human renal carcinoma cells by infection with retroviral vectors harboring the murine inducible nitric oxide synthase gene. Hum Gene Ther 1998; 9:845-85.

[42] Lehrman S. Virus treatment questioned after gene therapy death. Nature. 1999; 401:517-8

[43] Read T. Sorensen DR, Mahesparan R, et al Local endostatin treatment of gliomas administered by microencapsulated producer cells. *Nat Biotechnol* 2001; 19:29-34.

[44] Von der Leyen HE, Dzau VJ. Therapeutic potential of nitric oxide synthase gene manipulation. *Circulation*. 2001;103:2760-5.
[45] Chen AF, O'Brien T, Katusic ZS. Transfer and expression of recombinant nitric oxide synthase genes in the cardiovascular system. *Trends Pharmacol Sci*. 1998,19:276-86.
[46] Fukumura D, Gohongi T, Kadambi A, Izumi Y, Ang J, Yun CO, Buerk DG, Huang PL, Jai RK. Predominant role of endothelial nitric oxide synthase in vascular endothelial growth factor-induced angiogenesis and vascular permeability. *Proc Natl Acad Sci USA*. 2001,98:2604-9.
[47] Tang CH & Grimm EA Depletion of endogenous nitric oxide enhances cisplatin-induced apoptosis in a p53 dependent manner in melanoma cell lines.2004 *J Biol Chem* 279, 288-298

In: New Angiogenesis Research
Editor: Roberta V. Zubar, pp. 63-96

ISBN 1-59454-239-2

Chapter IV

Hemostasis and Angiogenesis

Ali Amirkhosravi*, Farooq A. Siddiqui, Sarfraz Ahmad and John L. Francis

Florida Hospital Institute of Translational Research

Abstract

Hemostasis refers to the physiological systems that maintain circulating blood fluidity under normal conditions, though primed to react rapidly to prevent blood loss following vascular injury. Four fundamental components comprise the hemostatic system: (1) the endothelium, (2) blood platelets, and the (3) coagulation and (4) fibrinolytic systems. Each of these systems has been shown to influence angiogenesis, though varied and as yet not fully understood.

The endothelium maintains blood fluidity by modulating vascular tone and permeability, by separating blood components from reactive subendothelial substances, and by producing inhibitors of coagulation and platelet aggregation. Endothelial cells are the operative players in angiogenesis. Platelets, which adhere to and occlude damaged blood vessels, anchor and accelerate clotting reactions by providing sites for adsorption, activation, and concentration of clotting factors. Platelets are also the source of many key angiogenesis mediators. The coagulation system consists of an explosive network of interlaced enzymatic reactions, regulated both by positive and negative feedback mechanisms, and designed to produce a fibrin clot. The fibrinolytic system limits clot formation and contributes to blood vessel repair mechanisms and endothelial cell re-growth, obviously vital to angiogenesis.

There is considerable evidence that the hemostatic system is not only activated in cancer but is also involved in the neovascularization and hematogenous metastasis of malignant disease. There are striking similarities between hemostasis and angiogenesis. First, both processes become activated during wound healing. Second, both processes are involved in coordinating endothelial cell stabilization and repair. Furthermore, substantial evidence suggest that a variety of cellular and protein components of the hemostatic

* Correspondence concerning this article should be addressed to Dr. Ali Amirkhosravi Florida Hospital Institute of Translational Research, 2501 North Orange Ave, Suite 786, Orlando, Florida 32804. Phone: 407-303-2443; Fax: 407-303-2441; e-mail: ali.amirkhosravi@flhosp.org.

system regulate the angiogenic process. Of central importance may be the presence on malignant cells of tissue factor and urokinase receptor. Also the expression on endothelial and tumor cells of protease-activated receptors that are activated by coagulation enzymes could be significant. Finally, proangiogenic growth factors such as vascular endothelial growth factor and inflammatory cytokines such as CD40 ligand present within circulating platelets could play important regulatory roles in angiogenesis following coagulation activation. The present review article first provides an overview of hemostasis. Second, the complex relationship between hemostasis and cancer and the similarities between hemostatic and angiogenic processes are discussed. Third, the known positive and negative hemostatic regulators of angiogenesis are identified and the potential regulatory functions of the key components are highlighted. Finally, the application of anti-hemostatic agents as potential treatment strategies and future directions are discussed in the context of relevant experimental studies.

Key words: Hemostasis, Coagulation, Platelets, Fibrinolysis, angiogenesis

Overview of the Hemostatic System

The hemostatic system is designed to maintain blood in a fluid state under normal physiological conditions. This system is also primed to rapidly react to vascular injury to prevent blood loss by sealing the damaged segment of the vessel wall. Four major components make up the hemostatic system. These are 1) the vascular endothelium; 2) the blood platelets; 3) the coagulation system and 4) the fibrinolytic system.

The **vascular endothelial cells** maintain blood fluidity by separating blood's hemostatic components from reactive subendothelial structures. In addition, the highly anionic endothelium produces inhibitors of platelet aggregation (prostacyclin and nitric oxides) and blood coagulation (thrombomodulin and heparan sulphate). Finally, the endothelial cells regulate vascular tone and permeability by producing endothelins and nitric oxides that cause vasoconstriction and vasodilation respectively [1].

Platelets participate in hemostasis by first adhering to the damaged area of the vasculature. They then spread on the exposed subendothelial matrix, and secrete their internal constituents that include molecules involved in both hemostasis and wound healing. Additional platelets delivered to the site of injury, adhere initially to the basal layer of adherent platelets and subsequently to one another thus forming large aggregates. Furthermore, during these processes, activated platelet membrane sites accelerate coagulation by adsorbing and concentrating circulating clotting factors and by providing the phospholipid surface for coagulation complex formation. Due to their negatively charged surface and absence of binding sites, platelets do not adhere to normal endothelium. However, following vascular injury, binding sites such as von Willebrand factor (vWF) and fibronectin become available and platelet binding can occur via glycoprotein (GP)Ib/IX complex and integrin receptors respectively [2]. Aggregation is mediated by glycoproteins IIb/IIIa (GPIIb/IIIa) bridged to GPIIb/IIIa on another activated platelet by fibrinogen [3]. Platelets contain different types of granules in which intracellular constituents are sequestered. These include α-granules (which store platelet-derived growth factor [PDGF], fibrinogen, vWF, and platelet factor-4 [PF4], for example), dense granules (containing serotonin, ADP and calcium) and lysosomes (containing acid hydrolases) [4].

Platelets can become activated by several agonists such as thrombin, collagen, ADP, epinephrine, and arachidonic acid. Activation occurs after these agonists bind to their specific receptors on the platelet surface [5]. Following receptor-mediated stimulation, the platelet cytoskeletal contractile apparatus becomes activated, and result in the fusion of granular envelope with the membranes of intracellular canaliculi followed by external release of granule contents.

The **coagulation mechanism** is composed of a series of reactions that function as a biological amplifier and culminate in the conversion of soluble circulating fibrinogen into a fibrin meshwork at the site of vascular injury providing stability to the hemostatic plug of platelets. In this system, relatively few initiating substances sequentially and proteolytically activate a cascade of circulating precursor proteins (the coagulation factor enzymes). The major site for almost all coagulation factors is the liver hepatocyte, although some are synthesized in platelets and endothelial cells. Almost all clotting factors are serine proteinases (having a serine residue at their active center).

The coagulation cascade is initiated by the transmembrane glycoprotein tissue factor (TF). Under normal physiological conditions, TF expression is limited to extravascular sites that are only exposed to blood upon vascular injury. Following vascular or endothelial cell injury, circulating factor (F) VII binds to the exposed TF receptor and undergoes proteolytic activation to become the serine protease FVIIa [6]. In addition, TF can bind to FVIIa (which comprises 1% of the total plasma FVII [7] directly. This TF-VIIa complex acts in concert with membrane phospholipid (PL) to convert circulating factors IX and X to IXa and Xa, respectively (Figure 1). FXa is the active catalytic component of the "prothrombinase" complex which converts circulating prothrombin to thrombin. Thrombin activates platelets and cleaves fibrinopeptides A and B from soluble fibrinogen to form insoluble fibrin. In addition, thrombin converts FXIII to FXIIIa which chemically crosslinks the fibrin clot. Tissue factor-dependent reactions are regulated by the natural plasma protein inhibitor "tissue factor pathway inhibitor" (TFPI). TFPI can react with and inhibit FXa and/or form a quaternary inhibitory complex with TF, FVIIa, and FXa on the cell membrane [8,9]. Other natural coagulation inhibitors that control coagulation include antithrombin (AT) which blocks factors IXa, Xa and thrombin, and activated protein C (APC) that regulates thrombin generation by inhibiting coagulation factors Va and VIIIa.

When a fibrin clot is formed following vascular injury, it becomes remodeled and subsequently removed in order to restore normal blood flow. The **fibrinolytic system** is the primary mechanism responsible for enzymatic degradation of fibrin [10]. This mechanism acts to limit the persistence of fibrin and prevent its inappropriate extension. Like the coagulation mechanism, the proteolytic enzymes within the fibrinolytic system circulate as inert proenzymes and their activity is enhanced by spatial and conformational changes that occur when they are adsorbed on to molecules in order to localize their activity.

The enzyme plasmin is the active terminal product of the fibrinolytic system. Plasmin is formed by enzymatic activation of the inert circulating proenzyme plasminogen by plasminogen activators. The latter include the tissue-type plasminogen activator (t-PA) produced in most tissue cells as well as the vascular endothelium and urokinase-like plasminogen activator (u-PA) which is found in the urine, tears and saliva. u-PA can activate plasminogen in the absence of fibrin, whereas t-PA has a specific binding site for fibrin [10]. In response to the generation of an intravascular thrombus, endothelial cells release t-PA to initiate localized thrombolysis. The rate of clot dissolution is dependent on the binding of plasminogen, activators and inhibitors to the thrombus. Thrombus degradation results in the formation of soluble fibrin degradation products (FDPs) [11]. Any plasmin released into the blood is neutralized by α_2- antiplasmin, thus preventing non-specific degradation of plasma proteins. Additional regulation of fibrinolysis comes from plasminogen activator inhibitor-1 (PAI-1) secreted by endothelial cells and activated platelets.

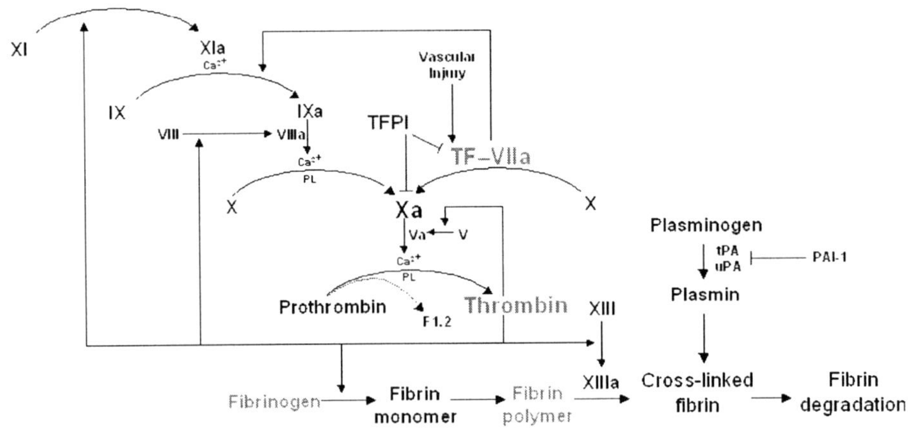

Figure 1: Diagramatic overview of the coagulation and fibrinolytic systems.

Hemostatic Abnormalities in Cancer

The relationship between cancer and vascular thrombosis was first reported over 130 years ago [12] by the French Physician Armand Trousseau who observed a high incidence of thromboembolic disease (TED) in patients with gastric carcinoma. He also suggested that thrombophlebitis may be symptomatic of cancer of other internal organs. Ever since, substantial clinical, laboratory, pharmacological and histologic evidence has accumulated in support of this relationship. It is now well established that many cancer patients exhibit a hypercoagulable state or low-grade disseminated intravascular coagulation (DIC). Not all tumor types are equally associated with thrombotic events; patients with tumors of the lung, pancreas and gastrointestinal tract tend to be more hypercoagulable than those with breast or renal cancer [13]. In addition, the prevalence of (TED) varies depending on the treatment protocol [14, 15]

Laboratory evidence of intravascular coagulation and/or fibrinolytic activation is present in the majority of cancer patients [16-20] Thrombocytopenia (platelet count $<150\text{x}10^9/\text{l}$) is present in up to 28% of patients with disseminated cancer [18,21,22]. Thrombocytosis (platelet count $>400\text{x}10^9/\text{l}$) is more common and is found in 10-57% of patients [18,21]. Hyperfibrinogenemia is found in 50 to 80% of cancer patients [23,24] and fibrinogen levels in patients with malignancy increase during the terminal phase [23]. Since the activation of the fibrinolytic pathway usually occurs in response to the intravascular activation of coagulation, evidence for the former is frequently observed in cancer patients. These include elevated levels of fibrin degradation products (FDPs) [19,21], decreased plasminogen levels [21] and increased plasmin-antiplasmin complex [25]. Finally, molecular markers of hemostatic activation are commonly elevated in cancer patients. For example, plasma fibrinopeptide A (FpA) is a sensitive indicator of *in vivo* coagulation activation and is elevated in most patients with malignant disease [26,27]. Furthermore, FpA levels increase as the patients become terminally ill, and persistently raised levels indicate treatment failure and a poor prognosis [20]. Other markers such as prothrombin F1.2 and thrombin-antithrombin (TAT) complex, have been studied in cancer patients, with broadly similar results [28,29]. Overall, the measurement of sensitive molecular markers of hemostatic activation are more helpful than routine coagulation tests in demonstrating hypercoagulability in patients with cancer.

The histological evidence linking hemostasis and malignancy is based on the commonly observed fibrin deposition in and around tumors. Although the exact process of extravascular fibrin formation remains unclear, it is well established that fibrin is an integral part of the stroma of many solid tumors [30,31]. The generation of tumor stroma has been likened to inappropriate wound healing [32] and is essential for significant tumor growth. Finally, pharmacological evidence from animal models show that anti-hemostatic therapies can influence tumor growth and dissemination. Collectively, these evidence strongly indicate that hemostasis is adversely affected by cancer. However, the effects of cancer on hemostasis do not constitute a unidirectional relationship. Rather, it is becoming increasingly apparent that components of the hemostatic system may have a role in tumor growth, angiogenesis and metastasis suggesting that activation of the coagulation and/or fibrinolytic pathways in cancer patients is not merely an epiphenomenon of the disease. Thus, a better understanding of this relationship may lead to novel treatments for malignant disease. The present review article focuses on the possible contributions of the hemostatic system to the process of angiogenesis in cancer.

Wound Healing: The Link between Hemostasis and Tumor Angiogenesis

Since the proposal of the hypothesis that tumor growth is angiogenesis-dependent over three decades ago [33], the process of angiogenesis has received intensive laboratory investigation. Neovascularization is not only required for the growth of solid tumors beyond a small size (2-3 mm), but also provides routes for dissemination. Thus, the processes of angiogenesis and metastasis are tightly related.

Angiogenesis and hemostasis share several characteristics. First, both processes are anatomically and functionally integrated with the vasculature. Second, both processes operate under the control of several stimulatory and inhibitory factors. Third, both processes can remain quiescent for prolonged periods of time, but can be activated during wound healing [34]. Indeed, malignant tumors have often been referred to as "wounds that do not heal" [32]. Hemorrhage from damaged blood vessels after an injury is normally followed by the rapid coagulation of extravasated plasma due to contact with tissue factor [35]. The resultant clot consisting of platelets, fibrin, fibronectin and trapped blood cells, serves as a provisional stroma into which inflammatory cells migrate [36,37]. These events are followed by migration of new blood capillaries and fibroblasts that produce and deposit connective tissue matrix components. The resultant highly vascular tissue is known as "granulation" tissue and is eventually remodeled, as blood vessels are resorbed and fibroblasts disappear [38-40] finally giving rise to a scar tissue. The spillage of plasma into extravascular space also occurs during tumor stroma formation. This occurs usually due to the secretion of vascular permeability factor (VPF) by the tumor cells. This factor renders nearby vessels hyperpermeable to plasma proteins [41-42]. The fibrin generated in the tumor stroma typically persists within that structure, an occurence that is not observed in the healing wound. In the latter, fibrin as well as fibronectin appear only transiently [43-44]. It has been argued that the persistent as well as abundant fibrin deposited in some tumors may serve as a "cocoon" that hinders the infiltration of immune cells into the tumor structure [45-47].

Platelets participate in wound healing at various stages. Initially, they contibute towards the formation of the hemostatic plug and the generation of a provisional matrix that initiate the wound healing process [48]. Later, platelets may play a role by offering platelet-derived growth factor (PDGF) that can attract and stimulate the growth of fibroblasts [49,48]. In contrast, there is no extravascular presence of platelets in solid tumors. However, many tumor cell types are equipped with a procoagulant surface and adequate membrane properties to mimic platelet-like functions in wound healing such as generating prothrombinase [50,51].

During tumor growth, the demand for oxygen and growth factors results in the formation of "new" network of blood vessels. In addition, in certain circumstances, vessel cooption can occur from adjacent tissues [52]. Indeed, tumors and wounds are both generally hypoxic tissues, due to the deposition of fibrinous and collagenous material that act as barriers between tumor cells and blood vessels [44,53]. Moreover, the integrity of the newly formed blood vessels in tumors is not optimal resulting in a diminished blood supply compared to adjacent normal tissues [54]. Considering the major similarities (and relatively minor differences) in the processes of wound healing and tumor stroma formation, the concept of wound healing as a paradigm for the generation of tumor stroma would make sense. Furthermore, this paradigm could be regarded as the basis for the broad inter-relationship between activated hemostatic mechanisms and angiogenesis.

Coagulation Components that Influence Angiogenesis

A. Tissue Factor

TF is a 47-kDa transmembrane glycoprotein and is a unique member of the superfamily of cytokine receptors. As mentioned above, TF is the main initiator of the coagulation cascade and TF has also been shown to play an important role in blood vessel formation during embryogenesis. Mice deficient in TF exhibit impaired vascular integrity, defective blood vessel development of the yolk sac and suffer embryonic lethality by day 10.5 [55-57]. Similar defective vessel-induced lethality is observed in vascular endothelial growth factor (VEGF-) deficient mice [58,59], pointing to a functional inter-relationship between TF and VEGF. Later studies in tumor angiogenesis have provided strong evidence in support of this inter-relationship.

Physiologically, TF expression is limited to extravascular sites such as subendothelial layers of the vessel wall. Pathologically, however, TF could be inappropriately expressed on the surface of monocytes, macrophages and tumor cells. Cellular TF can be induced in response to inflammatory cytokines and due to malignant transformation [60]. Indeed, aberrant TF expression by monocyte/macrophages and/or tumor cells is in part responsible for the hypercoagulability associated with cancer. Surface TF expression has been demonstrated in several tumor cell types (but not in their corresponding normal tissues) including non-small-cell lung carcinoma [61,62], breast cancer [63,64], colorectal carcinomas [65-67], pancreatic cancer [68], leukemia [69] and gliomas [70]. Importantly, increasing TF expression in tumor cells positively correlates with VEGF, increased angiogenesis and reduced survival rates [61]. In colon cancer for example, TF expression correlates significantly with clinical stage as well as Dukes'classification [67]. Furthermore, TF-positive colon carcinomas present high VEGF expression and microvascular density more frequently than TF-negative tumors [67]. Indeed, immunohistochemical studies have demonstrated TF and VEGF colocalization in human lung and breast cancers [71].

Expression of TF on the vascular endothelial cells has been demonstrated *in vitro* but rarely *in vivo* and in human disease. Under normal physiologic conditions, plasmatic growth factors constantly activate the phosphatidyl 3-kinase (PI3-K)-Akt signaling pathway that causes the suppression of TF production in vascular endothelial cells [72]. However, a study by Contrino and colleagues [73] has shown that TF may be a marker of the initiation of angiogenesis in human breast cancer. In this study, TF was localized to the vascular endothelial cells (or tumor cells) within the tumors of seven patients with invasive breast cancer but not in the endothelial or tumor cells of benign tumors from ten patients. It was therefore postulated that TF may be involved in the "switch" to angiogenic phenotype.

Malignant transformation and tumor progression are genetically controlled events [74], and it is well established that the acquisition of the angiogenic phenotype is necessary for progression to a malignant phenotype. In addition to genetic alterations, tumor environmental conditions such as cell-to-cell interactions [75], hypoxia [76], growth factors and inflammatory cytokines [77], could trigger or enhance the proangiogenic phenotype. The concept of the "angiogenic switch" is well accepted and involves an imbalance of pro-and antiangiogenic factors in the tumor microenvironment. These factors normally maintain endothelial cells in a quiescent state. Evidence so far points to a role for TF in possibly offsetting the angiogenic balance by upregulating VEGF [78] and/or downregulating the anti-angiogenic factor thrombospondin (TSP) [79]. Indeed, Abe and colleagues [78] have shown that low TF and VEGF producing human melanoma cells, when injected subcutaneously into immunocompromised mice, give rise to small, avascular tumors. However, when such cells are transfected with TF cDNA, an angiogenic phenotype was established as evidenced by vascular large tumors. The latter experimental observation strongly supports a role for TF in tumor neovascularization. Interestingly, there appears to be a converse relationship between TF and VEGF. VEGF has been shown to upregulate TF expression on endothelial cells by activating the early growth response-1 gene [80]. The VEGF-induced TF expression could be inhibited by angiopoietin-1 [81].

Following cellular activation, TF expression is usually rapid. The transcription factors specificity protein-1 (SP-1), activator protein-1 (AP-1) and nuclear factor-κB are involved in the regulation of both TF and VEGF possibly explaining their co-localization and co-regulation in many tumors [82]. TF-induced VEGF production requires the binding of activated factor VII to TF and subsequent generation of factor X and thrombin [83,84]. However, TF-mediated VEGF regulation could also occur independent of clotting via the ligand-binding extracellular domain of TF [78]. This cytoplasmic domain, which could be phosphorylated by protein kinase C (PKC)-mediated mechanisms [85], has been shown to regulate cytoskeletal reorganization, vascular remodeling via interaction with actin binding protein-280 (ABP-280) [86]. This protein contributes to the assembly of actin filaments. The specific effect of TF cytoplasmic domain on the cytoskeleton provides a molecular pathway by which TF could influence metastasis and possibly angiogenesis. Indeed, extacellular functions of TF/VIIa complex appear to cooperate with the functions of TF cytoplasmic domain to support metastasis [87,88]. In addition, a recent study by Belting and colleagues [89] showed that TF-VIIa complex, can promote both tumor and developmental angiogenesis through protease-activated receptor-2 (PAR-2) signaling, and that TF cytoplasmic domain negatively regulates PAR-2 signaling. This study also demonstrated that PAR-2-dependent angiogenesis is enhanced in mice from which the TF cytoplasmic domain has been deleted. It is therefore suggested that targeting the TF/VIIa signaling pathway may potentiate the efficacy of angiostatic treatments for cancer. Overall, there is compelling evidence to show that TF can influence angiogenesis by clotting-dependent as well as clotting-independent mechanisms.

B. Thrombin and Protease-Activated Receptors (PARs)

The actions of thrombin reflect yet another similarity between the processes of wound healing and angiogenesis. Thus following vascular injury, thrombin stimulates the proliferation and migration of normally quiescent endothelial cells for promotion of wound repair. Similar effects may be seen in the tumor microenvironment where thrombin activates the recruitment of new blood vessels into the developing tumor.

Thrombin is a multi-functional serine protease that is rapidly generated following coagulation activation. In addition to its direct function of fibrin formation, thrombin regulates various cellular functions via coagulation-independent mechanisms (Figure 2). It does so mainly by activating G-protein-coupled protease-activated receptors (PARs), which initiate signaling cascades. These receptors have a basic residue at P1 in the activating cleavage site [90]. The cleavage of these sites by any protease could trigger PAR signaling. Four PARs have been identified of which Human PAR-1 [91,92], PAR-3 [93] and PAR-4 [94,95], can be activated by thrombin. PAR-2 cannot be activated by thrombin but is activated by trypsin [96], tryptase [97] and coagulation factors VIIa and Xa [98,99]. Human platelets express PAR-1 and PAR-4 and it appears that these receptors can independently mediate thrombin signaling (PAR-1 at low concentrations and PAR-4 at high concentrations of thrombin) [90] . PAR-1, PAR-2 and PAR-4 are present on the surface of vascular endothelial cells. PAR-1 appears to be the predominant mediator of thrombin signaling in these cells. PAR-1 is also highly expressed in some tumor cell types [100,101], and there is a direct correlation between PAR expression and invasive potential in breast cancer [101]. Thrombin activation of PAR-1 on tumor cells has been shown to promote adhesion of tumor cells to endothelial cells, subendothelial matrix, fibronectin and vWF [102-104]. In a recent study, Hjortoe *et al.* [105] demonstrated that FVIIa binding to TF on breast carcinoma cells upregulates the interleukin-8 through a PAR-2-dependent mechanism that leads to increased migration and invasion.

There is a substantial body of evidence to indicate that thrombin can promote angiogenesis via direct as well as indirect mechanisms. First, thrombin can potentiate VEGF activity on endothelial cells apparently by up-regulating the expression of VEGF receptors on endothelial cells [106]. Both thrombin and VEGF can in turn, stimulate DNA synthesis in endothelial cells, either alone, or together in a synergistic manner [107]. Second, thrombin can facilitate the detachment and migration of endothelial cells. Thrombin-treated endothelial cells lose their ability to adhere to collagen IV or laminin [108]. This effect could be of significance to the angiogenic process since endothelial cells must overcome their attachment to basement membrane components in order to migrate, divide and form the lumen of new vessels. Interestingly, thrombin can also activate matrix metalloproteinase-2 (MMP-2), which locally degrades collagen IV to allow the migration of endothelial cells and expose other angiogenic factors that are available in the extracellular matrix [109]. Third, thrombin can upregulate $\alpha_v\beta_3$ integrin which is expressed on the surface of cells during neovascularization and vascular remodeling [110]. The important role of $\alpha_v\beta_3$ in angiogenesis is evident by extensive bleeding and embryonic death of mice with targeted deletion of α_v subunit gene [111]. Thrombin increases both mRNA and protein levels of $\alpha_v\beta_3$ in endothelial cells and this effect is abolished by the direct thrombin inhibitor, hirudin [112]. In addition, thrombin could serve as a ligand to $\alpha_v\beta_3$ integrin [112]. Ligand binding to $\alpha_v\beta_3$ induces signaling that influences cell attachment, migration and proliferation [113], processes that angiogenesis depends upon. Furthermore, *in vitro*, endothelial cells exhibit longer survival and decreased level of apoptosis when treated with immobilized thrombin [112]. This effect is $\alpha_v\beta_3$-dependent since it could be reversed by either anti-$\alpha_v\beta_3$ or the antagonist peptide cRGD. In normal hemostasis, thrombin is inactivated by antithrombin. This process occurs rapidly only in the presence of heparins. Extracellular matrix ECM-immobilized thrombin could possibly be protected from degradation and mediate cellular responses. In a pathological situation such as within a tumor, thrombin may become trapped in thrombi and can act as an angiogenic factor.

C. Fibrinogen and Fibrin

The blood vessels of tumors are typically leaky due to increased microvascular permeability. This hyperpermeability is mainly due to the effects of VEGF/vascular permeability factor. Fibrinogen as well as other clotting factors may therefore leak into the extravascular tissue. Extravasated fibrinogen binds to tumor cells and/or inflammatory cells, is cleaved by thrombin and eventually converted to cross-linked fibrin which could become deposited on and around tumor cells or tumor-associated inflammatory cells and serve as a provisional matrix that enhances further neovascularization [114]. Modulation of the tumor-associated fibrin can significantly affect the extent and stability of capillary tube formation *in vitro* [115]. For example, low molecular weight heparins modulate fibrin structure and thus affect angiogenesis *in vitro* [115]. Furthermore, the alpha chain of fibrin harboring RGD and transglutaminase sequences appears to be an important determinant for angiogenesis [115]. Endothelial cells [116], fibroblasts [117], smooth muscle cells, platelets [118], leukocytes [119], and tumor cells [120], can all bind specifically to fibrin matrices via integrin or non-integrin-mediated cell surface receptors. For example, the aforementioned RGD sequence of human fibrinogen is necessary for the interactions between fibrinogen and $\alpha_v\beta_3$ and $\alpha_5\beta_1$

integrins. Although the importance of $\alpha_v\beta_3$ in tumor angiogenesis remains uncertain due to inconsistent findings between pharmacological [121-123], and genetic ablation studies [111], it has been suggested that the amount of appropriate angiogenic matrix ligands could dictate the role of $\alpha_v\beta_3$ integrin in pathological angiogenesis [124]. Indeed, it has been shown that fibrin matrices surrounding the endothelial cells affect the mRNA expression of $\alpha_v\beta_3$ and thus provoke differential angiogenic states [125]. The $\alpha_v\beta_3$ receptors could provide survival signals to the endothelial cells as a result of direct interactions with fibrinogen/fibrin. During wound repair, the integrin expression of endothelial cells changes according to their surrounding matrices, thus controlling angiogenesis. In a growing tumor microenvironment, constant fibrin deposition will lead to persistent integrin expression on invading endothelial cells and sustained angiogenesis.

Non-integrin-mediated interactions with fibrin are mediated via the Bβ15-42 sequence which is exposed following the cleavage of fibrinopeptide B. It has been suggested that following fibrinogen/fibrin degradation, cryptic sites in these molecules are exposed that promote adhesion to cell surface receptors and subsequent intracellular signaling [126]. Fibrinogen/fibrin can be cleaved directly by thrombin or plasmin and form biologically active fragments including D and E [127]. These factors can elicit pro-angiogenic or anti-angiogenic activities that may contribute to tumor growth. Fibrin(ogen) fragment E stimulates the proliferation, migration and differentiation of human microvascular endothelial cells *in vitro* [128]. However, the same fragment inhibits migration and tubule formation of human dermal microvascular endothelial cells [129]. *In vivo*, fibrinogen fragment E stimulates angiogenesis with thrombin being instrumental in generating that activity.

Overwhelming evidence points to an important role for fibrin(ogen) in enhancing angiogenesis and tumor progression. However, the growth kinetics and angiogenesis of primary tumors in fibrinogen-deficient mice is similar to that in control mice indicating that fibrinogen is not essential for angiogenesis and primary tumor growth [130]. Finally, an *in vitro* study by Contrino *et al.* [131] showed that TF expression on human umbilical vein endothelial cells (HUVECs) is induced (150 fold) when co-cultured with fibrin. These authors showed that direct contact between fibrin and the endothelial cells was required for TF induction.

The Contact Coagulation Activation System in Angiogenesis

High molecular weight kininogen (HK), factor XII and prekallikrein (PK) are the three plasma proteins required for the activation of contact system or surface-mediated pathway. HK can bind to endothelial cell surface in association with PK [132]. PK is then activated by an endothelial serine protease to kallikrein, which cleaves FXII to FXIIa and prourokinase to urokinase [133,132]. Intact HK stimulates angiogenesis in a chorioallatoic membrane (CAM) assay possibly by liberating bradykinin [134]. In contrast, after cleavage by plasma kallikrein, cleaved HK (HKa) and its cell-binding domain 5 (D5), kininostatin, have a negative effect on angiogenesis and inhibit endothelial cell migration, proliferation and tube formation [134].

The Role of Platelets in Angiogenesis

The role of platelets in promoting blood-borne metastasis is now well accepted. However, their possible contributions to angiogenesis have not been investigated as thoroughly. In cancer, platelets undergo activation due to direct or indirect effects of tumor cells. Tumor cells or their membrane vesicles can induce platelet activation by physical binding. In addition, they can initiate coagulation and cause thrombin generation, which in turn reinforces aggregation and platelet-mediated tumor cell adhesion to vascular endothelial cells [135].

The involvement of platelets in the angiogenic process was initially hypothesized by Pinedo *et al.* [136]. Subsequently, evidence emerged that platelets promote tube formation by endothelial cells on matrigel in a glycoprotein-dependent manner [137]. It was also shown that VEGF-stimulated endothelial cells promote adhesion and activation of platelets [138]. Platelets also stimulate sprouting of endothelial cells in *in vitro* models of angiogenesis, an effect that can be inhibited by GPIIb/IIIa receptor antagonists [139]. Platelet-endothelial bridging may involve platelet GPIIb/IIIa integrin and platelet degranulation resulting in the secretion of angiogenic factors such as VEGF [140].

Table 1: Potential Regulators of angiogenesis carried by platelets.

Positive Regulators	Negative Regulators
VEGF A and VEGF C	Thrombospondin
CD40L	PF4
PDGF	Plasminogen fragment (angiostatin)
IGF	Fibronectin fragment (45KD)
HGF	TFPI
EGF	α2- antiplasmin
Fibrinogen	α2-macroglobulin
Platelet microparticles	β-thromboglobulin
Angiopoietin-1	
Fibronectin	
Vitronectin	
PAI-1	

Platelets are numerous (2-3 x 10^8/ml) in blood and contain abundant stores of angiogenic and mitogenic factors. Platelets have a half-life of approximately 5-7 days [141] and may provide tumors with a potentially continuous supply of angiogenic factors. Platelets contain both positive and negative regulators of angiogenesis (Table 1). These regulators are mostly within the platelets and are exposed and/or released following platelet activation. In addition, platelet membranes carry growth factor receptors including functional VEGF receptors (VEGFR-1 and VEGFR-2) on their surface [142]. Although VEGF itself does not cause platelet activation, addition of exogenous VEGF to thrombin-stimulated platelets potentiates platelet aggregation [143]. Platelets also express receptor tyrosine kinase (Tie-1) and platelet activation results in increased expression of this receptor [144]. Tie-1 is expressed predominantly on endothelial cells and has an essential role in blood vessel formation. Platelet Tie-1 receptor could potentially modulate endothelial cell function by competing with other receptors for signaling Tie ligands [145]. Another example is platelet-derived growth factor-α (PDGF-α) receptor which is localized on both platelets and their progenitors, megakaryocytes, where they enhance their proliferation [146]. In this review, a number of important platelet-associated angiogenic regulators are discussed in more detail.

Vascular Endothelial Growth Factor (VEGF)

One of the strongest links between platelets and angiogenesis is the presence of VEGF within platelets. Platelet VEGF ($VEGF_{121}$ and $VEGF_{165}$) is released following activation [147,148]. VEGF is secreted from platelets along with β-thromboglobulin, indicating that it is stored in the α-granules [149]. We have shown that the release of VEGF from platelets could be inhibited by blockade of GPIIb/IIIa receptor [150]. In cancer, platelet numbers strongly correlate with serum VEGF concentration in breast, colorectal, renal and ovarian cancer patients, and IL-6 has been postulated to be a strong regulator of platelet VEGF release [151-153].

Thrombocytosis is relatively common in cancer patients. Although underlying mechanisms for its occurrence are not fully understood [145], increased levels of thrombopoietin (TPO) [154] and tumor-related humoral factors with TPO-like activity or cytokines (such as IL-6, IL-1, GMCSF) may be at least partially responsible [155-158].The possibility of platelet VEGF contributing to neovascularization of tumors at distant sites is interesting and worth investigating. It is well established that circulating tumor cells can bind and activate platelets prior to adhesion to the vascular endothelium of distant organs. It is conceivable that tumor cell-induced activated platelets can release VEGF and induce microvessel permeability (Figure 3). This would not only promote extravasation of cancer cells but also could induce neoangiogenesis in distant sites [145]. In addition, by inducing endothelial fenestration, platelet VEGF (as well as VEGF from other sources, e.g. tumor cells themselves) may facilitate the egress of other hemostatic proteins to the extravascular space. As mentioned earlier, VEGF can induce the expression of TF and MMPs in endothelial cells [159]. VEGF also enhances the transendothelial migration of monocytes and is a chemotactic factor for monocytes and mast cells [160] which are known to contribute to tumor angiogenesis [161-163].

CD40 and CD40 Ligand (CD40L)

CD40 is a transmembrane protein homologous to the tumor necrosis factor (TNF) receptor (TNFR). This receptor was first described as a constitutive cell-surface antigen on human bladder carcinoma cells and B cells [164,165]. CD40 was subsequently shown to be constitutively expressed on monocytes, macrophages and dendritic cells [166] and more recently identified on the surface of vascular endothelial cells and platelets [167,168]. CD40 ligand (CD40L, TRAP, gp39, or CD154) is a transmembrane homologue of tumor necrosis factor-α (TNF-α) that was originally described as a surface molecule on activated T cells and later, on stimulated mast cells and basophils [169-171]. Henn and colleagues [172] demonstrated that platelets contain preformed CD40L that rapidly appears on the platelet surface following stimulation by thrombin. CD40L is subsequently cleaved from the membrane and released as a soluble form.

We and others have shown that >95% of circulating CD40L is contained in platelets [173,168]. The engagement of platelet-derived membrane-bound CD40L with CD40 on endothelial cells induces the expression of TF and elicits an inflammatory reaction of the endothelium characterized by expression of intracellular adhesion molecule (ICAM-1), vascular cell adhesion molecule (VCAM-1) and E-selectin and secretion of IL-8 [172]. Interactions between CD40L and CD40 have pluripotent functions in inflammation, including the production of cytokines, chemokines and growth factors such as VEGF by endothelial cells. Treatment of HUVECs and monocytes with soluble CD40L induces VEGF mRNA (approximately 4-fold) and increases proliferation of endothelial cells in a VEGF-dependent manner [174]. Furthermore, subcutaneous injection of soluble CD40L in immunodeficient mice induces VEGF expression and marked angiogenesis *in vivo* [174]. In a mouse model of Kaposi's sarcoma, Biancone *et al.* [175] have demonstrated that CD40 supports tumor cell survival, growth and neovasculaization. Since abundant (ng) amounts of CD40L are persent in human platelets and since platelets are often activated, it is reasonable to suggest that platelet-derived CD40L (especially soluble CD40L) could have a significant stimulatory effect on tumor angiogenesis by binding to endothelial and/or tumor cell CD40 receptors. In addition, it is also possible for platelet-derived CD40L to bind CD40 on resting platelets and cause further platelet activation [176].

The platelet alpha granules contain many pro-angiogenic proteins. These include basic FGF (bFGF) [177] which enhances migration, proliferation and differentiation of endothelial cells [178] and hepatocyte growth factor (HGF) which promotes motility and matrix invasion of epithelial cells and enhances VEGF expression by endothelial cells [179]. Platelets contain insulin-like growth factor (IGF), which exerts mitogenic and anti-apoptotic effects and its expression is correlated with microvessel density in tumor tissue [180]. Other factors include epidermal growth factor (EGF), which has been shown to upregulate VEGF mRNA expression in tumor and endothelial cells [181,182] ; Angiopoietin-1, which is essential for blood vessel development via stabilization of proliferating endothelial cells and is released following thrombin activation [183]; Platelet-derived growth factor (PDGF) which induces angiogenesis via stimulating VEGF expression in tumor and endothelial cells and recruits pericytes to neovessels [184]; Transforming growth factor β-1 (TGF-β1) which regulates the activity of VEGF-VEFGR system [185] and increase EC survival [186].

In addition to releasing soluble factors, activated platelets can shed membrane microparticles (PMP). These particles range from (0.1-1μm) and have been shown to promote proliferation, survival, migration and tube formation in HUVECs *in vitro* [187]. Kim *et al*, [187] further demonstrated that heat-treated PMP did not significantly decrease the angiogenic activity in HUVEC compared with untreated PMP. However, when PMPs were treated with activated charcoal which removes the lipid growth factors, the angiogenic activity was significantly reduced, indicating that the lipid component of PMPs may contribute to the pro-angiogenic effect of these particles.

Platelets also contain a number of anti-angiogenic factors. Platelet factor4 (PF4) was the first hemostatic protein demonstrated to be an inhibitor of angiogenesis *in vivo* [188]. This tetrameric protein binds to the surface of heparin-like glycosaminoglycans on endothelial cells [189]. PF-4 is unable to directly inhibit tumor cell growth *in vitro* but strongly inhibits the growth of endothelial cells [190,191] . The mechanism of inhibition by PF4 is not clear, but it has been demonstrated that PF-4 slows down the passage of endothelial cells through S phase of the cell cycle [191]. In addition, PF-4 inhibits mitogen-activated protein (MAP) kinases and induces p21 in HUVECs [192,193]. PF-4 also inhibits the binding of FGF-2 and VEGF to their respective cell surface receptors [194,195]. Finally, several PF4 fragments and modified molecules have been made that exhibit anti-angiogenic properties [196].

Thrombospondin (TSP-1) is another constituent of platelet granules known to act as angiogenesis inhibitor. This protein binds tissue factor pathway inhibitor (TFPI) [197] thus localizing of TFPI to the extravascular surfaces. This may allow TFPI to potentially inhibit TF-dependent coagulation and angiogenesis.

Plasminogen activator inhibitor (PAI-1) is also present in platelets. The information regarding the effect of PAI-1 on angiogenesis is somewhat controversial [198]. However, reduced tumor growth and angiogenesis has been observed in PAI-1-deficient mice [199].

The Role of the Fibrinolytic System in Tumor Angiogenesis

One of the essential steps of the angiogenic process is the proteolytic degradation of the extracellular matrix that surrounds both the capillary sprouts and the migrating tumor cells. Enzymes of the fibrinolytic system as well as the matrix metalloproteinase family contribute to these processes. As mentioned above, plasmin is the principal active component of the fibrinolytic system. This protease is involved in the hydrolysis of fibrin and many other extracellular proteins. In angiogenesis, plasmin formation occurs mainly via the action of u-PA on plasminogen [200]. u-PA binds to a specific u-PA receptor (u-PAR), which is expressed on the surface of endothelial cells and many tumor cell types [201]. The localization of this complex is associated with the integrin adhesion molecules such as $\alpha_3\beta_1$ [202] which are important in endothelial cell interactions with the extracellular matrix. The cell surface u-PAR/u-PA interaction significantly increases fibrinolysis in the cell surface area, thus causing proteolysis of nearby matrices (Figure 4). Functional u-PAR/u-PA has been shown to be increased at the cell surface of the leading edge of migrating endothelial cells [203,204]. Moreover, u-PA expression is often elevated in malignant tissues compared to the surrounding tissue or benign tumors [205]. u-PA-deficient mice are resistant to melanoma progression [206] and exhibit decreased formation of new vessels [207] while u-PA antibodies or antisense oligonucleotides have been shown to inhibit both local tumor invasion and metastasis [208-210]. Fibrinolysis can be inhibited at different steps by physiological inhibitors present in blood. Plasmin activity is inhibited by its physiological inhibitor, α_2-antiplasmin, whereas u-PA is inhibited by PAI-1 [211]. Paradoxically, however, high levels of PAI-1 are predictive of a poor prognosis for survival of patients with cancer [212]. PAI-1 could potentially protect the extracellular matrix from excessive degradation by plasmin which could result in better endothelial cell migration and assembly of tumor vessels [212-214]. Thus it appears that plasmin proteolysis is essential for tumor angiogenesis. However, it must be tightly controlled in order to allow vessel stabilization and maturation.

The u-PA/plasmin and MMP systems cooperate to regulate the focal proteolytic activity on cell surfaces. Specifically, the u-PA/plasmin pathway directly activates the pro-forms of

MMPs, and increases the total proteolytic activity [215-218]. In addition, MMPs can inactivate PAI-1 and α_2-antiplasmin thereby increasing u-PA/plasmin proteolysis [219,220].

Plasminogen appears to be essential for optimum angiogenesis since it is responsible for plasmin formation. However, one of its internal proteolytic fragments, angiostatin, is a specific angiogenesis inhibitor and is produced by plasminogen hydrolysis either by u-PA or by metaloproteinases (MMP-3, MMP-7 or MMP-9) [221-224]. The structure of angiostatin includes the first four kringle domains of plasminogen [225]. Angiostatin is produced by the primary tumor and inhibits the metastasis of that tumor. Its relatively longer half-life compared to proangiogenic factors may be the reason why it inhibits the growth of metastases but not that of the primary tumor itself [226]. Although angiostatin specifically and effectively inhibits endothelial cell proliferation, the exact mechanism of its anti-angiogenic action is not completely understood. Suggestions include inhibition of G2/M transition of the endothelial cell cycle [227] and induction of endothelial cell apoptosis [228,229]. A short fragment of angiostatin (kringle 1-3) produces an even more potent anti-tumor effect than kringle 1-4 and has entered clinical trials in human cancer therapy [230].

Hemostatic Interventions as Anti-Angiogenic Approaches

A. Targeting Tissue Factor

There is no doubt that a broad and complex interface exists between vascular hemostasis, wound healing and tumor angiogenesis. A large number of *in vivo* and even larger number of *in vitro* studies of hemostatic components have shown enhancement or inhibition of angiogenesis pointing to a significant potential for anti-hemostatic approaches in cancer therapy. A better understanding of hemostasis-angiogenesis interrelationship *in vivo* is required in order to find a suitable anti-hemostatic approach against angiogenesis. In addition, the possibilty of thrombotic or hemorrahgic side effects must be carefully considered.

The apparent selective expression of TF on the vascular endothelial cells of malignant but not benign tumors, makes it a logical candidate for targeted cancer therapy. Furthermore, inhibition of TF activity is not likely to cause inappropriate bleeding. There is considerable evidence to indicate that TF-initiated coagulation generates potent positive regulators of angiogenesis. However, the exact mechanisms by which *in vivo* angiogenesis is supported by these regulators are not completely understood. In addition, TF also serves as a coreceptor in PAR signaling and there are emerging data to link angiogenesis to PAR activation by TF-initiated coagulation-independent mechanisms [89].

Antibody targeting of TF causes significant tumor debulking in murine models. For example, using a fusion protein consisting of an antibody fragment specific for the oncofetal ED-B domain of fibronectin (only expressed by blood vessels of malignant but not benign tissues) fused to the extracellular domain of tissue factor, Nilsson *et al.* [231] selectively targeted tumor blood vessels *in vivo* and selectively caused complete infarction of three types of solid tumors in mice. In another elegant study, a vector coding for an immunoconjugate molecule consisting of the Fc domain of IgG1 immunoglobulin and a mutated mouse factor VII was injected directly into primary tumors that expressed TF. This resulted in tumor shrinkage due to a cytolytic immune response directed against the Fc domain component of the conjugate that was selectively localized to the TF expressing tumor [232]. Finally, TFPI inhibits both tumor growth and metastasis in mice [233], [234]. There is convincing evidence that the TF signaling pathway is involved in angiogenesis both independently or more likely in cooperation with other signaling pathways dependent for example, on PAR-2 and PDGF [89]. In murine tumor models, we and others have shown that intravenous injection of a monoclonal anti-TF antibody not only inhibits experimental metastasis but also delays primary tumor growth [235,236] . Overall, TF-targeted strategies could be among the most promising anti-tumor approaches for human cancer therapy.

B. Targeting Thrombin Generation by Anticoagulants

For many years, anticoagulants such as heparin and warfarin have been used to treat and/or prevent thromboembolism in a variety of patients including those patients with malignancy. Several studies with low-molecular weight heparins (LMWHs) point to potential survival advantages among cancer patients. Due to their more predictable anticoagulant effect, the use of LMWHs has increased significantly in recent years. The results indicate that LMWH is equally, if not more beneficial to cancer patients in terms of survival, compared to unfractionated heparin (UFH) [237,238]. For example, meta-analysis of nine studies revealed that patients with venous thromboembolism and cancer who received LMWH had a significant improvement in 3-month mortality rate compared with those who received UFH [239].

One possible explanation of heparin's apparently anti-cancer effects is that these anticoagulants inhibit angiogenesis. Folkman and colleagues [240] showed that heparin or heparin fragment administered with cortisone inhibited angiogenesis, caused tumor regression and prevented metastasis. In this study, most inhibition was observed when the combination of heparin and cortisone was used. Similar results were obtained by Thorpe *et al* [241], who used non-anticoagulating heparin-steroid conjugates. It appears that heparin may inhibit angiogenesis via anticoagulant- and/or non-anticoagulant-dependent mechanisms. Heparins have been shown to inhibit tumor cell proliferation, migration and invasion [242] and could potentially interact with growth factors involved in endothelial cell prolifreration. However, under certain conditions (e.g. coronary artery disease), heparins may promote angiogenesis [243]. This inconsistency is probably due to the heterogeneity and complex involvement of a large number of substances [244]. LMWH seem to inhibit angiogenesis better than UFH and have an increased ability to block thrombin-induced platelet aggregation, greater interactions with vascular endothelium and the ability to stimulate platelet production [244]. Overall, anticoagulant adjuvant therapy in cancer holds promise. The development of thrombin receptor antagonists may also be an effective approach since proangiogenic actions of thrombin could be inhibited specifically, and such agents may be easier to use in the clinic than heparins or other anticoagulants. However, in order to reach definitive conclusions, carefully designed prospective randomized placebo-controlled clinical trials should be performed on specific preparations in patients controlled for tumor type, stage of disease, performance status and standard therapy given.

C. Anti-Platelet Therapy

As mentioned above, platelets could potentially enhance angiogenesis by multiple mechanisms. This, coupled with the role of platelets in promoting hematogenous metastasis, makes platelets a reasonable target for cancer therapy. It has been postulated that a "true" anti-angiogenic agent should not only inhibit tumor growth but also should suppress hematogenous metastasis [245]. A number of animal studies including two from our laboratory have demonstrated that inhibition of GPIIb/IIIa blocks experimental metastasis and tumor cell induced-thrombocytopenia [140,150,246]. There are little data available however, to suggest that chronic inhibition of platelets could interfere with neovascularization and suppression of tumor growth. One study has shown that a combined inhibition of platelet GPIIb/IIIa and $\alpha_v\beta_3$ integrin is more effective in inhibiting tumor growth and angiogenesis compared to blockade of $\alpha_v\beta_3$ alone [140] . In addition, the $F(ab')_2$ fragment of m7E3 anti GPIIb/IIIa antibody exhibits both anti-metastatic and anti-angiogenic effects [139] .

Prostacyclin analogues or inhibitors of thromboxane A2 synthase have been shown to inhibit tumor cell-induced platelet aggregation and metastases [247]. However, prostacyclin could not be regarded as an anti-cancer drug due to a lack of effect on many tumor types [248]. Aspirin interferes with platelet α-granule release but does not inhibit the release of VEGF from platelets [249]. A better understanding of the contribution of platelets to the angiogenic process is required in order to determine the most suitable anti-platelet approach in conjunction with standard cancer treatments.

D. Anti-Fibrinolytic Therapy

The u-PA/plasmin and MMP pathways appear to cooperate in regulating the proteolytic activities required in angiogenesis and metastasis. Based on their compelling experimental effects, MMP inhibitors have been studied in clinical trials. However, for the most part, the results of these studies have been disappointing suggesting that the involvement of the matrix metalloproteinases in tumor progression is more complex. The use of anti-fibrinolytic agents in cancer may be problematic since these agents could likely exacerbate the hypercoagulable state already present in patients with malignant disease.

Clearly, the inter-relationship between the hemostatic and angiogenic processes is complex and highly intricate. There are many cellular and protein components of the hemostatic system which positively or negatively regulate angiogenesis. However, very little is known about the coordination of these mechanisms. More information is needed regarding the timing and the sequence of interactions between various hemostatic components and tumor vessel formation and the challenge remains in designing safe therapeutic approaches. For example, Kuenan and associates [250], showed that the potent angiogenesis inhibitor SU5416, which blocks VEGFR-1 and VEGFR-2 may alter the hemostatic properties of endothelial cells. In the latter study on patients with advanced cancer, a significant increase in endogenous thrombin potential, and of parameters reflecting endothelial cell activation (von Willebrand antigen, soluble tissue factor, and soluble E-selectin) was observed in all patients as a result of treatment. Furthermore, a significant number of thromboembolic events (nine events in eight of nineteen patients) were observed. The investigators hypothesized that VEGF-deprived endothelial cells (after exposure to SU5416) become activated and more susceptible to damage by chemotherapeutic agents. This endothelial reaction can become further aggrevated by platelet activation and local liberation of VEGF.

Ideally, because of the relationship between hemostasis and angiogenesis, anti-angiogenic agents should be selected for their ability to exert minimal effects on bleeding and thrombosis.

References

[1] Passauer,J., Lassig,G., Bussemaker,E., Pistrosch,F., and Gross,P. 2004. Reduced endothelin-1- and nitric oxide-mediated arteriolar tone in hypertensive renal transplant recipients. *Kidney Int 65*:1782-1789.

[2] Pytela,R., Pierschbacher,M.D., Ginsberg,M.H., Plow,E.F., and Ruoslahti,E. 1986. Platelet membrane glycoprotein IIb/IIIa: member of a family of Arg-Gly-Asp--specific adhesion receptors. *Science 231*:1559-1562.

[3] Shattil,S.J., Hoxie,J.A., Cunningham,M., and Brass,L.F. 1985. Changes in the platelet membrane glycoprotein IIb.IIIa complex during platelet activation. *J Biol Chem 260*:11107-11114.

[4] Holmsen H. 1993. *Platelet secretion and energy metabolism. In Hemostasis and Thrombosis: basic principals and clinical practice.* J.Hirsh, Marder,V.J., Salzman,E.W., and Colman RW., editors. Philadelphia.

[5] Colman RW., Marder,V.J., Salzman,E.W., and Hirsh,J. 1994. *Overview of Hemostasis. In Hemostasis and Thrombosis*. Colman RW., Hirsh,J., Marder,V.J., and Salzman,E.W., editors. J.P. Lippincott, 3-18.

[6] Nemerson,Y. and Repke,D. 1985. Tissue factor accelerates the activation of coagulation factor VII: the role of a bifunctional coagulation cofactor. *Thromb.Res. 40*:351-358.

[7] Morrissey,J.H., Macik,B.G., Neuenschwander,P.F., and Comp,P.C. 1993. Quantitation of activated factor VII levels in plasma using a tissue factor mutant selectively deficient in promoting factor VII activation. *Blood 81*:734-744.

[8] Gemmell,C.H., Broze,G.J., Turitto,V.T., and Nemerson,Y. 1990. Utilization of a continuous flow reactor to study the lipoprotein-associated coagulation inhibitor (LACI) that inhibits tissue factor. *Blood 76*:2266-2271.

[9] Bajaj,M.S., Birktoft,J.J., Steer,S.A., and Bajaj,S.P. 2001. Structure and biology of tissue factor pathway inhibitor. *Thromb.Haemost. 86*:959-972.

[10] Collen,D. 1980. On the regulation and control of fibrinolysis. Edward Kowalski Memorial Lecture. *Thromb Haemost 43*:77-89.

[11] Francis,C.W., Marder,V.J., and Martin,S.E. 1980. Plasmic degradation of crosslinked fibrin. I. Structural analysis of the particulate clot and identification of new macromolecular-soluble complexes. *Blood 56*:456-464.

[12] Trousseau,A. 1865. *Phlegmasia alba dolens*. In Clinique Medicale de l'Hotel de Paris. Balliere, 654-656.

[13] Dvorak,H.F. 1987. Thrombosis and Cancer. *Human Pathol. 18*:275-284.

[14] Rickles,F.R. and Levine,M.N. 2001. Epidemiology of thrombosis in cancer. *Acta Haematol. 106*:6-12.

[15] Hillen,H.F. 2000. Thrombosis in cancer patients. *Ann.Oncol. 11 Suppl 3*:273-276.

[16] Peck,S.D. and Reiquam,C.W. 1973. Disseminated intravascular coagulation in cancer patients: supportive evidence. *Cancer 31*:1114-1119.

[17] Sun,N.C.J., Bowie,E.J.W., Kazmier,F.J., Elveback,L.R., and Owen,C.A. 1974. Blood coagulation studies in patients with cancer. *Mayo.Clin.Proc. 49*:636-641.

[18] Sun,N.C.J., McAfee,W.M., Hum,G.J., and Weiner,J.M. 1979. Hemostatic abnormalities in malignancy, a prospective study of one hundred eight patients. Part 1. Coagulation studies. *Am.J.Clin.Pathol. 71*:10-16.

[19] Bick,R.L. 1978. Alterations of haemostasis associated with malignancy. Etiology, pathophysiology, diagnosis and management. *Semin.Thromb.Hemost. 5*:1-26.

[20] Rickles,F.R., Edwards,R.L., Barb,C., and Cronlund,M. 1983. Abnormalities of blood coagulation in patients with cancer. Fibrinopeptide A generation and tumor growth. *Cancer 51*:301-307.

[21] Kies,M.S., Posch,J.J., Giolama,J.P., and Rubin,R.N. 1980. Haemostatic function in cancer patients. *Cancer 46*:831-837.

[22] Miller,S.P., Sanchez-Avalos,J., Stefanski,T., and Zuckerman,L. 1967. Coagulation disorders in cancer I. Clinical and laboratory studies. *Cancer 20*:1452-1465.

[23] Edwards,R.L., Rickles,F.R., Moritz,T.E., Henderson,W.G., Zacharski,L.R., Forman,W.B., Cornell,C.J., O'Donnell,J.F., Headley,E., Kim,S.-H. et al. 1987. Anormalities of blood coagulation tests in patients with cancer. *Am.J.Clin.Pathol. 88*:596-602.

[24] Davis,R.B., Theologides,A., and Kennedy,B.J. 1969. Comparative studies of blood coagulation and platelet aggregation in patients with cancer and non-malignant diseases. *Ann.Int.Med. 71*:67-80.

[25] Taguchi,O., Gabazza,E.C., Yoshida,M., Yamakami,T., Kobayashi,H., and Shima,T. 1996. High plasma level of plasmin-a2-plasmin inhibitor complex is predictor of poor prognosis in patients with lung cancer. *Clin.Chim.Acta 244*:69-81.

[26] Mombelli,G., Roux,A., Haeberli,A., and Staub,P.W. 1982. Comparison of 125I-fibrinogen kinetics and fibrinopeptide A in patients with disseminated neoplasias. *Blood 60*:381-388.

[27] Peuscher,F.W., Cleton,F.J., Armstrong,L., Stoepman,E.A., van Dalen,X., van Mourik,J.A., and van Aken,W.G. 1980. Significance of plasma fibrinopeptide A (FPA) in patients with malignancy. *J.Lab.Clin.Med. 96*:5-14.

[28] Seitz,R., Rappe,N., Kraus,M., Immel,A., Wolf,M., Maasberg,M., Egbring,R., Pfab,R., and Havemann,K. 1993. Activation of coagulation and fibrinolysis in patients with lung cancer - relation to tumour stage and prognosis. *Blood Coag.Fibrinol. 4*:249-254.

[29] Tripodi,A., Mannucci,P.M., Chantarangkul,V., Bottasso,B., Arbini,A.A., Dellabella,S., and Scorza,R. 1993. Markers of procoagulant imbalance in patients with localized melanomas and autoimmune disorders. *Br.J Haematol. 84*:670-674.

[30] Day,E.D., Planinsek,J.A., and Pressman,D. 1959. Localization in vivo of radioiodinated anti-rat-fibrin antibodies and radioiodinated rat fibrinogen in the murphy rat lymphosarcoma and in other transplantable rat tumors. *J.Natl.Cancer Inst. 22*:413-426.

[31] Dvorak,H.F., Senger,D.R., and Dvorak,A.M. 1983. Fibrin as a component of the tumour stroma: origins and biological significance. *Cancer Metast.Rev. 2*:41-73.

[32] Dvorak,H.F. 1986. Tumors: Wounds that do not heal. Similarities between tumor stroma generation and wound healing. *N.Engl.J.Med. 315*:1650-1659.

[33] Folkman,J. 1971. Tumor angiogenesis: therapeutic implications. *N Engl J Med 285*:1182-1186.

[34] Folkman,J., Browder,T., and Palmblad,J. 2001. Angiogenesis research: guidelines for translation to clinical application. *Thromb Haemost 86*:23-33.

[35] Bach,R., Nemerson,Y., and Konigsberg,W. 1981. Purification and characterisation of bovine tissue factor. *J.Biol.Chem. 256*:8324-8331.

[36] Dvorak,H.F., Senger,D.R., and Dvorak,A.M. 1984. *Fibrin formation: Implications for tumor growth and metastasis. In Hemostatic Mechanisms and Metastasis.* K.V.Honn and Sloane,B.F., editors. Martinus Nijhoff, Boston. 96-114.

[37] Clark,R.A.F. and Colvin,R.B. 1985. *Wound repair. In Plasma fibrinogen structure and function.* J.McDonagh, editor. Marcel Dekker, New York. 197-262.

[38] Dvorak,H.F., Form,D.M., Manseau,E.J., and Smith,B.D. 1984. Pathogenesis of desmoplasia. I. Immunofluorescence identification and localization of some structural proteins of line 1 and line 10 guinea pig tumors and of healing wounds. *J Natl Cancer Inst. 73*:1195-1205.

[39] Senger,D.R., Brown,L.F., Claffey,K.P., and Dvorak,H.F. 1994. Vascular permeability factor, tumor angiogenesis and stroma generation. *Invasion and Metastasis 14*:385-394.

[40] Robbins SL, Cotran,R.S., and Kumar,V. 1984. *Pathologic basis of disease.* W.B.Saunders, editor. Philadelphia.

[41] Senger,D.R., Brown,L.F., Claffey,K.P., and Dvorak,H.F. 1994. Vascular permeability factor, tumor angiogenesis and stroma generation. *Invasion and Metastasis 14*:385-394.

[42] Dvorak,H.F., Brown,L.F., Detmar,M., and Dvorak,A.M. 1995. Vascular permeability factor/vascular endothelial growth factor, microvascular hyperpermeability, and angiogenesis. *Am J Pathol 146*:1029-1039.

[43] Szendroi,M., Lapis,K., Zalatnai,A., Robert,L., and Labat-Robert,J. 1984. Appearance of fibronectin in putative preneoplastic lesions and in hepatocellular carcinoma during chemical hepatocarcinogenesis in rats and in human hepatomas. *J Exp Pathol 1:*189-199.

[44] Cole,M.A., Crawford,D.W., Warner,N.E., and Puffer,H.W. 1983. Correlation of regional disease and in vivo PO2 in rat mammary adenocarcinoma. *Am J Pathol 112:*61-67.

[45] Dvorak,H.F. and Dvorak,A.M. 1982. *Immunohistochemical characterization of inflammatory cells that infiltrate tumors. In Tumor immunity in prognosis: the role of mononuclear cell infiltration.* Haskill S, editor. Marcel Dekker, New York. 279-307.

[46] Dvorak,H.F., Form DM, Manseau,E.J., and Smith BD. 1984. Pathogenesis of desmoplasia. I. Immunofluorescence identification and localization of some structural proteins of line 1 and line 10 guinea pig tumors and of healing wounds. *J.Nat.Cancer.Inst 73*:1195-1205.

[47] Ciano,P.S., Colvin,R.B., Dvorak,A.M., McDonagh,J., and Dvorak,H.F. 1986. Macrophage migration in fibrin gel matrices. *Lab Invest 54*:62-70.

[48] Ross,R., Raines,E.W., and Bowen-Pope,D.F. 1986. The biology of platelet-derived growth factor. *Cell 46*:155-169.

[49] Karpatkin,S. and Holmsen H. 1983. Biochemistry and function of platelets. *In Hematology.* W.J.Williams, Beutler E, Erslev AJ, and Lichtman MA, editors. McGraw-Hill, New York.

[50] Tracy,P.B., Nesheim,M.E., and Mann,K.G. 1981. Coordinate binding of factor Va and factor Xa to the unstimulated platelet. *J Biol Chem 256*:743-751.

[51] van de Water,L., Tracy,P.B., Aronson,D., Mann,K.G., and Dvorak,H.F. 1985. Tumor cell generation of thrombin via functional prothrombinase assembly. *Cancer Res 45:*5521-5525.

[52] Holash,J., Maisonpierre,P.C., Compton,D., Boland,P., Alexander,C.R., Zagzag,D., Yancopoulos,G.D., and Wiegand,S.J. 1999. Vessel cooption, regression, and growth in tumors mediated by angiopoietins and VEGF. *Science 284*:1994-1998.

[53] Knighton,D.R., Hunt,T.K., Scheuenstuhl,H., Halliday,B.J., Werb,Z., and Banda,M.J. 1983. Oxygen tension regulates the expression of angiogenesis factor by macrophages. *Science 221*:1283-1285.

[54] Folkman,J. 1985. Tumor angiogenesis. *Adv Cancer Res 43*:175-203.

[55] Carmeliet,P., Mackman,N., Moons,L., Luther,T., Gressens,P., Van Vlaenderen,I., Demunck,H., Kasper,M., Breier,G., Evrard,P. et al. 1996. Role of tissue factor in embryonic blood vessel development. *Nature 383*:73-75.

[56] Bugge,T.H., Xiao,Q., Kombrinck,K.W., Flick,M.J., Holmbäck,K., Danton,H.J.S., Colbert,M.C., Witte,D.P., Fujikawa,K., Davie,E.W. et al. 1996. Fatal embryonic bleeding events in mice lacking tissue factor, the cell-associated initiator of blood coagulation. *PNAS USA 93*:6258-6263.

[57] Toomey,J.R., Kratzer,K.E., Lasky,N.M., Stanton,J.J., and Broze,G.J., Jr. 1996. Targeted disruption of the murine tissue factor gene results in embryonic lethality. *Blood 88*:1583-1587.

[58] Carmeliet,P., Moons,L., Dewerchin,M., Mackman,N., Luther,T., Breier,G., Ploplis,V., Muller,M., Nagy,A., Plow,E. et al. 1997. Insights in vessel development and vascular disorders using targeted inactivation and transfer of vascular endothelial growth factor, the tissue factor receptor, and the plasminogen system. *Ann N Y Acad Sci 811*:191-206.

[59] Ferrara N. 1996. Vascular Endothelial Growth Factor. *Eur.J.Cancer* 32A:2413-2422.

[60] Peppelenbosch,M.P. and Versteeg,H.H. 2001. Cell biology of tissue factor, an unusual member of the cytokine receptor family. *Trends Cardiovasc Med 11*:335-339.

[61] Koomagi,R. and Volm,M. 1998. Tissue-factor expression in human non-small-cell lung carcinoma measured by immunohistochemistry: correlation between tissue factor and angiogenesis. *Int J Cancer 79*:19-22.

[62] Sawada,M., Miyake,S., Ohdama,S., Matsubara,O., Masuda,S., Yakumaru,K., and Yoshizawa,Y. 1999. Expression of tissue factor in non-small-cell lung cancers and its relationship to metastasis. *Br J Cancer 79*:472-477.

[63] Contrino,J., Hair,G., Kreutzer,D.L., and Rickles,F.R. 1996. In situ detection of tissue factor in vascular endothelial cells: correlation with the malignant phenotype of human breast disease [see comments]. *Nat.Med. 2*:209-215.

[64] Ueno,T., Toi,M., Koike,M., Nakamura,S., and Tominaga,T. 2000. Tissue factor expression in breast cancer tissues: its correlation with prognosis and plasma concentration. *Br J Cancer 83*:164-170.

[65] Seto,S., Onodera,H., Kaido,T., Yoshikawa,A., Ishigami,S., Arii,S., and Imamura,M. 2000. Tissue factor expression in human colorectal carcinoma: correlation with hepatic metastasis and impact on prognosis. *Cancer 88*:295-301.

[66] Shigemori,C., Wada,H., Matsumoto,K., Shiku,H., Nakamura,S., and Suzuki,H. 1998. Tissue factor expression and metastatic potential of colorectal cancer. *Thromb Haemost 80*:894-898.

[67] Nakasaki,T., Wada,H., Shigemori,C., Miki,C., Gabazza,E.C., Nobori,T., Nakamura,S., and Shiku,H. 2002. Expression of tissue factor and vascular endothelial growth factor is associated with angiogenesis in colorectal cancer. *Am.J.Hematol. 69*:247-254.

[68] Ueda,C., Hirohata,Y., Kihara,Y., Nakamura,H., Abe,S., Akahane,K., Okamoto,K., Itoh,H., and Otsuki,M. 2001. Pancreatic cancer complicated by disseminated intravascular coagulation associated with production of tissue factor. *J Gastroenterol 36*:848-850.

[69] Hair,G.A., Padula,S., Zeff,R., Schmeizl,M., Contrino,J., Kreutzer,D.L., De Moerloose,P., Boyd,A.W., Stanley,I., Burgess,A.W. et al. 1996. Tissue factor expression in human leukemic cells. *Leukemia Res 20*:1-11.

[70] Guan,M., Su,B., and Lu,Y. 2002. Quantitative reverse transcription-PCR measurement of tissue factor mRNA in glioma. *Mol.Biotechnol. 20*:123-129.

[71] Shoji,M., Hancock,W.W., Abe,K., Micko,C., Casper,K.A., Baine,R.M., Wilcox,J.N., Danave,I., Dillehay,D.L., Matthews,E. et al. 1998. Activation of coagulation and angiogenesis in cancer: immunohistochemical localization in situ of clotting proteins and vascular endothelial growth factor in human cancer. *Am J Pathol 152*:399-411.

[72] Blum,S., Issbruker,K., Willuweit,A., Hehlgans,S., Lucerna,M., Mechtcheriakova,D., Walsh,K., von der,A.D., Hofer,E., and Clauss,M. 2001. An inhibitory role of the phosphatidylinositol 3-kinase-signaling pathway in vascular endothelial growth factor-induced tissue factor expression. *J Biol Chem 276*:33428-33434.

[73] Contrino,J., Hair,G., Kreutzer,D.L., and Rickles,F.R. 1996. In situ detection of tissue factor in vascular endothelial cells: Correlation with the malignant phenotype of human breast disease. *Nat. Med. 2*:209-215.

[74] Hanahan,D. and Folkman,J. 1996. Patterns and emerging mechanisms of the angiogenic switch during tumorigenesis. *Cell 86:*353-364.

[75] Rak,J., Mitsuhashi,Y., Sheehan,C., Tamir,A., Viloria-Petit,A., Filmus,J., Mansour,S.J., Ahn,N.G., and Kerbel,R.S. 2000. Oncogenes and tumor angiogenesis: differential modes of vascular endothelial growth factor up-regulation in ras-transformed epithelial cells and fibroblasts. *Cancer Res 60*:490-498.

[76] Mazure,N.M., Chen,E.Y., Yeh,P., Laderoute,K.R., and Giaccia,A.J. 1996. Oncogenic transformation and hypoxia synergistically act to modulate vascular endothelial growth factor expression. *Cancer Res 56*:3436-3440.

[77] Viloria-Petit,A., Crombet,T., Jothy,S., Hicklin,D., Bohlen,P., Schlaeppi,J.M., Rak,J., and Kerbel,R.S. 2001. Acquired resistance to the antitumor effect of epidermal growth factor receptor-blocking antibodies in vivo: a role for altered tumor angiogenesis. *Cancer Res 61*:5090-5101.

[78] Abe,K., Shoji,M., Chen,J., Bierhaus,A., Danave,I., Micko,C., Casper,K., Dillehay,D.L., Nawroth,P.P., and Rickles,F.R. 1999. Regulation of vascular endothelial growth factor production and angiogenesis by the cytoplasmic tail of tissue factor [In Process Citation]. *Proc Natl Acad Sci U S A 96*:8663-8668.

[79] Zhang,Y., Deng,Y., Luther,T., Müller,M., Ziegler,R., Waldherr,R., Stern,D.M., and Nawroth,P.P. 1994. Tissue factor controls the balance of angiogenic and antiangiogenic properties of tumor cells in mice. *J.Clin.Invest. 94*:1320-1327.

[80] Mechtcheriakova,D., Wlachos,A., Holzmuller,H., Binder,B.R., and Hofer,E. 1999. Vascular endothelial cell growth factor-induced tissue factor expression in endothelial cells is mediated by EGR-1. *Blood 93*:3811-3823.

[81] Kim,I., Oh,J.L., Ryu,Y.S., So,J.N., Sessa,W.C., Walsh,K., and Koh,G.Y. 2002. Angiopoietin-1 negatively regulates expression and activity of tissue factor in endothelial cells. *FASEB J. 16*:126-128.

[82] Rickles,F.R., Patierno,S., and Fernandez,P.M. 2003. Tissue factor, thrombin, and cancer. *Chest 124*:58S-68S.

[83] Ollivier,V., Bentolila,S., Chabbat,J., Hakim,J., and de Prost,D. 1998. Tissue factor-dependent vascular endothelial growth factor production by human fibroblasts in response to activated factor VII. *Blood 91:*2698-2703.

[84] Ollivier,V., Chabbat,J., Herbert,J.M., Hakim,J., and de Prost,D. 2000. Vascular endothelial growth factor production by fibroblasts in response to factor VIIa binding to tissue factor involves thrombin and factor Xa. *Arterioscler Thromb Vasc Biol 20:*1374-1381.

[85] Shoji,M., Abe,K., Nawroth,P.P., and Rickles,F.R. 1997. Molecular mechanisms linking thrombosis and angiogenesis in cancer. *Trends. Cardiovasc. Med 7*:52-59.

[86] Ott,I., Fischer,E.G., Miyagi,Y., Mueller,B.M., and Ruf,W. 1998. A role for tissue factor in cell adhesion and migration mediated by interaction with actin-binding protein 280. *J Cell Biol 140*:1241-1253.

[87] Mueller,B.M. and Ruf,W. 1998. Requirement for binding of catalytically active factor VIIa in tissue factor-dependent experimental metastasis. *J Clin Invest 101*:1372-1378.

[88] Bromberg, M. E, Konigsberg, W. H, Madison, J., Pawashe, A., and Garen, A. 1995. Tissue factor promotes melanoma metastasis by a pathway independent of blood coagulation. *Proc.Natl.Acad.Sci.USA 92*, 8205-8209.

[89] Belting,M., Dorrell,M.I., Sandgren,S., Aguilar,E., Ahamed,J., Dorfleutner,A., Carmeliet,P., Mueller,B.M., Friedlander,M., and Ruf,W. 2004. Regulation of angiogenesis by tissue factor cytoplasmic domain signaling. *Nat.Med. 10*:502-509.

[90] Coughlin,S.R. 2001. Protease-activated receptors in vascular biology. *Thromb Haemost 86*:298-307.

[91] Vu,T.K., Hung,D.T., Wheaton,V.I., and Coughlin,S.R. 1991. Molecular cloning of a functional thrombin receptor reveals a novel proteolytic mechanism of receptor activation. *Cell 64*:1057-1068.

[92] Rasmussen,U.B., Vouret-Craviari,V., Jallat,S., Schlesinger,Y., Pages,G., Pavirani,A., Lecocq,J.P., Pouyssegur,J., and Obberghen-Schilling,E. 1991. cDNA cloning and expression of a hamster alpha-thrombin receptor coupled to Ca2+ mobilization. *FEBS Lett 288*:123-128.

[93] Ishihara,H., Connolly,A.J., Zeng,D., Kahn,M.L., Zheng,Y.W., Timmons,C., Tram,T., and Coughlin,S.R. 1997. Protease-activated receptor 3 is a second thrombin receptor in humans. *Nature 386*:502-506.

[94] Xu,W.F., Andersen,H., Whitmore,T.E., Presnell,S.R., Yee,D.P., Ching,A., Gilbert,T., Davie,E.W., and Foster,D.C. 1998. Cloning and characterization of human protease-activated receptor 4. *Proc Natl Acad Sci U S A 95*:6642-6646.

[95] Kahn,M.L., Zheng,Y.W., Huang,W., Bigornia,V., Zeng,D., Moff,S., Farese,R.V., Jr., Tam,C., and Coughlin,S.R. 1998. A dual thrombin receptor system for platelet activation. *Nature 394*:690-694.

[96] Nystedt,S., Emilsson,K., Wahlestedt,C., and Sundelin,J. 1994. Molecular cloning of a potential proteinase activated receptor. *Proc Natl Acad Sci U S A 91*:9208-9212.

[97] Molino,M., Barnathan,E.S., Numerof,R., Clark,J., Dreyer,M., Cumashi,A., Hoxie,J.A., Schechter,N., Woolkalis,M., and Brass,L.F. 1997. Interactions of mast cell tryptase with thrombin receptors and PAR-2. *J Biol Chem 272*:4043-4049.

[98] Camerer,E., Rottingen,J.-A., Iversen,J.-G., and Prydz,H. 1996. Coagulation factors VII and X induce Ca++ oscillations in Madin-Darby canine kidney cells only when proteolytically active. *J Biol.Chem. 271*:29034-29042.

[99] Camerer,E., Huang,W., and Coughlin,S.R. 2000. Tissue factor- and factor X-dependent activation of protease-activated receptor 2 by factor VIIa. *Proc Natl Acad Sci US A.;97*:5255.-60. 97:5255-5260.

[100] Wojtukiewicz,M.Z., Tang,D.G., Ben-Josef,E., Renaud,C., Walz,D.A., and Honn,K.V. 1995. Solid tumor cells express functional "tethered ligand" thrombin receptor. *Cancer Res. 55*:698-704.

[101] Even-Ram,S., Uziely,B., Cohen,P., Grisaru-Granovsky,S., Maoz,M., Ginzburg,Y., Reich,R., Vlodavsky,I., and Bar-Shavit,R. 1998. Thrombin receptor overexpression in malignant and physiological invasion processes. *Nat Med 4*:909-914.

[102] Klepfish,A., Greco,M.A., and Karpatkin,S. 1993. Thrombin stimulates melanoma tumor-cell binding to endothelial cells and subendothelial matrix. *Int.J Cancer 53*:978-982.

[103] Wojtukiewicz,M.Z., Tang,D.G., Ciarelli,J.J., Nelson,K.K., Walz,D.A., Diglio,C.A., Mammen,E.F., and Honn,K.V. 1993. Thrombin increases the metastatic potential of tumor cells. *Int.J Cancer 54*:793-806.

[104] Nierodzik,M.L., Klepfish,A., and Karpatkin,S. 1995. Role of platelets, thrombin, integrin IIb-IIIa, fibronectin and von Willebrand factor on tumor adhesion in vitro and metastasis in vivo. *Thromb.Haemost. 74*:282-290.

[105] Hjortoe,G.M., Petersen,L.C., Albrektsen,T., Sorensen,B.B., Norby,P.L., Mandal,S.K., Pendurthi,U.R., and Rao,L.V. 2004. Tissue factor-factor VIIa-specific up-regulation of IL-8 expression in MDA-MB-231 cells is mediated by PAR-2 and results in increased cell migration. *Blood 103*:3029-3037.

[106] Tsopanoglou,N.E. and Maragoudakis,M.E. 1999. On the mechanism of thrombin-induced angiogenesis. Potentiation of vascular endothelial growth factor activity on endothelial cells by up-regulation of its receptors. *J Biol Chem 274*:23969-23976.

[107] Tsopanoglou,N.E. and Maragoudakis,M.E. 2004. Role of thrombin in angiogenesis and tumor progression. *Semin Thromb Hemost 30*:63-69.

[108] Tsopanoglou,N.E. and Maragoudakis,M.E. 1998. On the mechanism of thrombin-induced angiogenesis: inhibition of attachment of endothelial cells on basement membrane components. *Angiogenesis 1*:192-200.

[109] Maragoudakis,M.E., Kraniti,N., Giannopoulou,E., Alexopoulos,K., and Matsoukas,J. 2001. Modulation of angiogenesis and progelatinase a by thrombin receptor mimetics and antagonists. *Endothelium 8*:195-205.

[110] Eliceiri,B.P. and Cheresh,D.A. 2001. Adhesion events in angiogenesis. *Curr Opin Cell Biol 13*:563-568.

[111] Bader,B.L., Rayburn,H., Crowley,D., and Hynes,R.O. 1998. Extensive vasculogenesis, angiogenesis, and organogenesis precede lethality in mice lacking all alpha v integrins. *Cell 95*:507-519.

[112] Tsopanoglou,N.E., Andriopoulou,P., and Maragoudakis,M.E. 2002. On the mechanism of thrombin-induced angiogenesis: involvement of alphavbeta3-integrin. *Am J Physiol Cell Physiol 283*:C1501-C1510.

[113] Giancotti,F.G. and Ruoslahti,E. 1999. Integrin signaling. *Science 285*:1028-1032.

[114] Nagy,J.A., Brown,L.F., Senger,D.R., Lanir,N., van de Water,L., Dvorak,A.M., and Dvorak,H.F. 1989. Pathogenesis of tumor stroma generation: a critical role for leaky blood vessels and fibrin deposition. *Biochim.Biophys.Acta 948*:305-326.

[115] van Hinsbergh,V.W., Collen,A., and Koolwijk,P. 2001. Role of fibrin matrix in angiogenesis. *Ann N Y Acad Sci* 936:426-437.

[116] Dejana,E., Languino,L.R., Polentarutti,N., Balconi,G., Ryckewaert,J.J., Larrieu,M.J., Donati,M.B., Mantovani,A., and Marguerie,G. 1985. Interaction between fibrinogen and cultured endothelial cells. Induction of migration and specific binding. *J Clin Invest 75*:11-18.

[117] Brown,L.F., Lanir,N., McDonagh,J., Tognazzi,K., Dvorak,A.M., and Dvorak,H.F. 1993. Fibroblast migration in fibrin gel matrices. *Am J Pathol 142*:273-283.

[118] Degen,J.L., Drew,A.F., Palumbo,J.S., Kombrinck,K.W., Bezerra,J.A., Danton,M.J., Holmback,K., and Suh,T.T. 2001. Genetic manipulation of fibrinogen and fibrinolysis in mice. *Ann N Y Acad Sci 936*:276-290.

[119] Altieri,D.C., Mannucci,P.M., and Capitanio,A.M. 1986. Binding of fibrinogen to human monocytes. *J Clin Invest 78*:968-976.

[120] Felding-Habermann,B., Ruggeri,Z.M., and Cheresh,D.A. 1992. Distinct biological consequences of integrin alpha v beta 3-mediated melanoma cell adhesion to fibrinogen and its plasmic fragments. *J Biol Chem 267*:5070-5077.

[121] Brooks,P.C., Montgomery,A.M., Rosenfeld,M., Reisfeld,R.A., Hu,T., Klier,G., and Cheresh,D.A. 1994. Integrin alpha v beta 3 antagonists promote tumor regression by inducing apoptosis of angiogenic blood vessels. *Cell 79*:1157-1164.

[122] Brooks,P.C., Stromblad,S., Klemke,R., Visscher,D., Sarkar,F.H., and Cheresh,D.A. 1995. Antiintegrin alpha v beta 3 blocks human breast cancer growth and angiogenesis in human skin. *J Clin Invest 96*:1815-1822.

[123] Friedlander,M., Brooks,P.C., Shaffer,R.W., Kincaid,C.M., Varner,J.A., and Cheresh,D.A. 1995. Definition of two angiogenic pathways by distinct alpha v integrins. *Science 270*:1500-1502.

[124] Reynolds,L.E., Wyder,L., Lively,J.C., Taverna,D., Robinson,S.D., Huang,X., Sheppard,D., Hynes,R.O., and Hodivala-Dilke,K.M. 2002. Enhanced pathological angiogenesis in mice lacking beta3 integrin or beta3 and beta5 integrins. *Nat Med 8*:27-34.

[125] Feng,X., Clark,R.A., Galanakis,D., and Tonnesen,M.G. 1999. Fibrin and collagen differentially regulate human dermal microvascular endothelial cell integrins: stabilization of alphav/beta3 mRNA by fibrin1. *J Invest Dermatol 113*:913-919.

[126] Fernandez,P.M., Patierno,S.R., and Rickles,F.R. 2004. Tissue factor and fibrin in tumor angiogenesis. *Semin Thromb Hemost 30*:31-44.

[127] Doolittle,R.F. 1981. Fibrinogen and fibrin. *Sci Am 245*:126-135.

[128] Bootle-Wilbraham,C.A., Tazzyman,S., Thompson,W.D., Stirk,C.M., and Lewis,C.E. 2001. Fibrin fragment E stimulates the proliferation, migration and differentiation of human microvascular endothelial cells in vitro. *Angiogenesis 4*:269-275.

[129] Bootle-Wilbraham,C.A., Tazzyman,S., Marshall,J.M., and Lewis,C.E. 2000. Fibrinogen E-fragment inhibits the migration and tubule formation of human dermal microvascular endothelial cells in vitro. *Cancer Res 60*:4719-4724.

[130] Palumbo,J.S. and Degen,J.L. 2001. Fibrinogen and tumor cell metastasis. *Haemostasis 31 Suppl* 1:11-15.

[131] Contrino,J., Goralnick,S., Qi,J.F., Hair,G., Rickles,F.R., and Kreutzer,D.L. 1997. Fibrin induction of tissue factor expression in human vascular endothelial cells. *Circulation 96*:605-613.

[132] Colman,R.W. 2004. The contact system and angiogenesis: potential for therapeutic control of malignancy. *Semin Thromb Hemost 30*:45-61.

[133] Shariat-Madar,Z., Mahdi,F., and Schmaier,A.H. 2002. Identification and characterization of prolylcarboxypeptidase as an endothelial cell prekallikrein activator. *J Biol Chem 277*:17962-17969.

[134] Colman,R.W. 2002. Inhibition of angiogenesis by a monoclonal antibody to kininogen as well as by kininostatin which block proangiogenic high molecular weight kininogen. *Int Immunopharmacol 2*:1887-1894.

[135] Karpatkin,S., Nierodzik,M.L., and Klepfish,A. 1996. Role of platelets and thrombin in cancer. *Vessels 2*:17-23.

[136] Pinedo,H.M., Verheul,H.M., D'Amato,R.J., and Folkman,J. 1998. Involvement of platelets in tumour angiogenesis? *Lancet 352*:1775-1777.

[137] Pipili-Synetos,E., Papadimitriou,E., and Maragoudakis,M.E. 1998. Evidence that platelets promote tube formation by endothelial cells on matrigel. *Br J Pharmacol 125*:1252-1257.

[138] Verheul,H.M., Jorna,A.S., Hoekman,K., Broxterman,H.J., Gebbink,M.F., and Pinedo,H.M. 2000. Vascular endothelial growth factor-stimulated endothelial cells promote adhesion and activation of platelets. *Blood 96*:4216-4221.

[139] Trikha,M., Zhou,Z., Timar,J., Raso,E., Kennel,M., Emmell,E., and Nakada,M.T. 2002. Multiple roles for platelet GPIIb/IIIa and alphavbeta3 integrins in tumor growth, angiogenesis, and metastasis. *Cancer Res 62*:2824-2833.

[140] Trikha,M. and Nakada,M.T. 2002. Platelets and cancer: implications for antiangiogenic therapy. *Semin Thromb Hemost 28*:39-44.

[141] Heyns,A.D., Lotter,M.G., Badenhorst,P.N., van Reenen,O.R., Pieters,H., Minnaar,P.C., and Retief,F.P. 1980. Kinetics, distribution and sites of destruction of 111indium-labelled human platelets. *Br J Haematol 44*:269-280.

[142] Browder,T., Folkman,J., and Pirie-Shepherd,S. 2000. The hemostatic system as a regulator of angiogenesis. *J Biol Chem 275*:1521-1524.

[143] Selheim,F., Holmsen,H., and Vassbotn,F.S. 2002. Identification of functional VEGF receptors on human platelets. *FEBS Lett 512*:107-110.

[144] Tsiamis,A.C., Hayes,P., Box,H., Goodall,A.H., Bell,P.R., and Brindle,N.P. 2000. Characterization and regulation of the receptor tyrosine kinase Tie-1 in platelets. *J Vasc Res 37*:437-442.

[145] Sierko,E. and Wojtukiewicz,M.Z. 2004. Platelets and angiogenesis in malignancy. *Semin Thromb Hemost 30*:95-108.

[146] Selheim,F., Fukami,M.H., Holmsen,H., and Vassbotn,F.S. 2000. Platelet-derived-growth-factor-induced signalling in human platelets: phosphoinositide-3-kinase-dependent inhibition of platelet activation. *Biochem J 350* 2:469-475.

[147] Mohle,R., Green,D., Moore,M.A., Nachman,R.L., and Rafii,S. 1997. Constitutive production and thrombin-induced release of vascular endothelial growth factor by human megakaryocytes and platelets. *Proc Natl Acad Sci U S A 94*:663-668.

[148] Banks,R.E., Forbes,M.A., Kinsey,S.E., Stanley,A., Ingham,E., Walters,C., and Selby,P.J. 1998. Release of the angiogenic cytokine vascular endothelial growth factor (VEGF) from platelets: significance for VEGF measurements and cancer biology. *Brit.J.Cancer 77*:956-964.

[149] Wartiovaara,U., Salven,P., Mikkola,H., Lassila,R., Kaukonen,J., Joukov,V., Orpana,A., Ristimaki,A., Heikinheimo,M., Joensuu,H. et al. 1998. Peripheral blood platelets express VEGF-C and VEGF which are released during platelet activation. *Thromb Haemost 80*:171-175.

[150] Amirkhosravi,A., Amaya,M., Siddiqui,F.A., Biggerstaff,J., Meyer,T., and Francis,J.L. 1999. Blockade of GpIIb/IIIa inhibits the release of vascular endothelial growth factor (VEGF) from tumor cell-activated platelets and experimental metastasis. *Platelets 10*:285-292.

[151] Salgado,R., Vermeulen,P.B., Benoy,I., Weytjens,R., Huget,P., Van Marck,E., and Dirix,L.Y. 1999. Platelet number and interleukin-6 correlate with VEGF but not with bFGF serum levels of advanced cancer patients. *Br J Cancer 80*:892-897.

[152] Benoy,I., Salgado,R., Colpaert,C., Weytjens,R., Vermeulen,P.B., and Dirix,L.Y. 2002. Serum interleukin 6, plasma VEGF, serum VEGF, and VEGF platelet load in breast cancer patients. *Clin Breast Cancer 2:*311-315.

[153] Werther,K., Christensen,I.J., and Nielsen,H.J. 2002. Determination of vascular endothelial growth factor (VEGF) in circulating blood: significance of VEGF in various leucocytes and platelets. *Scand J Clin Lab Invest 62*:343-350.

[154] Uppenkamp,M., Makarova,E., Petrasch,S., and Brittinger,G. 1998. Thrombopoietin serum concentration in patients with reactive and myeloproliferative thrombocytosis. *Ann Hematol 77*:217-223.

[155] Corbett,G. and Perry,D.J. 1983. Significance of thrombocytosis. *Lancet 1*:77.

[156] Gastl,G., Plante,M., Finstad,C.L., Wong,G.Y., Federici,M.G., Bander,N.H., and Rubin,S.C. 1993. High IL-6 levels in ascitic fluid correlate with reactive thrombocytosis in patients with epithelial ovarian cancer. *Br J Haematol 83*:433-441.

[157] Estrov,Z., Talpaz,M., Mavligit,G., Pazdur,R., Harris,D., Greenberg,S.M., and Kurzrock,R. 1995. Elevated plasma thrombopoietic activity in patients with metastatic cancer-related thrombocytosis. *Am J Med 98*:551-558.

[158] Suzuki,A., Takahashi,T., Nakamura,K., Tsuyuoka,R., Okuno,Y., Enomoto,T., Fukumoto,M., and Imura,H. 1992. Thrombocytosis in patients with tumors producing colony-stimulating factor. *Blood 80*:2052-2059.

[159] Zucker,S., Mirza,H., Conner,C.E., Lorenz,A.F., Drews,M.H., Bahou,W.F., and Jesty,J. 1998. Vascular endothelial growth factor induces tissue factor and matrix metalloproteinase production in endothelial cells: Conversion of prothrombin to thrombin results in progelatinase A activation and cell proliferation. *Int.J.Cancer 75*:780-786.

[160] Clauss,M., Gerlach,M., Gerlach,H., Brett,J., Wang,F., Familletti,P.C., Pan,Y.C.E., Olander,J.V., Connolly,D.T., and Stern,D. 1990. Vascular-permeability factor - a tumor-derived polypeptide that induces endothelial-cell and monocyte procoagulant activity, and promotes monocyte migration. *J. Exp. Med. 172*:1535-1545.

[161] Ohta,M., Kitadai,Y., Tanaka,S., Yoshihara,M., Yasui,W., Mukaida,N., Haruma,K., and Chayama,K. 2003. Monocyte chemoattractant protein-1 expression correlates with macrophage infiltration and tumor vascularity in human gastric carcinomas. *Int J Oncol 22*:773-778.

[162] Balkwill,F. and Mantovani,A. 2001. Inflammation and cancer: back to Virchow? *Lancet 357*:539-545.

[163] Coussens,L.M., Raymond,W.W., Bergers,G., Laig-Webster,M., Behrendtsen,O., Werb,Z., Caughey,G.H., and Hanahan,D. 1999. Inflammatory mast cells up-regulate angiogenesis during squamous epithelial carcinogenesis. *Genes Dev 13*:1382-1397.

[164] Paulie,S., Ehlin-Henriksson,B., Mellstedt,H., Koho,H., Ben Aissa,H., and Perlmann,P. 1985. A p50 surface antigen restricted to human urinary bladder carcinomas and B lymphocytes. *Cancer Immunol Immunother 20*:23-28.

[165] Clark,E.A. and Ledbetter,J.A. 1986. Activation of human B cells mediated through two distinct cell surface differentiation antigens, Bp35 and Bp50. *Proc Natl Acad Sci U S A 83*:4494-4498.

[166] Van Kooten,C. and Banchereau,J. 1996. CD40-CD40 ligand: a multifunctional receptor-ligand pair. *Adv Immunol 61*:1-77.

[167] Karmann,K., Hughes,C.C., Schechner,J., Fanslow,W.C., and Pober,J.S. 1995. CD40 on human endothelial cells: inducibility by cytokines and functional regulation of adhesion molecule expression. *Proc Natl Acad Sci U S A 92*:4342-4346.

[168] Henn,V., Steinbach,S., Buchner,K., Presek,P., and Kroczek,R.A. 2001. The inflammatory action of CD40 ligand (CD154) expressed on activated human platelets is temporally limited by coexpressed CD40. *Blood 98*:1047-1054.

[169] Armitage,R.J., Fanslow,W.C., Strockbine,L., Sato,T.A., Clifford,K.N., Macduff,B.M., Anderson,D.M., Gimpel,S.D., Davis-Smith,T., Maliszewski,C.R. et al. 1992. Molecular and biological characterization of a murine ligand for CD40. *Nature 357*:80-82.

[170] Graf,D., Korthauer,U., Mages,H.W., Senger,G., and Kroczek,R.A. 1992. Cloning of TRAP, a ligand for CD40 on human T cells. *Eur J Immunol 22*:3191-3194.

[171] Gauchat,J.F., Aubry,J.P., Mazzei,G., Life,P., Jomotte,T., Elson,G., and Bonnefoy,J.Y. 1993. Human CD40-ligand: molecular cloning, cellular distribution and regulation of expression by factors controlling IgE production. *FEBS Lett 315*:259-266.

[172] Henn,V., Slupsky,J.R., Grafe,M., Anagnostopoulos,I., Forster,R., Muller-Berghaus,G., and Kroczek,R.A. 1998. CD40 ligand on activated platelets triggers an inflammatory reaction of endothelial cells. *Nature 391*:591-594.

[173] Amirkhosravi,A., Amaya,M., Desai,H., and Francis,J.L. 2002. Platelet-CD40 ligand interaction with melanoma cell and monocyte CD40 enhances cellular procoagulant activity. *Blood Coagul.Fibrinolysis 13*:505-512.

[174] Melter,M., Reinders,M.E., Sho,M., Pal,S., Geehan,C., Denton,M.D., Mukhopadhyay,D., and Briscoe,D.M. 2000. Ligation of CD40 induces the expression of vascular endothelial growth factor by endothelial cells and monocytes and promotes angiogenesis in vivo. *Blood 96*:3801-3808.

[175] Biancone, L., Cantaluppi, V., Boccellino, M., Del Sorbo, L., Russo, S., Albini, A., Stamenkovic, I., and Camussi, G. 1999. Activation of CD40 favors the growth and vascularization of Kaposi's sarcoma. *J Immunol 163*:6201-6208.

[176] Inwald, D.P., McDowall, A., Peters, M.J., Callard, R.E., and Klein, N.J. 2003. CD40 is constitutively expressed on platelets and provides a novel mechanism for platelet activation. *Circ Res 92*:1041-1048.

[177] Brunner, G., Nguyen, H., Gabrilove, J., Rifkin, D.B., and Wilson, E.L. 1993. Basic fibroblast growth factor expression in human bone marrow and peripheral blood cells. *Blood 81*:631-638.

[178] Friesel, R. and Maciag, T. 1999. Fibroblast growth factor prototype release and fibroblast growth factor receptor signaling. *Thromb Haemost 82*:748-754.

[179] Tomita, N., Morishita, R., Taniyama, Y., Koike, H., Aoki, M., Shimizu, H., Matsumoto, K., Nakamura, T., Kaneda, Y., and Ogihara, T. 2003. Angiogenic property of hepatocyte growth factor is dependent on upregulation of essential transcription factor for angiogenesis, ets-1. *Circulation 107*:1411-1417.

[180] Bustin, S.A., Dorudi, S., Phillips, S.M., Feakins, R.M., and Jenkins, P.J. 2002. Local expression of insulin-like growth factor-I affects angiogenesis in colorectal cancer. *Tumour Biol 23*:130-138.

[181] Valter, M.M., Wiestler, O.D., Pietsche, T., and Pietsch, T. 1999. Differential control of VEGF synthesis and secretion in human glioma cells by IL-1 and EGF. *Int J Dev Neurosci 17*:565-577.

[182] Ravindranath, N., Wion, D., Brachet, P., and Djakiew, D. 2001. Epidermal growth factor modulates the expression of vascular endothelial growth factor in the human prostate. *J Androl 22*:432-443.

[183] Li, J.J., Huang, Y.Q., Basch, R., and Karpatkin, S. 2001. Thrombin induces the release of angiopoietin-1 from platelets. *Thromb Haemost 85*:204-206.

[184] Guo, P., Hu, B., Gu, W., Xu, L., Wang, D., Huang, H.J., Cavenee, W.K., and Cheng, S.Y. 2003. Platelet-derived growth factor-B enhances glioma angiogenesis by stimulating vascular endothelial growth factor expression in tumor endothelia and by promoting pericyte recruitment. *Am J Pathol 162*:1083-1093.

[185] Breier, G., Blum, S., Peli, J., Groot, M., Wild, C., Risau, W., and Reichmann, E. 2002. Transforming growth factor-beta and Ras regulate the VEGF/VEGF-receptor system during tumor angiogenesis. *Int J Cancer 97*:142-148.

[186] Vinals, F. and Pouyssegur, J. 2001. Transforming growth factor beta1 (TGF-beta1) promotes endothelial cell survival during in vitro angiogenesis via an autocrine mechanism implicating TGF-alpha signaling. *Mol Cell Biol 21*:7218-7230.

[187] Kim, H.K., Song, K.S., Chung, J.H., Lee, K.R., and Lee, S.N. 2004. Platelet microparticles induce angiogenesis in vitro. *Br J Haematol 124*:376-384.

[188] Taylor, S. and Folkman, J. 1982. Protamine is an inhibitor of angiogenesis. *Nature 297*:307-312.

[189] Pluda, J.M. and Parkinson, D.R. 1996. Clinical implications of tumor-associated neovascularization and current antiangiogenic strategies for the treatment of malignancies of pancreas. *Cancer 78*:680-687.

[190] Maione, T.E., Gray, G.S., Hunt, A.J., and Sharpe, R.J. 1991. Inhibition of tumor growth in mice by an analogue of platelet factor 4 that lacks affinity for heparin and retains potent angiostatic activity. *Cancer Res 51*:2077-2083.

[191] Gupta, S.K. and Singh, J.P. 1994. Inhibition of endothelial cell proliferation by platelet factor-4 involves a unique action on S phase progression. *J Cell Biol 127*:1121-1127.

[192] Gentilini, G., Kirschbaum, N.E., Augustine, J.A., Aster, R.H., and Visentin, G.P. 1999. Inhibition of human umbilical vein endothelial cell proliferation by the CXC chemokine, platelet factor 4 (PF4), is associated with impaired downregulation of p21(Cip1/WAF1). *Blood 93*:25-33.

[193] Sulpice, E., Bryckaert, M., Lacour, J., Contreres, J.O., and Tobelem, G. 2002. Platelet factor 4 inhibits FGF2-induced endothelial cell proliferation via the extracellular signal-regulated kinase pathway but not by the phosphatidylinositol 3-kinase pathway. *Blood 100*:3087-3094.

[194] Perollet, C., Han, Z.C., Savona, C., Caen, J.P., and Bikfalvi, A. 1998. Platelet factor 4 modulates fibroblast growth factor 2 (FGF-2) activity and inhibits FGF-2 dimerization. *Blood 91*:3289-3299.

[195] Gengrinovitch, S., Greenberg, S.M., Cohen, T., Gitay-Goren, H., Rockwell, P., Maione, T.E., Levi, B.Z., and Neufeld, G. 1995. Platelet factor-4 inhibits the mitogenic activity of VEGF121 and VEGF165 using several concurrent mechanisms. *J Biol Chem 270*:15059-15065.

[196] Bikfalvi, A. and Gimenez-Gallego, G. 2004. The control of angiogenesis and tumor invasion by platelet factor-4 and platelet factor-4-derived molecules. *Semin Thromb Hemost 30*:137-144.

[197] Mast, A.E., Stadanlick, J.E., Lockett, J.M., Dietzen, D.J., Hasty, K.A., and Hall, C.L. 2000. Tissue factor pathway inhibitor binds to platelet thrombospondin-1. *J Biol Chem 275*:31715-31721.

[198] Ploplis, V.A., Balsara, R., Sandoval-Cooper, M.J., Yin, Z.J., Batten, J., Modi, N., Gadoua, D., Donahue, D., Martin, J.A., and Castellino, F.J. 2004. Enhanced in vitro proliferation of aortic endothelial cells from plasminogen activator inhibitor-1-deficient mice. *J Biol Chem 279*:6143-6151.

[199] McMahon, G.A., Petitclerc, E., Stefansson, S., Smith, E., Wong, M.K., Westrick, R.J., Ginsburg, D., Brooks, P.C., and Lawrence, D.A. 2001. Plasminogen activator inhibitor-1 regulates tumor growth and angiogenesis. *J Biol Chem 276*:33964-33968.

[200] Bell, W.R. 1996. The fibrinolytic system in neoplasia. *Semin Thromb Hemost 22*:459-478.

[201] Pepper, M.S., Montesano, R., Mandriota, S.J., Orci, L., and Vassalli, J.D. 1996. Angiogenesis: a paradigm for balanced extracellular proteolysis during cell migration and morphogenesis. *Enzyme Protein 49*:138-162.

[202] Chapman, H.A. and Wei, Y. 2001. Protease crosstalk with integrins: the urokinase receptor paradigm. *Thromb Haemost 86*:124-129.

[203] Estreicher, A., Muhlhauser, J., Carpentier, J.L., Orci, L., and Vassalli, J.D. 1990. The receptor for urokinase type plasminogen activator polarizes expression of the protease to the leading edge of migrating monocytes and promotes degradation of enzyme inhibitor complexes. *J Cell Biol 111*:783-792.

[204] Pepper, M.S., Sappino, A.P., Stocklin, R., Montesano, R., Orci, L., and Vassalli, J.D. 1993. Upregulation of urokinase receptor expression on migrating endothelial cells. *J Cell Biol 122*:673-684.

[205] Engelse,M.A., Hanemaaijer,R., Koolwijk,P., and van Hinsbergh,V.W. 2004. The fibrinolytic system and matrix metalloproteinases in angiogenesis and tumor progression. *Semin Thromb Hemost 30*:71-82.

[206] Shapiro, R.L., Duquette, J.G., Roses, D.F., Nunes, I., Harris, M.N., Kamino, H., Wilson, E.L., and Rifkin, D.B. 1996. Induction of primary cutaneous melanocytic neoplasms in urokinase-type plasminogen activator (uPA)-deficient and wild-type mice: cellular blue nevi invade but do not progress to malignant melanoma in uPA-deficient animals. *Cancer Res 56*:3597-3604.

[207] Oh, C.W., Hoover-Plow, J., and Plow, E.F. 2003. The role of plasminogen in angiogenesis in vivo. *J Thromb Haemost 1*:1683-1687.

[208] Ossowski, L., Russo-Payne, H., and Wilson, E.L. 1991. Inhibition of urokinase-type plasminogen activator by antibodies: the effect on dissemination of a human tumor in the nude mouse. *Cancer Res 51*:274-281.

[209] Ossowski, L. and Reich, E. 1983. Antibodies to plasminogen activator inhibit human tumor metastasis. *Cell 35*:611-619.

[210] Ossowski, L. 1988. Plasminogen activator dependent pathways in the dissemination of human tumor cells in the chick embryo. *Cell 52*:321-328.

[211] Collen, D. and Lijnen, H.R. 1986. The fibrinolytic system in man. *Crit Rev Oncol Hematol 4*:249-301.

[212] Bajou, K., Masson, V., Gerard, R.D., Schmitt, P.M., Albert, V., Praus, M., Lund, L.R., Frandsen, T.L., Brunner, N., Dano, K. et al. 2001. The plasminogen activator inhibitor PAI-1 controls in vivo tumor vascularization by interaction with proteases, not vitronectin. Implications for antiangiogenic strategies. *J Cell Biol 152*:777-784.

[213] Gutierrez, L.S., Schulman, A., Brito-Robinson, T., Noria, F., Ploplis, V.A., and Castellino, F.J. 2000. Tumor development is retarded in mice lacking the gene for urokinase-type plasminogen activator or its inhibitor, plasminogen activator inhibitor-1. *Cancer Res 60*:5839-5847.

[214] Loskutoff, D.J., Curriden,S.A., Hu,G., and Deng,G. 1999. Regulation of cell adhesion by PAI-1. *Apmis 107*:54-61.

[215] Koolwijk,P., Sidenius,N., Peters,E., Sier,C.F., Hanemaaijer,R., Blasi,F., and van Hinsbergh,V.W. 2001. Proteolysis of the urokinase-type plasminogen activator receptor by metalloproteinase-12: implication for angiogenesis in fibrin matrices. *Blood 97*:3123-3131.

[216] Andolfo, A., English, W.R., Resnati, M., Murphy, G., Blasi, F., and Sidenius, N. 2002. Metalloproteases cleave the urokinase-type plasminogen activator receptor in the D1-D2 linker region and expose epitopes not present in the intact soluble receptor. *Thromb Haemost 88*:298-306.

[217] Festuccia, C., Dolo, V., Guerra, F., Violini, S., Muzi, P., Pavan, A., and Bologna, M. 1998. Plasminogen activator system modulates invasive capacity and proliferation in prostatic tumor cells. *Clin Exp Metastasis 16*:513-528.

[218] Davis, G.E., Pintar Allen, K.A., Salazar, R., and Maxwell, S.A. 2001. Matrix metalloproteinase-1 and -9 activation by plasmin regulates a novel endothelial cell-mediated mechanism of collagen gel contraction and capillary tube regression in three-dimensional collagen matrices. *J Cell Sci 114*:917-930.

[219] Lijnen, H.R., Arza, B., Van Hoef, B., Collen, D., and Declerck, P.J. 2000. Inactivation of plasminogen activator inhibitor-1 by specific proteolysis with stromelysin-1 (MMP-3). *J Biol Chem 275*:37645-37650.

[220] Lijnen, H.R., Van Hoef, B., and Collen, D. 2001. Inactivation of the serpin alpha(2)-antiplasmin by stromelysin-1. *Biochim Biophys Acta 1547*:206-213.

[221] Dong, Z., Kumar, R., Yang, X., and Fidler, I.J. 1997. Macrophage-derived metalloelastase is responsible for the generation of angiostatin in Lewis lung carcinoma. *Cell 88*:801-810.

[222] Lijnen, H.R., Ugwu, F., Bini, A., and Collen, D. 1998. Generation of an angiostatin-like fragment from plasminogen by stromelysin-1 (MMP-3). *Biochemistry 37*:4699-4702.

[223] Gately, S., Twardowski, P., Stack, M.S., Cundiff, D.L., Grella, D., Castellino, F.J., Enghild,J., Kwaan,H.C., Lee,F., Kramer,R.A. et al. 1997. The mechanism of cancer-mediated conversion of plasminogen to the angiogenesis inhibitor angiostatin. *Proc Natl Acad Sci U S A 94*:10868-10872.

[224] Gately, S., Twardowski, P., Stack, M.S., Patrick, M., Boggio, L., Cundiff, D.L., Schnaper, H.W., Madison, L., Volpert, O., Bouck, N. et al. 1996. Human prostate carcinoma cells express enzymatic activity that converts human plasminogen to the angiogenesis inhibitor, angiostatin. *Cancer Res 56*:4887-4890.

[225] O'Reilly, M.S., Holmgren, L., Shing, Y., Chen, C., Rosenthal, R.A., Moses, M., Lane, W.S., Cao, Y., Sage, E.H., and Folkman, J. 1994. Angiostatin: A novel angiogenesis inhibitor that mediates the suppression of metastases by a Lewis lung carcinoma. *Cell 79*:315-328.

[226] Folkman, J. 1995. Seminars in Medicine of the Beth Israel Hospital, Boston. Clinical applications of research on angiogenesis. *N Engl J Med 333*:1757-1763.

[227] Griscelli, F., Li, H., Bennaceur-Griscelli, A., Soria, J., Opolon, P., Soria, C., Perricaudet, M., Yeh, P., and Lu, H. 1998. Angiostatin gene transfer: inhibition of tumor growth in vivo by blockage of endothelial cell proliferation associated with a mitosis arrest. *Proc Natl Acad Sci U S A 95*:6367-6372.

[228] Lucas, R., Holmgren, L., Garcia, I., Jimenez, B., Mandriota, S.J., Borlat, F., Sim, B.K., Wu, Z., Grau, G.E., Shing, Y. et al. 1998. Multiple forms of angiostatin induce apoptosis in endothelial cells. *Blood 92*:4730-4741.

[229] Claesson-Welsh, L., Welsh, M., Ito, N., Anand-Apte, B., Soker, S., Zetter, B., O'Reilly, M., and Folkman, J. 1998. Angiostatin induces endothelial cell apoptosis and activation of focal adhesion kinase independently of the integrin-binding motif RGD. *Proc Natl Acad Sci U S A 95*:5579-5583.

[230] Cao, Y., Ji, R.W., Davidson, D., Schaller, J., Marti, D., Sohndel, S., McCance, S.G., O'Reilly,M.S., Llinas,M., and Folkman,J. 1996. Kringle domains of human angiostatin. Characterization of the anti-proliferative activity on endothelial cells. *J Biol Chem 271*:29461-29467.

[231] Nilsson, F., Kosmehl, H., Zardi, L., and Neri, D. 2001. Targeted delivery of tissue factor to the ED-B domain of fibronectin, a marker of angiogenesis, mediates the infarction of solid tumors in mice. *Cancer Res. 61*:711-716.

[232] Hu, Z. and Garen, A. 2001. Targeting tissue factor on tumor vascular endothelial cells and tumor cells for immunotherapy in mouse models of prostatic cancer. *Proc.Natl.Acad.Sci.U.S.A 98*:12180-12185.

[233] Hembrough, T.A., Swartz, G.M., Papathanassiu, A., Vlasuk, G.P., Rote, W.E., Green, S.J., and Pribluda, V.S. 2003. Tissue factor/factor VIIa inhibitors block angiogenesis and tumor growth through a nonhemostatic mechanism. *Cancer Res 63*:2997-3000.

[234] Amirkhosravi, A., Meyer, T., Chang, J.Y., Amaya, M., Siddiqui, F., Desai, H., and Francis, J.L. 2002. Tissue factor pathway inhibitor reduces experimental lung metastasis of B16 melanoma. *Thromb.Haemost. 87*:930-936.

[235] Francis, J.L. and Amirkhosravi, A. 2002. Effect of antihemostatic agents on experimental tumor dissemination. *Semin.Thromb.Hemost. 28*:29-38.

[236] Wen, J., Wong, H.C., and Jiao, J. 2003. Tissue factor as an anti-cancer target: anti-tissue factor monoclonal antibody inhibits tumor growth and metastasis in nude mice. *Blood 102*:809a (Abstr.)

[237] Prandoni, P., Lensing, A.W., Buller, H.R., Carta, M., Cogo, A., Vigo, M., Casara, D., Ruol, A., and Ten Cate, J.W. 1992. Comparison of subcutaneous low-molecular-weight heparin with intravenous standard heparin in proximal deep-vein thrombosis. *Lancet 339*:441-445.

[238] Cosgrove, R.H., Zacharski, L.R., Racine,E., and Andersen,J.C. 2002. Improved cancer mortality with low-molecular-weight heparin treatment: a review of the evidence. *Semin Thromb Hemost 28*:79-87.

[239] Hettiarachchi, R.J., Smorenburg, S.M., Ginsberg, J., Levine, M., Prins, M.H., and Buller, H.R. 1999. Do heparins do more than just treat thrombosis? The influence of heparins on cancer spread. *Thromb Haemost 82*:947-952.

[240] Folkman, J., Langer, R., Linhardt, R.J., Haudenschild, C., and Taylor, S. 1983. Angiogenesis inhibition and tumor regression caused by heparin or a heparin fragment in the presence of cortisone. *Science 221*:719-725.

[241] Thorpe, P.E., Derbyshire,E.J., Andrade,S.P., Press,N., Knowles,P.P., King,S., Watson,G.J., Yang,Y.C., and Rao-Bette,M. 1993. Heparin-steroid conjugates: new angiogenesis inhibitors with antitumor activity in mice. *Cancer Res 53*:3000-3007.

[242] Smorenburg, S.M. 2001. Inhibition of angiogenesis with heparin? *Haemostasis* 31 Suppl 1:25-29.

[243] Quyyumi, A.A., Diodati, J.G., Lakatos, E., Bonow, R.O., and Epstein, S.E. 1993. Angiogenic effects of low molecular weight heparin in patients with stable coronary artery disease: a pilot study. *J Am Coll Cardiol 22*:635-641.

[244] Zacharski, L.R. and Ornstein, D.L. 1998. Heparin and cancer. *Thromb Haemost 80*:10-23.

[245] Nierodzik, M.L., Klepfish,A., and Karpatkin,S. 1995. Role of platelets, thrombin, integrin IIb-IIIa, fibronectin and von Willebrand factor on tumor adhesion in vitro and metastasis in vivo. *Thromb. Haemost 74*:282-290.

[246] Amirkhosravi, A., Mousa, S.A., Amaya, M., Blaydes, S., Desai, H., Meyer, T., and Francis, J.L. 2003. Inhibition of tumor cell-induced platelet aggregation and lung metastasis by the oral GpIIb/IIIa antagonist XV454. *Thromb.Haemost. 90*:549-554.

[247] Mehta, P., Lawson, D., Ward, M.B., Lee-Ambrose, L., and Kimura, A. 1986. Effects of thromboxane A2 inhibition on osteogenic sarcoma cell-induced platelet aggregation. *Cancer Res 46*:5061-5063.

[248] Karpatkin, S., Ambrogio, C., and Pearlstein, E. 1984. Lack of effect of in vivo prostacyclin on the development of pulmonary metastases in mice following intravenous injection of CT26 colon carcinoma, Lewis lung carcinoma, or B16 amelanotic melanoma cells. *Cancer Res 44*:3880-3883.

[249] Ma, L., Elliott, S.N., Cirino, G., Buret, A., Ignarro, L.J., and Wallace, J.L. 2001. Platelets modulate gastric ulcer healing: role of endostatin and vascular endothelial growth factor release. *Proc Natl Acad Sci U S A 98*:6470-6475.

[250] Kuenen, B.C., Levi,M., Meijers,J.C., van Hinsbergh,V.W., Berkhof,J., Kakkar,A.K., Hoekman,K., and Pinedo,H.M. 2003. Potential role of platelets in endothelial damage

observed during treatment with cisplatin, gemcitabine, and the angiogenesis inhibitor SU5416. *J Clin Oncol 21*:2192-2198.

In: New Angiogenesis Research
Editor: Roberta V. Zubar, pp. 97-112

ISBN 1-59454-239-2

Chapter V

Pericytes and Angiogenesis

Sho-ichi Yamagishi[1,*], Yosuke Inagaki[1], Kazuo Nakamura[1], Masayoshi Takeuchi[2] and Tsutomu Imaizumi[1]

[1]Department of Internal Medicine III, Kurume University School of Medicine, Kurume, Japan

[2]Department of Biochemistry, Hokuriku University, Kanazawa, Japan

Abstract

Microvessels are composed of two types of cells, endothelial cells and pericytes. Pericytes are elongated cells of the mesodermal origin, which partially surround the endothelial cells of small vessels. As pericytes contain contractile muscle filaments on their endothelial cell side, they have been regarded for a long time just as microvascular counterparts of smooth muscle cells, and implicated in the regulation of capillary tone. However, recent understandings of pericyte biology suggest that pericytes play an important role in the maintenance of microvascular homeostasis. Indeed, pericyte loss or dysfunction has been involved in the pathogenesis of various types of disorders. In this review, we discuss pericyte biology and molecular mechanisms of pericyte loss or dysfunction in angiogenesis-related disorders such as diabetic angiopathy and tumor growth and expansion. We also review here potential therapeutic strategies to prevent pericyte loss or dysfunction in these devastating diseases.

Key words: AGEs, atherosclerosis, diabetic retinopathy, oxidative stress, PEDF, tumor growth

* Correspondence concerning this article should be addressed to Sho-ichi Yamagishi MD, PhD, Department of Internal Medicine III, Kurume University School of Medicine, Kurume 830-0011, Japan; Tel; +81-942-31-7580; Fax; +81-942-31-7707; E-mail: shoichi@med.kurume-u.ac.jp.

1. Introduction

Angiogenesis, the formation of new capillary networks, is physiologically essential for embryogenesis, reproduction and wound healing, and is also related to various pathological states, including diabetic retinopathy, tumor growth and metastasis, and rheumatoid arthritis [1, 2]. The process of angiogenesis is known to be composed of several steps, namely, proteolytic degradation of the basement membrane, migration and proliferation of endothelial cells (ECs), and the formation of capillary tubes, which finally become enveloped in the recruited pericytes [3].

Pericytes are elongated cells of the mesodermal origin, wrapping around and along ECs of small vessels [4]. Since pericytes have contractile actin- and myosin-filaments in addition to a corresponding anatomical topology in vascular walls, they have so far been regarded as the microvascular counterpart of smooth muscle cells, and involved in the regulation of capillary tonus [5, 6]. However, development of pericyte-EC co-culture systems has revealed that pericytes could play an important role in the maintenance of microvascular homeostasis. Indeed, pericyte loss or dysfunction has been involved in the pathogenesis of various types of disorders. In this review, we discuss pericyte biology and molecular mechanisms of pericyte loss or dysfunction in angiogenesis-related disorders such as diabetic angiopathy and tumor growth and expansion. We also review here potential therapeutic strategies to prevent pericyte loss or dysfunction in these devastating diseases.

2. Pericyte Characteristics

(I) Structure and Distribution

Pericytes are long, slender polymorphic cells with numerous branching processes, and encircle ECs of small arterioles, capillaries, and venules [7]. Pericytes are embedded within a basement membrane which surrounds the capillary tubes. Pericytes contribute to the formation of the basement membrane, and their processes penetrate it to directly contact the underlying ECs [8]. The ratios of pericytes to ECs vary significantly in different tissues; the greater pericyte number and coverage, the better the microvascular barrier function (retina, brain > lung > skeltal muscle >cardiac muscle > adrenal gland, an so on) [9].

(II) Biology

Pericytes contain contractile muscle filaments on their EC side. They have been regarded for a long time just as microvascular counterparts of smooth muscle cells, and implicated in the regulation of capillary tone [4]. However, D'Amore and her colleague developed a procedure for isolating pericytes from small vessels in 1983, and enabled us to elucidate the functional roles and biological characteristics of pericytes [10]. By using pericyte-EC co-culture systems, we, along with others, have found that pericytes not only regulate the growth, but also preserve the prostacyclin-producing ability and protect against lipid-peroxide-induced injury of ECs, thus playing an important role in the maintenance of microvascular homeostasis [11, 12]. Therefore, pericyte loss and the resultant disturbance of functional interaction between pericytes and ECs could be involved in the pathogenesis of angiogenesis-related disorders such as diabetic vascular complications and tumor growth and expansion [13].

Signals that mediate these functional interactions between pericytes and ECs might involve cell surface molecules, because the EC overgrowth inhibition and stimulation of prostacyclin production were accomplished by direct contact of ECs to pericytes. D'Amore *et al.* demonstrated that an active form of transforming growth factor-β (TGF-β) was produced by co-cultures of ECs and pericytes and that antibodies against TGF-β added to the co-culture systems abolished the growth inhibitory effects of pericytes on neighboring ECs [14]. Further, they demonstrated that TGF-β not only induced pericyte differentiation but also stabilized capillary-like structures in a three-dimensional model of *in vitro* angiogenesis [15]. These observations suggest that a candidate molecule that would mediate the functional interactions between pericytes and ECs is TGF-β.

3. Pericytes and Angiogenesis-Related Disorders

(1) Diabetic Retinopathy

(I) Role of Pericytes in Diabetic Retinopathy

Diabetic retinopathy is one of the most important microvascular complications in diabetes and is a leading cause of acquired blindness among the people of occupational age [16]. The lesions of diabetic retinopathy can be grouped into those associated with background, preproliferative and proliferative retinopathy.

The earliest histopathological hallmark of diabetic retinopathy is loss of pericytes [17]. Normally, the ratio of ECs to pericytes in the retinal capillaries is 1:1, but its levels are reported to decrease to 1:4 after several years of diabetes and eventually to 1:10 with even longer diabetic exposure [17, 18]. In parallel with loss of pericytes, several characteristic changes including thickening of the basement membrane, hyperpermeability, and formation of microaneurysm are observed [19, 20]. These structural and functional abnormalities are followed by microvascular occlusion in the retinas, which ultimately progresses to proliferative changes associated with neovascularization [19, 20]. It has been postulated that many of these changes are the consequent of the loss of pericytes. Pericytes negatively control the growth of neighboring ECs under physiological conditions [10]. They also preserve the EC function, including the ability to produce prostacyclin, a potent anti-thrombogenic prostanoid, and are protective against lipid peroxide-induced EC injury [11]. These observations suggest that loss of pericytes could predispose the vessels to angiogenesis, thrombogenesis, and EC injury, thus leading to full clinical expression of diabetic retinopathy.

Recently, Hammes *et al.* investigated the role of capillary coverage with pericytes in early diabetic retinopathy and the contribution to proliferative retinopathy using mice with a single functional allele of platelet-derived growth factor-B (PDGF-B(+/-) mice) [21]. They demonstrated in their studies that retinal capillary coverage with pericytes is crucial for the survival of ECs, particularly under stress conditions such as diabetes, and that pericyte deficiency leads to reduced inhibition of EC proliferation, thus promoting angiogenesis in the retinopathy of prematurity model. Our *in vitro* [11] and their recent *in vivo* [21] observations provide a basis for understanding why diabetic retinopathy develops consequent to pericyte loss, the earliest histopathological hallmarks of diabetic retinopathy.

(ii) Role of Advanced Glycation End Products (AGEs) in Pericyte Loss or Dysfunction

A non-enzymatic reaction between ketones or aldehydes and the amino groups of proteins contributes to the aging of proteins and to pathological complications of diabetes [22-25]. Under hyperglycemic conditions in diabetes, this process begins with the conversion of reversible Schiff base adducts, and then to more stable, covalently-bound Amadori rearrangement products. Over a course of days to weeks, these early glycation products undergo further reactions and rearrangements to become irreversible crossed-linked, fluorescent protein derivatives termed AGEs.

Retinal pericytes accumulate AGEs during diabetes [26], which would be expected to have a detrimental influence on pericyte survival and function [27]. AGEs are toxic to retinal pericytes *in vitro*. We have found that AGEs not only induce growth retardation and apoptotic cell death of, but also exert an immediate toxicity to, retinal pericytes [28, 29]. Antisense DNA complementary mRNA coding for a receptor for AGEs (RAGE) reversed the AGE-induced decrease in viable cell number of pericytes, while overexpression of RAGE potentiated the deleterious effects of AGEs. These results suggest that the AGE effects on pericytes could be mediated through the interactions with RAGE. Further, an anti-oxidant *N*-acetylcysteine (NAC) completely reversed the toxic effects of AGEs, thus suggesting that the AGE-RAGE-induced ROS generation mediated these harmful effects on pericytes [30]. We have recently found that beraprost sodium, a prostacyclin analogue, or forskolin, an activator of adenylate cyclase, protects against the AGE-induced injury in retinal pericytes by suppressing ROS generation [31]. Since cyclic AMP elevating agents were known to block ROS generation in neutrophils by inhibiting NADPH oxidase activity [32], NADPH oxidase might be a source of ROS production elicited by AGEs and also be a target of beraprost sodium.

Vascular endothelial growth factor (VEGF) is a specific mitogen to ECs, also known as vascular permeability factor, and is generally thought to be involved in the pathogenesis of proliferative diabetic retinopathy. Indeed, some clinical observations have demonstrated that VEGF level in ocular fluid is positively correlated with the activity of neovascularization in diabetic retinopathy [33, 34]. Recently, VEGF level was also found to be associated with the breakdown of the blood-retinal barrier, thus being involved in microvascular hyperpermeability in background retinopathy [35]. Exposure of retinal cells including pericytes to preformed AGEs is known to cause significant up-regulation of this growth factor both *in vitro* and *in vivo* [29, 36-38]. These observations suggest that AGEs are also involved in progression of diabetic retinopathy by inducing VEGF. Although the molecular mechanisms of VEGF overexpression elicited by AGEs are not fully understood, our recent investigation has shown that the AGE-RAGE interaction might increase VEGF gene transcription by NADPH oxidase-mediated ROS generation [39, 40].

Angiopoietin (ang)-Tie receptor interaction plays an important role in both physiological and pathological angiogenesis as well [41]. Engagement of tie-2 by ang-1 has been known to promote recruitment of pericytes, thereby supporting the establishment and maintenance of vascular integrity; while ang-2 is a naturally occurring antagonist of ang-1, and induces the loosening of contacts between ECs and pericytes [41-43]. AGEs increase a ratio of ang-2 to ang-1 mRNA level and simultaneously up-regulate VEGF mRNA levels in microvascular ECs. A plastic window for blood vessel remodeling is defined by pericyte coverage of the preformed endothelial network [44]. Therefore, the AGE-induced pericyte apoptosis and increased ratio of ang-2/ang-1 in ECs could disrupt the pericyte-EC interactions, thus promoting angiogeneis by acting in concert with VEGF. Recently, recombinant ang-1 has been found to restore the activity of ECs to form an organized, mature vascular architecture, thus preventing retinal edema and hemorrhage in the complete absence of pericytes in mice models [45]. These observations suggest the potential of ang-1 as a new therapeutic modality for pericyte dropout in diseases such as diabetic retinopathy.

The above-discussed *in vitro* and *in vivo* effects of AGEs strongly suggest a pathological role for these senescent macroproteins in diabetic retinopathy. Further, serum levels of AGEs are found to be correlated to severity of diabetic retinopathy with both type 1 and type 2 diabetes [46, 47]. Therefore, inhibition of AGE formation, blockade of AGE-RAGE interactions, or the downstream signaling pathways has been supposed to be potential therapeutic strategies in the prevention of diabetic retinopathy.

The hydrazine compound aminoguanidine is the first AGE inhibitor discovered [48, 49]. Treatment of diabetic rats for 26 weeks with aminoguanidine prevented a 2.6-fold accumulation of AGE products at branching sites of pre-capillary arterioles and thereby prevented abnormal EC proliferation and significantly diminished pericyte dropout [50]. A multicenter clinical trial revealed that pimagedine (aminoguanidine) slowed the progression of diabetic retinopathy, although it was terminated early due to safety concerns [51, 52].

Amadorins have an ability to scavenge dicarbonyls and therefore inhibit the conversion of Amadori intermediates into AGEs [53, 54]. The derivative of vitamin B_6, pyridoxamine, has been shown to an efficacious and specific post-Amadori inhibitor, with the ability to prevent up-regulation of retinal basement membrane-associated genes and capillary dropout [55].

Compared to the strategy of preventing AGE formation, the manupulation of the AGE signal pathways as a therapeutic option in diabetic retinopathy remains much less developed. However, recently, we have found that pigment epithelium-derived factor (PEDF), one of the superfamily of serine protease inhibitors with potent neuronal differentiating activity in human retinoblastoma cells [56], inhibits the AGE-induced pericyte apoptosis and EC proliferation and activation through its anti-oxidative properties [30, 57]. Since the levels of vitreal PEDF are decreased in angiogenic eye diseases such as proliferative diabetic retinopathy [58], substitution of PEDF may disrupt inappropriate retinal cell responses to AGEs, thus being a promising strategy for treatment of patients with diabetic retinopathy.

(iii) Role of the Polyol Pathway in Pericyte Loss or Dysfunction

The polyol pathway consists of two enzymes, aldose reductase (AR) and sorbitol dehydrogenase (SDH); the former is the first enzyme in the polyol pathway, that catalyzes reduction of glucose to sorbitol, while the latter is the second one, that converts sorbitol into fructose using NAD^+ as a cofactor [59]. The polyol pathway is activated under hyperglycemic conditions, and is considered to play an important role in the development of diabetic neuropathy in addition to other complications [60-63]. Intracellular sorbitol accumulation and decline in NADPH contents caused by increases in AR flux has been postulated to induce osmotic damage and oxidative stress, respectively. However, in human studies, AR inhibitors have only a partial effect against early phase of diabetic retinopathy [64-67]. Such negative findings have fueled controversy surrounding the contribution of AR in diabetic retinopathy.

Increased flux through SDH can lead to an increased ratio of NADH/NAD that may alter lipid metabolism and increase production of ROS, thus contributing to the development of diabetic microangiopathies (pseudohypoxia hypothesis) [68]. This redox imbalance may be associated with impaired regulation of retinal blood flow in humans with diabetes and in nondiabetic acutely hyperglycemic animals [69]. In order to further examine a functional role of SDH in diabetic retinopathy, we studied effects of SDH overexpression on glucose toxicity to cultured retinal pericytes [70]. High glucose modestly increased ROS generation, decreased DNA synthesis and up-regulated VEGF mRNA levels in retinal pericytes. SDH overexpression was found to significantly stimulate ROS generation in high glucose-exposed pericytes, and subsequently potentiate the cytopathic effects of glucose. An anti-oxidant NAC, completely prevented these deleterious effects of SDH overexpression on pericytes. Further, blockade of the polyol pathway was found to significantly prevent vascular hyperpermeability, the characteristic changes of the early phase of diabetic retinopathy, in streptozotocin-induced diabetic rats. These observations suggest that SDH-mediated conversion of sorbitol into fructose and the resultant ROS generation may play a role in the pathogenesis of diabetic retinopathy. Since fructose is a stronger glycating agent than glucose, intracellular AGE formation via the SDH pathway might be involved in glucose toxicity to retinal pericytes [71].

(iv) Role of the Renin-Angiotensin in Pericyte Loss or Dysfunction

The local RAS is activated under diabetes [72]. We have recently found that angiotensin II (AII) stimulated intracellular ROS generation in retinal pericytes through an interaction with type 1 receptor. Further, AII decreased DNA synthesis and simultaneously up-regulated VEGF mRNA levels in pericytes, both of which were blocked by treatment with telmisartan, a newly developed AII type 1 receptor antagonist, or an anti-oxidant NAC [73, 74]. These results suggest that AngII-type 1 receptor interaction could induce pericyte loss and dysfunction through intracellular ROS generation, thus being involved in diabetic retinopathy. Since AII induces the VEGF receptor KDR (kinase insert domain-containing receptor) expression in retinal microvascular ECs, the retinal RAS might augment the permeability- and angiogenesis-inducing activity of VEGF, thus being implicated in the progression of diabetic retinopathy as well [75].

Blockade of the RAS by inhibitors of angiotensin converting enzyme or AII type 1 receptor antagonists can reduce retinal overexpression of VEGF and hyperpermeability and neovascularization in experimental diabetes [76-78]. Funatsu *et al.* recently found that the vitreous fluid level of AII was significantly correlated with that of VEGF, and both of them were significantly higher in patients with active proliferative diabetic retinopathy than in those with quiescent proliferative diabetic retinopathy [79]. These findings further support the concept that AII contributes to development and progression of proliferative diabetic retinopathy in combination with VEGF. In the EUCLID Study, the angiotensin converting enzyme inhibitor, lisinopril, reduced the risk of progression of retinopathy by approximately 50%, and also significantly reduced the risk of progression to proliferative retinopathy although retinopathy was not a primary end-point and the study was not sufficiently powered for the eye-related outcomes [80].

(V) Role of Endothelin (ET) in Pericyte Loss

ET-1, a 21-amino acid peptide initially identified as a vasoconstrictor factor secreted by ECs, has been recently reported to be mitogenic to vascular smooth muscle cells and glomerular mesangial cells, both of which are regarded as as anatomical equivalents to pericytes in their respective vascular archetectures [81]. We have previously found that ET-1 is a responsible factor that mediates pericyte growth induced by ECs [12]. Pericytes express mRNA for the type A but not type B ET receptor. This indicates that pericytes possess a system efficiently responding to ET-1, because rank order of the binding affinity to the expressed receptor type is ET-1>ET-2>>ET-3 [82]. Responsiveness of pericytes to ET-1 was blunted under high glucose conditions [83]. Induction of resistance to ET-1's actions by elevated glucose levels in retinal pericytes might be involved in pericyte loss in early diabetic retinopathy.

(2) Atherosclerosis

(I) Role of Pericytes in Plaque Angiogenesis

Plaque neovascularization is comprised of a network of capillaries that arise from adventitial vasa vasorum and extend into the intimal layer of atherosclerotic lesions [84]. They are often found in areas rich in inflammatory cells such as macrophages and T cells, and have been considered to function as conduits for the entry of leukocytes and nutrients into the artery wall [85, 86]. Plaque vessels are also associated with plaque rupture, intraplaque hemorrhage, and unstable angina [87, 88]. Further, recently, inhibition of plaque angiogenesis is found to reduce macrophage accumulation and progression of advanced atherosclerosis in apolipoprotein E-deficient mice [89, 90]. These observations suggest that angiogenesis may be involved in plaque growth and lesion instability in atherosclerosis.

Atherosclerotic plaque is often hypoxic because diffusion from artery lumen is insufficient to meet the metabolic demands of the plaque [89]. We have previously shown that hypoxia could elicit angiogenesis through the production of paracrine VEGF by pericytes [91]. VEGF enhanced plaque formation and progression in atherosclerosis in animal models, and its expression was increased in human atheromatous plaque [92, 93]. These observations suggest that hypoxia could be involved in plaque angiogenesis by stimulating pericyte VEGF production *in vivo*.

AGEs, which exist in atherosclerotic plaque, also stimulate VEGF production in pericytes. Since AGEs predispose to thrombogenesis by inhibiting prostacyclin production and inducing plasminogen activator inhibitor-1 in microvascular ECs [94, 95], ischemia and the resultant hypoxia due to microthrombus formation in the atherosclerotic plaque may trigger VEGF expression, thus further promoting plaquc angiogenesis in advanced atherosclerosis [96].

(II) Role of Pericytes in Vascular Calcification

Vascular calcification is a common feature in advanced atherosclerosis [97] and also a predictor of future cardiovascular events such as unstable angina and myocardial infarction [98]. Although vascular calcification has long been regarded as an end-stage, degenerative process, recent works by Demer *et al.* revealed that it was an actively regulated process involving a subpopulation of artery wall cells, called calcifying vascular cells (CVC) [99,

100]. They also showed that CVC had the potential to differentiate along with other mesenchymal lineages such as osteoblasts, and their immunochemical characters were identical to those of pericytes [99, 101].

AGEs have the ability to induce the osteoblatic differentiation of pericytes, thus contributing to the development of vascular calcification in atherosclerosis [102]. Pericytes have the plasticity to differentiate into other mesenchymal cell types under various circumstances, and may function as resting stem cells to be converted into smooth muscle cells, macrophage-like phagocytes or osteoblasts [103, 104]. Indeed, under hypoxic conditions, pericytes are capable of exhibiting phenotypic characterisitics ascribed to osteoblasts [105]. These observations suggest that AGEs may be an alternative inducer of osteoblastic differentiation of pericytes. AGEs and hypoxia elicited angiogenesis and that vascular calcification was often associated with marked neovascularization in atherosclerosis, further supporting our concept that pericytes could play an important role in the pathogenesis of vascular calcification in atherosclerosis [106].

(3) Tumor Growth and Expansion

(I) Role of Pericytes in Tumor-Associated Angiogenesis

Tumors can not grow beyond a volume of 1-2 mm^3 without establishing a vascular supply because cells must be within 100-200 μm of a blood vessel to survive [107, 108]. A major event in tumor growth and expansion is the ‘angiogenic switch’, an alteration in the balance of pro-angiogenic and anti-angiogenic molecules that leads to tumor neovascularization [109]. Several lines of evidence implicate VEGF as the key factor involved in angiogenic switch in human tumors [110]. VEGF and its receptors are expressed at high levels in almost all tumors [110], and administration of antibodies (Abs) directed against VEGF or dominant negative forms of the VEGF receptor *flk-1* inhibited tumor growth in nude mice [111, 112].

We have shown previously that hypoxia, the principal cause of angiogenesis, can induce the proliferation of pericytes and ECs, two microvascular constituents [91]. Further, we have recently found that the hypoxic induction of pericyte growth can be ascribed at least partly to autocrine VEGF on the basis of the following evidence [113]. (1) Hypoxia stimulated the proliferation of pericytes. (2) Northern blot analysis revealed that levels of mRNA encoding VEGF increased as the atmospheric oxygen tension dropped; this was accompanied by an increase in *de novo* synthesis of VEGF proteins. (3) Pericytes were able to respond to exogenously added VEGF, resulting in a dose-dependent increase in the viable cell number. (4) Polyclonal antibodies against VEGF efficiently blocked the hypoxic induction of pericyte growth. (5) Pericytes expressed the gene for *fms*-like tyrosine kinase 1 (*flt1*) as the predominant form of VEGF receptor, and tyrosine phosphorylation of this receptor protein was enhanced by exposing the pericytes to hypoxia as it was when exposed to VEGF. (6) Antisense DNA complement of *flt1* mRNA abolished the hypoxia-induced stimulation of pericyte growth. (7) Exogenous VEGF stimulated the migration of pericytes in a dose-dependent manner. These results thus suggest that VEGF, which has so far been thought to be a specific mitogen for ECs [114], also acts on neighboring pericytes, and that the hypoxia-induced overproduction of VEGF could promote not only EC sprouting but also the recruitment of pericytes, thereby contributing to growth and expansion of tumors by stimulating the maturation of newly formed microvessels.

4. Conclusion

We review here molecular mechanisms of pericyte loss and dysfunction in various angiogenesis-related disorders. Inhibition of pericyte loss or dysfunction might be a novel potential therapeutic strategy for the treatments of patients with angiogenesis-related disorders such as diabetic vascular complications and tumors.

Acknowledgements

This work was supported in part by Grants of Venture Research and Development Centers from the Ministry of Education, Culture, Sports, Science and Technology, Japan (S.Y.).

References

[1] Folkman J, Haudenschild C. Angiogenesis in vitro. *Nature* 1980; 288: 551-6.

[2] Folkman J, Shing Y. Angiogenesis. *J Biol Chem* 1992; 267: 10931-4.

[3] D'Amore PA, Thompson RW. Mechanisms of angiogenesis. *Annu Rev Physiol* 1987; 49: 453-64.

[4] Sims DE. Recent advances in pericyte biology--implications for health and disease. *Can J Cardiol* 1991; 7: 431-43.

[5] Herman IM, D'Amore PA. Microvascular pericytes contain muscle and nonmuscle actins. *J Cell Biol* 1985; 101: 43-52.

[6] Joyce NC, Haire MF, Palade GE. Contractile proteins in pericytes. II. Immunocytochemical evidence for the presence of two isomyosins in graded concentrations. *J Cell Biol* 1985; 100: 1387-95.

[7] Gerhardt H, Betsholtz C. Endothelial-pericyte interactions in angiogenesis. *Cell Tissue Res* 2003; 314: 15-23.

[8] Hirschi KK, D'Amore PA. Pericytes in microvasculature. *Cardiovasc Res* 1996; 32: 687-98.

[9] Shepro D, Morel NM. Pericyte physiology. *FASEB J* 1993; 7: 1031-8.

[10] Gitlin JD, D'Amore PA. Culture of retinal capillary cells using selective growth media. *Microvasc Res* 1983; 26: 1455-62.

[11] Yamagishi S, Kobayashi K, Yamamoto H. Vascular pericytes not only regulate growth, but also preserve prostacyclin-producing ability and protect against lipid peroxide-induced injury of co-cultured endothelial cells. *Biochem Biophys Res Commun* 1993; 190: 418-25.

[12] Yamagishi S, Hsu CC, Kobayashi K, Yamamoto H. Endothelin 1 mediates endothelial cell-dependent proliferation of vascular pericytes. *Biochem Biophys Res Commun* 1993; 191: 840-6.

[13] Yamagishi S, Yonekura H, Yamamoto Y, Katsuno K, Sato F, et al. Advanced glycation end products-driven angiogenesis in vitro. Induction of the growth and tube formation of human microvascular endothelial cells through autocrine vascular endothelial growth factor. *J Biol Chem* 1997; 272: 8723-30.
[14] Antonelli-Orlidge A, Saunders KB, Smith SR, D'Amore PA. An active form of transforming growth factor-β was produced by co-cultures of ECs and pericytes. *Proc Natl Acad Sci USA* 1989; 86: 4544-8.
[15] Darland DC, D'Amore PA. TGF beta is required for the formation of capillary-like structures in three-dimensional cocultures of 10T1/2 and endothelial cells. *Angiogenesis* 2001; 4:11-20.
[16] L'Esperance FA, James WA, Judson PH. In: Lifkin H, Porte D Ed, The eye and diabetes mellitus. *Ellenberg and Rifkin's Diabetes Mellitus, Theory and Practice*. New York, Elsevier, 1990; 661-83.
[17] Cogan DG, Toussaint D, Kuwabara T. Retinal vascular patterns. IV. Diabetic retinopathy. *Arch Ophthalmo* 1961; 66: 366-78.
[18] Kuwabara T, Cogan DG. Retinal vascular patterns. VI. Mural cells of the retinal capillaries. *Arch Ophthalmo* 1963; 69: 492-502.
[19] Mandarino LJ. Current hypotheses for the biochemical basis of diabetic retinopathy. *Diabetes Care* 1992; 15: 1892-901.
[20] Frank RN. On the pathogenesis of diabetic retinopathy. A 1990 update. *Ophthalmology* 1991; 98: 586-93.
[21] Hammes HP, Lin J, Renner O, Shani M, Lundqvist A, et al. Pericytes and the pathogenesis of diabetic retinopathy. *Diabetes* 2002; 51: 3107-12.
[22] Brownlee M, Cerami A, Vlassara H. Advanced glycosylation end products in tissue and the biochemical basis of diabetic complications. *N Engl J Med* 1988; 318: 1315-21.
[23] Dyer DG, Blackledge JA, Thorpe SR, Baynes JW. Formation of pentosidine during nonenzymatic browning of proteins by glucose. Identification of glucose and other carbohydrates as possible precursors of pentosidine in vivo. *J Biol Chem* 1991; 266: 11654-60.
[24] Grandhee SK, Monnier VM. Mechanism of formation of the Maillard protein cross-link pentosidine. Glucose, fructose, and ascorbate as pentosidine precursors. *J Biol Chem* 1991; 266: 11649-53.
[25] Stitt AW. The role of advanced glycation in the pathogenesis of diabetic retinopathy. *Experimental and Molecular Pathology* 2003; 75: 95-108.
[26] Stitt AW, Li YM, Gardiner TA, Bucala R, Archer DB, et al. Advanced glycation end products (AGEs) co-locarize with AGE receptors in the retinal vasculature of diabetic and AGE-infused rats. *Am J Pathol* 1997; 150: 523-31.
[27] Sharma NK, Gardiner TA, Archer DB. A morphologic and autoradiographic study of cell death and regeneration in the retinal microvasculature of normal and diabetic rats. *Am J Ophthalmol* 1985; 100: 51-60.
[28] Yamagishi S, Hsu CC, Taniguchi M, Harada S, Yamamoto Y, et al. Receptor-mediated toxicity to pericytes of advanced glycosylation end products: a possible mechanism of pericyte loss in diabetic microangiopathy. *Biochem Biophys Res Commun* 1995; 213: 681-7.

[29] Yamagishi S, Amano S, Inagaki Y, Okamoto T, Koga K, et al. Advanced glycation end products-induced apoptosis and overexpression of vascular endothelial growth factor in bovine retinal pericytes. *Biochem Biophys Res Commun* 2002; 290: 973-8.

[30] Yamagishi S, Inagaki Y, Amano S, Okamoto T, Takeuchi M, et al. Pigment epithelium-derived factor protects cultured retinal pericytes from advanced glycation end product-induced injury through its antioxidative properties. *Biochem Biophys Res Commun* 2002; 296: 877-82.

[31] Yamagishi S, Amano S, Inagaki Y, Okamoto T, Takeuchi M, et al. Beraprost sodium, a prostaglandin I_2 analogue, protects against advanced gycation end products-induced injury in cultured retinal pericytes. *Mol Med* 2002; 8: 546-50.

[32] Ottonello L, Morone MP, Dapino P, Dallegri F. Tumor necrosis factor-alpha-induced oxidative burst in neutrophils adherent to fibronectin: effects of cyclic AMP-elevating agents. *Br J Haematol* 1995; 91: 566-70.

[33] Adamis AP, Miller JW, Bernal MT, D'Amico DJ, Folkman J, et al. Increased vascular endothelial growth factor levels in the vitreous of eyes with proliferative diabetic retinopathy. *Am J Ophthalmol* 1994; 118: 445-50.

[34] Aiello LP, Avery RL, Arrigg PG, Keyt BA, Jampel HD, et al. Vascular endothelial growth factor in ocular fluid of patients with diabetic retinopathy and other retinal disorders. *N Engl J Med* 1994; 331: 1480-7.

[35] Murata T, Ishibashi T, Khalil A, Hata Y, Yoshikawa H, et al. Vascular endothelial growth factor plays a role in hyperpermeability of diabetic retinal vessels. *Ophthalmic Res* 1995; 27: 48-52.

[36] Segawa Y, Shirao Y, Yamagishi S, Higashide T, Kobayashi M, et al. Upregulation of retinal vascular endothelial growth factor mRNAs in spontaneously diabetic rats without ophthalmoscopic retinopathy. A possible participation of advanced glycation end products in the development of the early phase of diabetic retinopathy. *Ophthalmic Res* 1998; 30: 333-9.

[37] Stitt AW, Bhaduri T, McMullen CB, Gardiner TA, Archer DB. Advanced glycation end products induce blood-retinal barrier dysfunction in normoglycemic rats. *Mol Cell Biol Res Commun* 2000; 3: 380-8.

[38] Lu M, Kuroki M, Amano S, Tolentino M, Keough K, et al. Advanced glycation end products increase retinal vascular endothelial growth factor expression. *J Clin Invest* 1998; 101: 1219-24.

[39] Okamoto T, Yamagishi S, Inagaki Y, Amano S, Koga K, et al. Angiogenesis induced by advanced glycation end products and its prevention by cerivastatin. *FASEB J* 2002; 16: 1928-30.

[40] Okamoto T, Yamagishi S, Inagaki Y, Amano S, Takeuchi M, et al. Incadronate disodium inhibits advanced glycation end products-induced angiogenesis in vitro. *Biochem Biophys Res Commun* 2002; 297: 419-24.

[41] Folkman J. D'Amore PA. Blood Vessel Formation: What Is Its Molecular Basis? *Cell* 1996; 87: 1153-5.

[42] Maisonpierre PC, Suri C, Jones PF, Bartunkova S, Wiegand SJ, et al. Angiopoietin-2, a Natural Antagonist for Tie2 That Disrupts in vivo Angiogenesis. *Science* 1997; 277: 55-60.

[43] Jonnes N, Iljin K, Dumont DJ, Alitalo K. Tie receptors: new modulators of angiogenic and lymphangiogenic responses. *Nat Rev Mol Cell Biol* 2001; 2: 257-67.

[44] Benjamin LE, Hemo I, Keshet E. A plasticity window for blood vessel remodelling is defined by pericyte coverage of the preformed endothelial network and is regulated by PDGF-B and VEGF. *Development* 1998; 125: 1591-8.

[45] Uemura A, Ogawa M, Hirashima M, Fujisawa T, Koyama S, Takagi H, Honda Y, Wiegand SJ, Yamcopoulos GD, Nishikawa S. Recombinant angiopoietin-1 restores higher-order architecture of growing blood vessels in mice in absence of mural cells. *J Clin Invest* 2002; 110: 1619-28.

[46] Miura J, Yamagishi S, Uchigata Y, Takeuchi M, Yamamoto H, et al. Serum levels of non-carboxymethyllysine advanced glycation endproducts are correlated to severity of microvascular complications in patients with Type 1 diabetes. *J Diabetes Complications* 2003; 17: 16-21.

[47] Koga K, Yamagishi S, Okamoto T, Inagaki Y, Amano S, et al. Serum levels of glucose-derived advanced glycation end products are associated with the severity of diabetic retinopathy in type 2 diabetic patients without renal dysfunction. *Int J Clin Pharmacol Res*. 2002; 22: 13-7.

[48] Brownlee M, Vlassara H, Kooney A, Ulrich P, Cerami A. Aminoguanidine prevents diabetes-induced arterial wall protein cross-linking. *Science* 1986; 232: 1629-32.

[49] Yamagishi S, Imaizumi T. Diabetic vascular complications: pathophysiology, biochemical basis, and potential therapeutic strategy. *Curr Pharma Des* 2004 (in press)

[50] Hammes HP, Martin S, Federlin K, Geisen K, Brownlee M. Aminoguanidine treatment inhibits the development of experimental diabetic retinopathy. *Proc Natl Acad Sci USA* 1991; 88: 11555-8.

[51] Vasan S, Foiles PG, Founds HW. Therapeutic potential of AGE inhibitors and breakers of AGE protein cross-links. *Expert Opin Investig Drugs* 2001; 10: 1977-87.

[52] Thornalley PJ. Use of aminoguanidine (Pimagedine) to prevent the formation of advanced glycation endproducts. *Arch Biochem Biophys* 2003; 419: 31-40.

[53] Khalifah RG, Baynes JW, Hudson BG. Amadorins: novel post-Amadori inhibitors of advanced glycation reactions. *Biochem Biophys Res Commun* 1999; 257: 251-8.

[54] Voziyan PA, Metz TO, Baynes JW, Hudson BG. A post-Amadori inhibitor pyridoxamine also inhibits chemical modification of proteins by scavenging carbonyl intermediates of carbohydrate and lipid degradation. *J Biol Chem* 2002;277: 3397-403.

[55] Stitt A, Gardiner TA, Alderson NL, Canning P, Frizzell N, et al. The AGE inhibitor pyridoxamine inhibits development of retinopathy in experimental diabetes. *Diabetes* 2002; 51: 2826-32.

[56] Tombran-Tink J, Chader CG, Johnson LV. PEDF: Pigment epithelium-derived factor with potent neuronal differentiative activity. *Exp Eye Res* 1991; 53: 411-4.

[57] Inagaki Y, Yamagishi S, Okamoto T, Takeuchi M, Amano S. Pigment epithelium-derived factor prevents advanced glycation end products-induced monocyte chemoattractant protein-1 production in microvascular endothelial cells by suppressing intracellular reactive oxygen species generation. *Diabetologia* 2003; 46: 284-7.

[58] Spranger J, Osterhoff M, Reimann M, Mohlig M, Ristow M, et al. Loss of the antiangiogenic pigment epithelium-derived factor in patients with angiogenic eye disease. *Diabetes* 2002; 50: 2641-5.

[59] Yabe-Nishimura C. Aldose reductase in glucose toxicity: a potential target for the prevention of diabetic complications. Pharmacol Rev 1998; 50: 21-33.

[60] Kinoshita JH, Nishimura C. The involvement of aldose reductase in diabetic complications. *Diabetes Metab Rev* 1998; 4: 323-37.

[61] Ghahary A, Luo JM, Gong YW, Chakrabarti S, Sima AA, et al. Increased renal aldose reductase activity, immunoreactivity, and mRNA in streptozocin-induced diabetic rats. *Diabetes* 1989; 38: 1067-71.

[62] Vinores SA, Campochiaro PA, Williams EH, May EE, Green WR, et al. Aldose reductase expression in human diabetic retina and retinal pigment epithelium. *Diabetes* 1988; 37: 1658-64.

[63] Tawata M, Ohtaka M, Hosaka Y, Onaya T. Aldose reductase mRNA expression and its activity are induced by glucose in fetal rat aortic smooth muscle (A10) cells. *Life Sci* 1992; 51: 719-26.

[64] Van Gerven JM, Boot JP, Lemkes HH, Van Best JA. Effects of aldose reductase inhibition with tolrestat on diabetic retinopathy in a six months double blind trial. *Doc Ophthalmol* 1994; 87: 355-65.

[65] Arauz-Pacheco C, Ramirez LC, Pruneda L, Sanborn GE, Rosenstock J, et al. The effect of aldose reductase inhibitor, ponalrestat, on the progression of diabetic retinopathy. *J Diabetes Complications* 1992; 6: 131-7.

[66] Tromp A, Hooymans JM, Barendsen BC, Van Doormaal JJ. The effects of an aldose reductase inhibitor on the progression of diabetic retinopathy. *Doc Ophthalmol* 1991; 78: 153-9.

[67] Sorbinil Retinopathy Trial Research Group. A randomized trial of sorbinil, an aldose reductase inhibitor, in diabetic retinopathy. *Arch Ophthalmol* 1990; 108: 1234-44.

[68] Williamson JR, Chang K, Frangos M, Hasan KS, Ido Y, et al. Hyperglycemic pseudohypoxia and diabetic complications. *Diabetes* 1993; 42: 801-13.

[69] Van den Enden MK, Nyengaard JR, Ostrow E, Burgan JH, Williamson JR. Elevated glucose levels increase retinal glycolysis and sorbitol pathway metabolism. Implications for diabetic retinopathy. *Invest Ophthalmol Vis Sci* 1995; 36: 1675-8

[70] Amano S, Yamagishi S, Kato N, Inagaki Y, Okamoto T, et al. Sorbitol dehydrogenase overexpression potentiates glucose toxicity to cultured retinal pericytes. *Biochem Biophys Res Commun* 2002; 299: 183-8.

[71] Amano S, Yamagishi S, Koda Y, Tsuneoka M, Soejima M, et al. Polymorphisms of sorbitol dehydrogenase (SDH) gene and susceptibility to diabetic retinopathy. *Med Hypotheses*. 2003; 60: 550-1.

[72] Anderson S. Role of local and systemic angiotensin in diabetic renal disease. *Kidney Int Suppl* 1997; 63: S107-10.

[73] Yamagishi S, Amano S, Inagaki Y, Okamoto T, Inoue H, et al. Angiotensin II-type 1 receptor interaction upregulates vascular endothelial growth factor messenger RNA levels in retinal pericytes through intracellular reactive oxygen species generation. *Drugs Exp Clin Res* 2003; 29: 75-80.

[74] Amano S, Yamagishi S, Inagaki Y, Okamoto T. Angiotensin II stimulates platelet derived growth factor-B gene expression in cultured retinal pericytes through intracellular reactive oxygen species generation. *Int J Tissue React* 2003;25: 51-5.

[75] Otani A, Takagi H, Suzuma K, Honda Y. Angiotensin II potentiates vascular endothelial growth factor-induced angiogenic activity in retinal microcapillary endothelial cells. *Circ Res* 1998; 82: 619-28.

[76] Nagisa Y, Shintani A, Nakagawa S. The angiotensin II receptor antagonist candesartan cilexetil (TCV-116) ameliorates retinal disorders in rats. *Diabetologia* 2001; 44: 883-8.
[77] Gilbert RE, Kelly DJ, Cox AJ, Wilkinson-Berka JL, Rumble JR, et al. Angiotensin converting enzyme inhibition reduces retinal overexpression of vascular endothelial growth factor and hyperpermeability in experimental diabetes. *Diabetologia* 2000; 43: 1360-7.
[78] Moravski CJ, Skinner SL, Stubbs AJ, Sarlos S, Kelly DJ, et al. The renin-angiotensin system influences ocular endothelial cell proliferation in diabetes: transgenic and interventional studies. *Am J Pathol* 2003; 162: 151-60.
[79] Funatsu H, Yamashita H, Nakanishi Y, Hori S. Angiotensin II and vascular endothelial growth factor in the vitreous fluid of patients with proliferative diabetic retinopathy. *Br J Ophthalmol* 2002; 86: 311-5.
[80] Chaturvedi N, Sjolie AK, Stephenson JM, Abrahamian H, Keipes M, et al. Effect of lisinopril on progression of retinopathy in normotensive people with type 1 diabetes. The EUCLID Study Group. EURODIAB Controlled Trial of Lisinopril in Insulin-Dependent Diabetes Mellitus. *Lancet* 1998; 351: 28-31.
[81] Imai T, Hirata Y, Emori T, Yanagisawa M, Masaki T, et al. Induction of endothelin-1 gene by angiotensin and vasopressin in endothelial cells. Hypertension 1992; 19: 753-7.
[82] Hosoda K, Nakao K, Hiroshi-Arai, Suga S, Ogawa Y, et al. Cloning and expression of human endothelin-1 receptor cDNA. *FEBS Lett* 1991; 287: 23-6.
[83] De la Rubia G, Oliver FJ, Inoguchi T, King GL. Induction of resistance to ET-1's biochemical actions by elevated glucose levels in retinal pericytes. *Diabetes* 1992; 41: 1533-9.
[84] Zhang Y, Cliff WJ, Schoefl GI, Higgins G. Immunohistochemical study of intimal microvessels in coronary atherosclerosis. *Am J Pathol* 1993; 143: 164-72.
[85] O'Brien ER, Garvin MR, Dev R, Stewart DK, Hinohara T, Simpson JB, Schwartz SM. Angiogenesis in human coronary atherosclerotic plaques. *Am J Pathol* 1994; 145: 883-94.
[86] O'Brien KD, McDonald TO, Chait A, Aleen MD, Alpers CE. Neovascular expression of E-selectin, ICAM-1, and VCAM-1 in human atherosclerosis and their relation to intimal leukocyte content. *Circulation* 1996; 93: 672-82.
[87] Moulton KS. Plaque angiogenesis and atherosclerosis. *Curr Atheroscler Rep* 2001; 3: 225-33.
[88] Tenaglia AN, Peters KG, SketchMH Jr, Annex BH. Neovascularization in atherectomy species from patients with unstable angina. *Am Heart J* 1998; 80: 2623-27.
[89] Moulton KS, Heller E, Konerdling MA, Flynn E, Palinski W, Folkman J. Angiogenesis inhibitors endostatin or TNP-470 reduce intimal neovascularization and plaque growth in apolipoprotein E-deficient mice. *Circulation* 1999; 99: 1726-32.
[90] Moulton KS, Vakili K, Zurakowski D, Soliman M, Butterfield C, Sylvin E, Lo KM, Gillies S, Javaherian K, Folkman J. Inhibition of plaque neovascularization reduces macrophage accumulation and progression of advanced atherosclerosis. *Proc Natl Acad Sci USA* 2003; 100: 4736-41.
[91] Nomura M, Yamagishi S, Harada S, Hayashi Y, Yamashima T, et al. Possible participation of autocrine and paracrine vascular endothelial growth factors in hypoxia-induced proliferation of endothelial cells and pericytes. *J Biol Chem* 1995; 270: 28316-24.

[92] Celletti FL, Waugh JM, Amabile PG, Brendolan A, Hilfiker PR, Dake MD. Vascular endothelial growth factor enhances atherosclerotic plaque progression. *Nat Med* 2001; 7: 425-9.

[93] Inoue M, Ueda M, Naruko T, Kojima A, komatsu R, Doi K, Ogawa Y, Tamura N, Takaya K, Igaki T, Yamashita J, Chun TH, Masatsugu K, Becker AE, Nakao K. Vascular endothelial growth factor (VEGF) expression in human coronary atherosclerotic lesions: possible pathophysiological significance of VEGF in progression of atherosclerosis. *Circulation* 1998; 98: 2108-16.

[94] Yamagishi S, Yamamoto Y, Harada S, Hsu CC, Yamamoto H. Advanced glycosylation end products stimulate the growth but inhibit the prostacyclin-producing ability of endothelial cells through interactions with their receptors. *FEBS Lett.* 1996; 384: 103-6

[95] Yamagishi S, Fujimori H, Yonekura H, Yamamoto Y, Yamamoto H. Advanced glycation endproducts inhibit prostacyclin production and induce plasminogen activator inhibitor-1 in human microvascular endothelial cells. *Diabetologia* 1998; 41: 1435-41.

[96] Yamagishi S, Kawakami T, Fujimori H, Yonekura H, Tanaka N, et al. Insulin stimulates the growth and tube formation of human microvascular endothelial cells through autocrine vascular endothelial growth factor. *Microvasc Res* 1999; 57: 329-39.

[97] Agatson AS, Janowitz WR, Hildner FJ, Zusmer NR, Viamonte M, Detrano R. Quantification of coronary artery calcium using ultrafast computed tomography. *J Am Coll Cardiol* 1990; 15: 827-32.

[98] Fitzgerald PJ, Ports TA, Yock PG. Contribution of localized calcium deposits to dissection after angioplasty. An observational study using intravascular ultrasound. *Circulation* 1992; 86: 64-70.

[99] Watson KE, Bostrom K, Ravindranath R, Lam T, Norton B, Demer LL. TGF-β1 and 25-hydroxycholesterol stimulate osteoblast-like vascular cells to calcify. *J Clin Invest* 1994; 93: 2106-13.

[100] Parhami F, Tintut Y, Ballard A, Fogelman AM, Demer LL. Leptin enhances the calcification of vascular cells. Artery wall as a target of leptin. *Cir Res* 2001; 88: 954-60.

[101] Tintut Y, Alfonso Z, Saini T, Radcliff K, Watson K, Bostrom K, Demer LL. Multilineage potential of cells from the artery wall. *Circulation* 2003; 108: 2505-10.

[102] Yamagishi S, Fujimori H, Yonekura H, Tanaka N, Yamamoto H. Advanced glycation endproducts accelerate calcification in microvascular pericytes. *Biochem Biophys Res Commun* 1999; 258: 353-7.

[103] Schor AM, Canfield AE, Sutton AB, LicBiol EA, Allen TD. Pericyte differentiation. *Clin Ortho Related Res* 1995; 313: 81-91.

[104] Doherty MJ, Ashton BA, Walsh S, Beresford JN, Grant ME, Canfield AE. Vascular pericytes express osteogenic potential in vitro and in vivo. *J Bone Miner Res* 1998; 13: 828-38.

[105] Reilly TM, Seldes R, Luchetti W, Brighton CT. Similarities in the phenotypic expression of pericytes and bone cells. *Clin Ortho Related Res* 1998; 346: 95-103.

[106] Barger AC, Beeuwkes R 3rd, Lainey LL, Silverman KJ. Hypothesis: vasa vasorum and neovascularization of human coronary arteries. A possible role in the pathophysiology of atherosclerosis. *N Engl J Med* 1984; 310: 175-7.

[107] Holmgren L, O'Reilly MS, Folkman J. Dormancy of micrometastases: balanced proliferation and apoptosis in the presence of angiogenesis suppression. *Nature Med* 1995; 1: 149-53.

[108] Carmeliet P, Jain RK. Angiogenesis in cancer and other diseases. *Nature* 2000; 407: 249-57.

[109] Fidler IJ, Ellis LM. The implications of angiogenesis for the biology and therapy of cancer metastasis. *Cell* 1994; 79: 185-8.

[110] Senger DR, van de Water L, Brown LF, Jnagy JA, Yeo KT, Yeo TK, Berse B, Jackman RW, Dvorak AM, Dvorak HF. Vascular permeability factor in tumor biology. *Cancer Metastasis Rev* 1993; 12: 303-24.

[111] Kim KJ, Li B, Winer J, Armanini M, Gillett N, Phillips HS, Ferrara N. Inhibition of vascular endothelial growth factor-induced angiogenesis suppresses tumor growth in vivo. *Nature* 1993; 362: 841-4.

[112] Millauer B, Shawver LK, Plate KH, Risau W, Ullrich A. Glioblastoma growth inhibited in vivo by a dominant-negative Flk-1 mutant. *Nature* 1994; 367: 576-9.

[113] Yamagishi S, Yonekura H, Yamamoto Y, Fujimori H, Sakurai S, et al. Vascular endothelial growth factor acts as a pericyte mitogen under hypoxic conditions. *Lab Invest* 1999; 79: 501-9.

[114] Yamagishi S, Amano S, Inagaki Y, Okamoto T, Takeuchi M, et al. Pigment epithelium-derived factor inhibits leptin-induced angiogenesis by suppressing vascular endothelial growth factor gene expression through anti-oxidative properties. *Microvasc Res* 2003; 65: 186-90.

In: New Angiogenesis Research
Editor: Roberta V. Zubar, pp. 113-129
ISBN 1-59454-239-2

Chapter VI

New Proteins from Snake Venom: Attractive Tools for Studying Angiogenesis

Ammar Gasmi[1] and Jacques Pouysségur[2]
[1]Laboratoire des Venins et Toxines, Institut Pasteur de Tunis, Tunisia
[2]Institute of Signaling, Developmental Biology and Cancer Research Nice, France

I. Abstract

cFour VEGF isoforms (A-D) mediate signaling through three members of the receptor-type tyrosine kinase family called VEGFR-1 (flt-1), VEGFR-2 (KDR) and VEGFR-3 (flt-4). Integrins contribute to the migration, adhesion, and anchorage-dependent survival mechanisms of vascular endothelial cells. They also have been implicated critically in supporting cytokine activation of the MAPK pathway, raising the possibility that $\alpha 1\beta 1$ and/or $\alpha 2\beta 1$ integrins collaborate with VEGF in promoting MAPK activation and angiogenesis. In this chapter, we will present the biochemical and physiological aspects of two groups of new molecules isolated from snake venom that affect angiogenesis. A novel VEGF-like heparin-binding proteins from snake venom capable of increasing capillary permeability were recently described. These proteins form homodimers linked by cysteine disulfide bonds. Each monomer is composed of 110 amino acids including eight cysteine residues and shares about 50% identity with human VEGF-A. Members of this family have been shown to induce strong arterial hypotension in rats and to strongly stimulate proliferation of vascular endothelial cells *in vivo*. They are also shown to be capable of promoting *in vitro* angiogenesis and to induce p42/p44 mitogen-activated protein kinases (MAPKs). All these activities are believed to be mediated through the specific activation of the kinase domain receptor VEGFR-2 (KDR). Besides VEGF-like proteins, the venom of *Viperidae* and *Crotalidaes* snake species contain another class of low molecular weight cystine-rich peptides called disintegrins that are known to be the most potent inhibitors of integrin function. These proteins initially characterized as platelet aggregation inhibitors were recently shown to strongly inhibit angiogenesis by interfering with the adhesion and migration of endothelial cells. Further studies on these new molecules will facilitate our understanding of the physiology and pathophysiology of vascular systems and will be helpful in the design of peptidomimetic inhibitors of angiogenesis in cancer therapy.

Key words: snake venom, angiogenesis, VEGF, integrins

II. Introduction to Angiogenesis

A. VEGF in Angiogenesis

Angiogenesis, a process by which new blood vessels form from pre-existing ones, is an essential process in reproduction, development, and wound repair. Unregulated angiogenesis is associated with many diseases, such as: arthritis, diabetes, ocular vascularization, proliferative retinopathy, tumor growth, and metastasis. Therefore, enhancing revascularization or inhibition of angiogenesis are considered as major targets for development of therapeutic drugs. Angiogenesis can be induced by a variety of growth factors such as VEGF and bFGF (basic fibroblast growth factor) [1,2] and by cell adhesion molecules such as integrins [3,4].

VEGF is a disulfide-linked dimeric glycoprotein, highly specific for vascular endothelial cells (ECs) [5] and was identified as a major mediator of both vasculogenesis and angiogenesis. VEGF is also known to cause permeabilization of blood vessels and to induce proliferation of vascular ECs [6,7]. All cells produce VEGF-A, however tumor cells generally overproduce VEGF, an action which promotes the vascular network necessary to support tumor growth. Inhibition of VEGF activity or VEGF-A has been found to suppress tumor growth in animal models [8]. In growing tumors and in the ischemic retina, hypoxia is the main regulator of VEGF expression through induction of the transcription factor hypoxia-inducible factor -1 [9]._VEGF-A forms several homodimeric molecular species consisting of polypeptides of different sizes generated by alternative splicing of the VEGF messenger RNA [10,11]. VEGF-A monomers of 121, 165, 189 or 206 amino acids are referred to, respectively as VEGF121, VEGF165, VEGF189 and VEGF206. The different VEGF splice variants differ in their ability to interact with heparin. VEGF121 does not bind to heparin, whereas VEGF165, VEGF189 and VEGF206 do with increasing affinity [12]. Loss of the heparin-binding domain results in a significant loss of the mitogenic activity of VEGF [13]. All these splice variants mediate their activities through the three members of the transmembrane receptor-type tyrosine kinase family called VEGFR-1, VEGFR-2 and VEGFR-3. The two first receptors are expressed on the cell surface of most blood ECs. While the third one is largely restricted to lymphatic ECs, the precise function of VEGFR-1 is still under debate [14]. Recent studies indicate, however, that VEGFR-1 is the dominant VEGF receptor on monocytes and is implicated in chemotaxis, tissue factor activation and also signaling and recruitment of stem cells and endothelial precursor cells [15,16,17]. VEGFR-2 is the major receptor, which appears to mediate via activation of intrinsic tyrosine kinase activity most of the VEGF effect. There is evidence to suggest that this receptor plays a role in capillary permeability, angiogenesis, chemotaxis, cell survival, and cell division [18]. VEGFR-3 is the major receptor for lymphatic endothelial cells in terms of mitogenic signaling and differentiation of the lymphatic network [19]. An additionally family of receptors, the neuropilins (NRPs) has also been identified and appear to function as co-receptors in modulating binding to other receptors without being active in signaling. When coexpressed in cells with VEGFR-2, NRP1 enhanced the binding of VEGF165 to VEGFR-2 and regulated angiogenesis through a VEGF-dependent pathway [20,21].

B. Implication of Integrins in Angiogenesis

In addition to cytokines, adhesion receptors belonging to the integrin family promote tumor angiogenesis by mediating cell migration, proliferation and survival of angiogenic ECs. Endothelial cells were shown to express many different integrin adhesion receptors during developmental or post-natal angiogenesis such as:

α1β1, α2β1, α3β1, α4β1, α5β1, α6β1, α6β4, α8β1, α9β1, αvβ1, αvβ3, αvβ5, and αvβ8 [22,23]. Some of these molecules are highly expressed on neovascular ECs and may emerge as a novel target for anti-angiogenic drugs [24]. αvβ3, an integrin upregulated in angiogenic ECs was the first to be described to be associated with tumor angiogenesis [25]. The implication of this integrin and also of αvβ5 in the positive regulation of angiogenesis was demonstrated by the fact that pharmacological agents directed against these integrins block the growth of new blood vessels on chick chorioallantoic membrane (CAM) induced by bFGF [4]. However, in contrast to previous reports, genetic deletion studies have recently shown that mice lacking αv integrins can support developmental angiogenesis and that neither αvβ3 nor αvβ5 integrins are required for this angiogenesis [26]. It was suggested that these integrins exert an inhibitor effect on angiogenesis by suppressing VEGFR-1 and VEGFR-2 mediated EC survival, by trans-dominantly blocking other integrins or by mediating the antiangiogenic activity of thrombospondins and other inhibitors of angiogenesis [27,28]. Further studies will be necessary to elucidate the precise molecular mechanisms of the involvement of these integrins in angiogenesis. This is important in determining rational strategies for any anti-angiogenic approach.

Results on other integrins in angiogenesis are not discrepant and several have been shown to be implicated in angiogenesis. Experiments revealed that genetic or pharmacological inhibition of expression or function of the collagen receptors, integrins α1β1 and α2β1, and of the integrin α5β1 and its ligand fibronectin clearly suppress angiogenesis [29,30,31,32]. The role of other vascular integrins such as α8β1, αvβ8 or α6β4 in tumor angiogenesis remains to be further clarified [24].

III. Snake Venom Proteins

Snake venom represents an extraordinary source of biological molecules. Many of these proteins have been highly purified and characterized. Besides the specific toxins affecting several aspects of nerve conduction, there are peptides and proteins with or without catalytic activity that have been shown to affect the vessel wall, platelets and blood coagulation. These proteins that are known to produce activating or inactivating effects on many of the various interactions of the hemostatic system may be employed to aid our understanding of basic biological mechanisms involved in heamostasis [33,34]. The human hemostatic system is based on a number of complicated interactions involving blood proteins, platelets, ECs, and the subendothelial structure. Their role, coordinated by a series of chemical signals, is mutually dependent. The bite of snakes can result in severe and various symptoms. It has been known that in general, venom of the *Elapidae* and *Hydrophiidae* families of snakes are recognized to be highly neurotoxic, causing death by blocking neuromuscular transmission. Whereas the venom proteins from the *Viperidae* family cause shock, intravascular clotting, systemic and local hemorrhage, edema, necrosis but also local vasodilatation, increased vascular permeability, and hypotension are usual responses elicited by snakebite envenomations.

Among the proteins contributing to the various symptoms of envenoming, many permeability factors have been identified. They are crucial for rapid dissemination of the toxins into the general circulation of the prey, and target blood capillaries by inducing an increase in their permeability and resulting in a hypotensive effect. These proteins have been extensively studied and are bradykinin potentiating serine proteases, responsible both for the conversion of angiotensin I into angiotensin II and for release of bradykinin from kininogen [35,36], or phospholipases A2 which induce a degranulation of mast cells and a release of histamine [37]. Recently, an additional set of selected molecules from snake venom that are able to permeabilize the vasculature and to solicit a strong hypotensive effect has been described. These proteins purified from snake venom after different chromatographic steps, in a relatively high yield (0.2%-0.6% of total venom proteins), were shown to be structurally related to the VEGF-A. They constitute novel members of the family of VEGF-like growth factors. We will classify these proteins under the group of snake venom VEGFs. Studies into their biological activities revealed a potent capacity to induce EC growth and angiogenesis, and thus make them very useful and attractive tools for studying vascular biology.

Another group of proteins called disintegrins have been purified from snake venom. These proteins are small molecular integrin antagonists that suppress angiogenesis and tumor progression in many animal models. They are present in viper venom in high amounts and were initially reported to be inhibitors of platelet aggregation due to antagonizing fibrinogen binding to platelet glycoprotein IIb/IIIa. They have now been shown to competitively inhibit the binding of adhesive ligands to a variety of integrin receptors of the β1 and β3 families [38,39]. Integrins have been shown to be involved in cell-cell and cell-substratum interactions. They serve as receptors for extracellular matrix proteins such as fibronectin, fibrinogen, vitronectin, collagen and laminin [40]. Disintegrins have received a great deal of attention and are being used in pre-clinical research to examine their possible therapeutic potential.

IV. Snake Venom VEGFs

A. Composition of the Group

Snake venom VEGFs include a group of proteins with a very potent capacity to stimulate capillary permeability as measured by the Miles assay [41]. The permeability test involves intradermal injection of purified snake venom protein to mice and measurement of the leakage of Evan's blue dye into the extravascular space. Several proteins belonging to this family have been recently isolated from snake venom. These proteins are the hypotensive factor (HF) present in *Vipera aspis aspis* venom [42], increasing capillary permeability protein (ICPP) purified from *Vipera lebetina* venom [43,44], Vammin and VR1 [45] described in the venom of *Vipera ammodytes ammodytes* and *Daboia russelli russelli*, respectively. Another protein, named svVEGF (snake venom VEGF) was subcloned from a cDNA sequence obtained from a cDNA library of venom glands from the snake *Bothrops insularis*. The recombinant protein expressed in *E. coli* was biologically characterized by its ability to increase vascular permeability [46].

B. Structure of Snake Venom VEGFs and Comparison with Human VEGF-A

Snake venom VEGFs is a family of disulfide linked homodimers of about 25 kD. Each monomer, with the N-terminal blocked by pyroglutamic acid, is composed of 110 aminoacids, 8 of which are cysteines with spacing identical to VEGF-A. The second and the fourth cysteine residues are involved in interchain disulfide bonds, whereas, Cys(1)-Cys(6), Cys(3)-Cys(7) and Cys(5)-Cys(8) form three intramolecular disulfide bonds [47]. Figure 1 shows the alignment of amino acid sequences of the different members of snake venom VEGFs and a segment of human VEGF165. Comparison of the sequences reveals that snake venom VEGFs exhibits high identity between themselves with a value of about 95% and display 50 % similarity with the N-terminal region of human VEGF165. It is also interesting to note that most of the important residues implicated in receptor binding, identified by site directed mutagenesis or examination of the crystal structure of human VEGF, are highly conserved [47,48]. Some of these residues are, however, not conserved as is the case of Glu67, a negatively charged residue, His86, Gln89 and Ile91 in human VEGF-A. These amino acids are replaced by Lys55, Arg74, Ser77 and Lys79 in snake venom VEGFs, a group including 3 positively charged residues. Another difference concerns Tyr25 in VEGF165 which is replaced by Ala or Val in snake venom VEGFs. An alanine mutation at this position was recently shown to be crucial in Flt-1 binding without affecting KDR binding [49]. These observations in important variation in charges and in some amino acids between mammalian and snake venom VEGFs may be explained by a unique and specific receptor selectivity for this group.

Moreover, some other notable structural differences were clearly identified. They concern the absence in snake venom VEGFs of asparagine linked glycosylation sites defined by the consensus sequence NXS/T and the absence of any similarity with the heparin-binding domain of VEGF. The precise role of glycosylation in the bioactivity of VEGF165 remains to be elucidated and studies into snake venom VEGFs may allow us to dissect this role [13]. Members of snake venom VEGFs were tested for their binding activity to heparin and found to have a relatively weak affinity for heparin-Sepharose. On these affinity columns, HF and SvVEGF were eluted with 0.3 M NaCl [42,46]. Under the same conditions, VEGF165 was reported to elute in the presence of 0.9 M NaCl [10]. The high negative charge density of heparin suggests that any specific heparin-binding site must have an excess of positive charges. The heparin-binding activity of VEGF has been localized to the carboxyl-terminal 55 residues of VEGF165, residues 111-165. The domain contains repeated Lys and Arg residues and is highly basic. It also contains 8 cysteine residues that form four disulfides bonds. Removal of this domain does not affect significantly the affinity of VEGF for its receptors, but is associated with a significant loss in bioactivity.

```
                         10          20          30          40          50
Vasp HF        1 <EVRPFLEVHERSACQARETLVSILQEYPDEISDIFRPSCVAVLRCSGCCTDESLKC
Vleb ICPP      1 <EVRPFPDVYQRSACQARETLVSILQEYPDEISDIFRPSCVAVLRCSGCCTDESLKC
Vamm Vammin    1 <EVRPFLEVHERSACQARETLVPILQEYPDEISDIFRPS-VAVLRCSGCCTDESMKC
Drus VR-1      1 <EVRPFLDVYQRSACQTRETLVSILQEHPDEISDIFRPSCVAVLRCSGCCTDESMKC
Bins svVEGF   25  QVMPFMEVYRHSVCQTRETLVSILEEHPDEVSHIFRPSCVTALRCGGCCTDESLKC
Bjar svVEGF   25  QVMPFMEVYRHSVCQPRETLVSILEEYPGEISHIFRPSCVTALRCGGCCTDESLEC
Hum VEGF      12 HEVVKFMDVYQRSYCHPIETLVDIFQEYPDEIEYIFKPSCVPLMRCGGCCNDEGLEC
                       20          30          40          50          60

              60          70          80          90          100
Vasp HF       TPVGKHTVDLQIMRVNPRTQSSKMEVMKFTEHTACECRPRRKQGEPD-----GPKE-KPR
Vleb ICPP     TPVGKHTVDMQIMRVNPRTQSSKMEVMKFTEHTACECRPRRKQGEPD-----GPKE-KPR
Vamm Vammin   TPVGKHTVDLQIMRVNPRTQSSKMEVMKFTEHTACECRPRRKQGEPD-----GPKE-KPR
Drus VR-1     TPVGKHTADIQIMRMNPRTHSSKMEVMKFMEHTACECRPRWKQGEPE-----GPKE--PR
Bins svVEGF   TATGKRSVGREIMRVDPHKGTSKTEVMQFTEHTDCECRPRSASGVNSRKHKRNPEEGEPRAKFPFV
Bjar svVEGF   TATGKRSVGREIMRLSPHKGTSEKEVMQFTEHTDCECRPRSASGVNSRKHKRNPEEGEPRAKFPFV
Hum VEGF      VPTEESNITMQIMRIKPHQGQHIGE-MSFLQHNKCECRPKKDRARQE--NPCGPCS-ERRKHLFVQ......55 residues....
               70   ▲     80        90          100           110 $heparin binding domain
```

Fig. 1 : Alignment of the amino acid sequences of the different snake venom VEGFs with that of human VEGF165 (P15692). HF [42], ICPP [44], vammin and VR-1 [45] were purified from *V. aspis aspis, V. lebetina, V. ammodytes ammodytes* and *D. russelli russelli*, respectively. The primary structure of svVEGF [46] was deduced from the nucleotide sequence of a cDNA clone isolated by screening the venomous gland cDNA library of the snake *B. insularis*. VEGF residues identified by site directed mutagenesis as being important for receptor binding are in bold [48]. Residues implicated in Flk-1/KDR binding (fœtal liver kinase/kinase insert domain containing receptor) along with the VEGF crystal structure are underlined [47]. The cysteines are boxed. Heparin binding domain (italic 55 residues). ▲ glycosylation site of VEGF.

We examined the different sequences of snake venom VEGFs for the distribution of acidic and basic amino acids. It is of note that a majority of acidic residues are concentrated in the N-terminal sequence of these proteins (Residues 1-54), whereas, a majority of basic residues are concentrated in the C-terminal parts of these molecules (Residues 55-98). Determination of the theoretical pI of ICPP a member of snake venom VEGFs with the Expasy Molecular Biology Server [50] showed a value of 8.47. The same program showed values of a pI of 7.94, 5.20 and 9.58 for VEGF165, VEGF120 and heparin binding domain (VEGF55), respectively. For the different parts of ICPP the pI were estimated to be 4.51 for residues 1-54, and 9.73 for residues 55-110. A molecular model of ICPP based on the crystal structure of VEGF1-98 [47] shows a similar folding and backbone structure for these proteins (unpublished data). The electrostatic potential gradient at the molecular surfaces clearly show a negative surface at the N-terminal part of ICPP and a positive surface at the C-terminal part of the molecule. For VEGF120 only a negative surface was seen. These observations suggest that the C-terminal part of snake venom VEGFs containing clusters of basic amino acids that probably harbor the heparin binding site for the acidic groups of heparin, whereas, the N-terminal regions of these molecules may interact with VEGF receptors. To establish exactly how snake venom VEGFs such as ICPP interact with VEGFR-2 and heparin more work on the structure/function relationships needs to be carried out and may require determination of the crystal structure of the complexes.

C. Effect of Snake Venom VEGFs on Angiogenesis

VEGF, a key regulator of physiological angiogenesis is also implicated in pathological angiogenesis associated with tumors but also in vascular permeability and EC survival. *In vitro*, VEGF causes microvascular ECs grown on 3D collagen gels to invade the underlying matrix and to form capillary-like tubules [5]. Members of snake venom VEGFs were tested for their effect on angiogenesis and compared to VEGF165. ICPP, a protein of this family was tested for its capacity to induce angiogenesis in two *in vitro* systems, growth and differentiation of mouse vascular ECs and DNA proliferation of human umbilical vascular endothelial cells HUVEC [44]. The first *in vitro* system exploited to assess ICPP-induced angiogenesis shows the capacity of a cytokine to promote the proliferation of embryonic vascular endothelial cell precursors and their capacity to differentiate into a vascular network. ICPP was found to be a potent molecule, which like VEGF, can induce a vascular-like network positive for the vascular specific marker CD31 after 12 days of differentiation. Although this assay did not allow accurate quantitation, ICPP at 10 ng/ml, was always found to be more potent than VEGF165 (10 ng/ml) in establishing a differentiated vascular network. The second *in vitro* system using HUVEC has shown that serum starved HUVEC are able to reinitiate DNA synthesis in response to VEGF165 or ICPP. DNA synthesis was stimulated 2-fold above basal with VEGF165 and 3-fold above basal with ICPP. Further preliminary studies performed with an ICPP antibody demonstrated cross reactivity between ICPP and VEGF165. Reinitiation of DNA synthesis in response to ICPP or VEGF165 was shown to be neutralized by F(ab')2 specific for ICPP, purified by affinity chromatography on ICPP covalently coupled to a CNBr-activated sepharose column. F(ab')2 fragments were obtained from anti-venom containing almost pure F(ab')2 plasma fractions which has been prepared in horse with *Vipera lebetina* venom and purified after ammonium sulfate precipitation and pepsin digestion (unpublished data). Other members of snake venom VEGFs were reported to strongly stimulate cultured vascular ECs *in vitro* and to have a potent mitogenic effect. The bioactivity of HF was tested with different cell types and found to affect only the growth of ECs [42]. Using bovine aortic ECs (BAEC), the percentages increase in cell growth with 10 nM of HF (final concentration) was approximately 150 to 210 % compared to the control. The cell growth induced by HF was however reported to be inhibited in the presence cycloheximide or a high concentration of heparin [42]. The growth factor activity of vammin was analyzed on cultured vascular ECs and found to induce endothelial proliferation at a level of about 266% compared to the control, while VEGF165 induced endothelial proliferation under the same condition at a level of about 190% [45]. Interestingly, snake venom VEGFs are usually found to induce more potent bioactivity than VEGF165.

D. Implication of VEGFR-2 Signaling in Snake Venom VEGFs Activities

The biological effects of VEGF-A are mediated by two receptor tyrosine kinases, VEGFR-1 and VEGFR-2. VEGFR-3 is a member of the same family of receptors but its biological activity is mediated via VEGF-C and VEGF-D [14]. In addition to these receptors, VEGF-A interacts with a family of coreceptors, the neuropilins. Members of snake venom VEGFs were found to induce potently angiogenesis but also to increase capillary permeability, and to enhance EC mitogenecity and MAP kinase activation. Studies of the receptors involved in these activities were performed by assays using VEGF receptor inhibitors or receptor binding ligands. The requirement for VEGF receptor signaling in transduction of a biological response to ICPP was demonstrated using a VEGF receptor tyrosine kinase inhibitor, an antagonist that can selectively inhibit the kinase activity associated with VEGFR-2 and VEGFR-1. The inhibitor used in the study is a molecule belonging to the anilinocinnoline family of compounds, referred as VTKI for VEGF receptor

Tyrosine Kinase Inhibitor. In isolated enzyme assays, VTKI was described to be a potent inhibitor of VEGFR-2 tyrosine kinase with submicromolar activity versus the kinase activity of VEGFR-1. In comparison to its inhibitory activity versus VEGFR-2 tyrosine kinase, VTKI demonstrated >2000- fold selectivity versus that associated with FGFR1 and EGFR-2. Results have shown that the mitogenic action of ICPP or VEGF is fully suppressed by VTKI. Moreover, ICPP-induced growth and differentiation was fully suppressed by the addition of this inhibitor suggesting that ICPP and VEGF use the same receptor system for *in vitro* angiogenesis [44].

More recently, the interactions between VEGF receptors and other snake venom VEGFs have been studied using a receptor-ligand binding protocol performed with surface plasmon resonance assay (SPR). Data clearly indicate that vammin, VR-1 and HF, snake venom VEGFs, bound to KDR-IgG with an equal affinity as to VEGF165. The same proteins were shown not to be able to interact with the other receptors of VEGF, Flt-1, Flt-4 or neuropilin-1 [45]. These finding prove that these factors exert their mitogenic, angiogenic and permeability-enhancing activities through the specific activation of KDR (VEGFR-2). Moreover, these results provide evidence that snake venom VEGFs are novel members of the family of VEGF-like growth factors.

V. Snake Venom Disintegrins

A. Different groups of Disintegrins

Disintegrins are derived proteolytically from the PII and PIII class of snake venom metalloproteinases composed of pre pro-metalloproteinase, disintegrin, and cysteine rich PIII domains [51,52]. Since the early characterization of the first two disintegrins, trigramin from the venom of *Trimeresurus gramineus* [53] and echistatin from *Echis carinatus* [54] close to 50 disintegrins have been isolated from viper and rattlesnake over the last decade, and their primary structures have been elucidated. They are a functionally homologous group of polypeptides, which may be divided into five groups according to their polypeptide length and number of disulfide bonds. They include , short-chain disintegrins, composed of 49-51 residues and four disulfide bonds such as echistatin and eristostatin [55,56], medium-chain disintegrins, containing approx. 70 amino acids and six disulfides bonds including triflavin [55], trigramin [53] and barbourin [57], and long-chain protein represented by bitistatin and salmosin, with 84-residues cross-linked by seven disulfide bonds [58,59]. The disintegrin domains of PIII snake-venom metalloproteinases with 100 amino acids including 16 cysteines residues, and the homodimeric and heterodimeric disintegrins like contortrostatin [60] and lebein [61] constitute the fourth and the fifth group, respectively.

B. Structure of Disintegrins

Most disintegrins are rich in disulfide bonds and contain a reactive RGD sequence in the carboxyl-terminal half of the molecule which is essential to their ability to block integrin interaction with ligand [62,63]. An exception to this is that the RGD motif has been shown to be substituted, in the A and B subunits of the dimeric disintegrin EC3 from *Echis carinatus suchoreki* venom, by VGD and MLD, respectively [64]. The inhibitory activity of EC3 towards α4 integrins is associated with the MLD sequence of its B subunit. The A subunit of EC3 contains a VGD motif, and the ability of EC3 to inhibit α5β1 resides in both subunits [64]. Another heterodimeric disintegrin, EMF10 isolated from *Eristocophis macmahomi* venom is an extremely potent and selective inhibitor of integrin α5β1. The selective recognition of α5β1 by EMF-10 is associated with the MGD sequence, a motif located in the active loop of the B subunit [65]. For CC8, an heterodimeric disintegrin isolated from the venom of *Cerastes cerastes*, the presence of a WGD motif has been reported to increase the inhibitory activity of this protein on αIIβ3, αvβ3 and α5β1 integrins [66]. Other disintegrins have been reported to have different motifs such as Barbourin, isolated from *Sistrurus m. barbouri* and for atrolysin E/D, purified from *Crotalus atrox* the motif RGD is replaced by KGD and MVD, respectively [57,67]. Disintegrins may also have an RGD motif in their sequences but do not act in an RGD-dependant manner. This is the case of lebein a newly discovered hetrodimeric disintegrin from *Vipera lebetina* venom [61] which was shown to interact with laminin-binding β1 integrins in a divalent cation-dependent and RGD-independent manner both *in vitro* and *in vivo* [68]. Through the potential to inhibit integrin-mediated cell attachment to laminins, lebein may be a valuable tool to influence laminin-dependent cell functions. These cell functions are of importance in complex physiological processes such as wound healing and tumor invasion. The amino acid sequences of several disintegrins are shown in Fig: 2. The specificity of disintegrins is due to their disulfide-bonding framework and specific amino acids in intercysteine loops. The high content of disulfide bonds plays a vital role in their stability and imposes distinct folding on the protein, with a specific orientation of the loop regions [69]. Furthermore, the crystal structure of trimestatin, a disintegrin found in snake venom and containing the cell adhesion recognition motif RGD, indicates that in addition to the RGD motif, the C-terminal region of the molecule is another potential binding site to integrin receptors [70].

```
               1        10        20        30        40        50        60        70        80
Obtustatin     ----------------------------CTTGPCCRQCKLKPAGTTCW--KTSLTSHYCTGKSCDCPLYPG---------
Echistatin     ---------------------------ECESGPCCRNCKFLKEGTICKRARGDDMDDYCNGKTCDCPRNPHKGPAT----
Triflavin      --GEECDCGSPSNPCCDAATCKLRPGAQCADGLCCDQCRFKKKRTICRIARGDFPDDRCTGQSADCPRWNGL--------
Salmosin       EAGEECDCGSPGNPCCDAATCKLRQGAQCAEGLCCDQCRFMKEGTICRRARGDDLDDYCNGISAGCPRNPFHA-------
Rhodostomin    -MGKECDCSSPENPCCDAATCKLRPGAQCGEGLCCEQCKFSRAGKICRIPRGDMPDDRCTGQSADCPRYHRR--------
Trimestatin    --GEECDCGSPSNPCCDAATCKLRPGAQCADGLCCDQCRFKKKRTICRIARGDFPDDRCTGQSADCPRWNGL--------
Contortrostatin--------DAPANPCCDAATCKLTTGSQCADGLCCDQCKFMKEGTVCRRARGDDLDDYCNGISAGCPRNPFH--------
EMF10A         --------MNSANPCCDPITCKPKKGEHCVSGPCCRNCKFLNPGTICKKGRGDNLNDYCTGVSSDCPRNPWKSEEED---
EMF10B         -----ELLQNSGNPCCDPVTCKPRRGEHCVSGPCCDNCKFLNAGTVCWPAMGDWNDDYCTGISSDCPRNPVFK-------
EC3 A          ---------NSVHPCCDPVKCEPREGEHCISGPCCRNCKFLRAGTNCKRAVGDDVDDYCSGITPDCPRNRYKGKED----
EC3 B          ---------NSVHPCCDPVKCEPREGEHCISGPCCRNCKFLNAGTICKRAMLDGLNDYCTGKSSDCPRNRYKGDED----
Lebein A       ---------NSGNPCCDPVTCKPRRGEHCVSGPCCRNCKFLNAGTICNRARGDDMNDYCTGISSDCPRNPYKD-------
Lebein B       ---------NSGNPCCDPVTCKPRRGWHCVSNPCCDNCKFMRAGTICNRARGDDMNDYCTGISSDCPRNPYKD-------
```

Fig. 2: Primary structure of members of snake venom disintegrins reported to affect angiogenesis. Among these proteins obtustatin (P83469) and echistatin (P17347) belong to the short-size disintegrins, Triflavin (P21859), Salmosin 2 (O93517), rhodostomin (AAA57568) and Trimestatin (1J2LA) are medium-size disintegrins and Contortrostatin (Q91AB0), EC3 (P81630, P81631), EM10 (P81742, P81743) and Lebein (P83253, P83254) are dimeric disintegrins. The sequences were obtained from the Swissprot databank and the accession numbers are indicated. The cysteines are boxed.

C. Effect of Disintegrins on Angiogenesis and their Mechanisms of Action

A large number of disintegrins have been shown to efficiently inhibit angiogenesis *in vitro* and *in vivo*, and may have clinical potential. Triflavin, an RGD containing peptide purified from *Trimeresurus flavoviridis* venom was reported to inhibit angiogenesis induced by TNF (α) in CAM. The relative activitiy of triflavin has a more powerful inhibitory effect than the anti-αvβ3 integrin monoclonal antibody on angiogenesis and in HUVEC adhesion and migration *in vitro* [71]. Accutin, purified from *Agkistrodon acutus* was shown to exhibit an effective antiangiogenic effect *in vivo* when assayed by using the 10-day-old embryo chick CAM model [72]. Salmosin, isolated from *Agkistrodon halys brevicaudus* was reported to disrupt *in vivo* angiogenesis in the chorioallantoic membrane induced with bFGF [73] and to inhibit the proliferation of B16F10 melanoma cells [74]. Contortrostatin obtained from *Agkistrodon contortrix contortrix* inhibits angiogenesis in breast cancer [75], and rhodostomin identified in the venom of *Calloselasma rhodostoma*, was reported to inhibit distinct steps in angiogenesis elicited by bFGF, and also to suppress *in vivo* murine melanoma tumor growth [76]. All these snake venom-derived disintegrins were shown to have antiangiogenesis potential presumably via selective blocking of αvβ3 integrins expressed on vascular ECs. However, recent data revealed that mice lacking β3 integrins or both β3 and β5 integrins not only support tumorogenesis, but as well have enhanced tumor growth [27,28]. This apparent paradox highlights the need for further evaluation of integrins as regulators of angiogenesis and of the mechanism of action of αv-integrin antagonists.

Other members of the disintegrin family have different mechanisms of action. A novel non RGD disintegrin, obtustatin [77], purified from the venom of *Vipera lebetina obtusa* and presenting some structural differences to the previously reported proteins was shown to be a potent and selective inhibitor of the α1β1 integrin *in vitro* and of angiogenesis *in vivo* suggesting novel approaches to the generation of angiogenesis inhibitors. Obustatin potently inhibited angiogenesis *in vivo* in the CAM assay, and in the Lewis lung syngeneic mouse model. The critical role of integrin α1β1 in VEGF-driven angiogenesis in the dermis has been established. This integrin provides critical support for vascular endothelial growth factor signaling, EC migration, and tumor angiogenesis [78]. More recently, another non RGD disintegrin like protein, alternagin-C, purified from the venom of the *Bothrops alternatus* was reported to be capable of triggering human neutrophil chemotaxis modulated by intracellular signals [79]. The activity of alternagin-C could be related to an ECD amino acid motif present in its sequence. Alternagin-C was also shown in a further report to interact with the major collagen I receptor, the α2β1 integrin, inhibiting collagen binding, to induce VEGF expression and to strongly activate Akt/PKB phosphorylation, a signaling event involved in endothelial survival and angiogenesis. The authors concluded that alternagin-C acts as a survival factor, promoting adhesion and EC proliferation [80]. The identification of new motifs could help to establish a correlation between sequences and integrin selectivity of these proteins.

In addition to the previously described activities members of disintegrins were shown to potently induce apoptosis. Integrin-mediated cell adhesion is necessary for the survival of many types of cells, and loss of adhesion causes apoptosis [6]. The mechanism by which disintegrin causes endothelial apoptosis remain, however, unclear. Wu and collaborators [81] have used rhodostomin in order to elucidate this phenomenon. The authors concluded that disintegrin-induced apoptosis is caused by a blockade of the endothelial integrin αnuβ3 and is also accompanied by a change in shape and the presence of mechanical stretches among cells. Disintegrins have been found to be effective anti-adhesion and anti-invasion agents for a number of different tumor systems. They bind to integrins on the surface of many cell types. From a medical point of view, the possibility that such studies may lead to the characterization of new integrin antagonists could be particularly important.

VI. Conclusion

Blood vessels provide an essential nutritive function for all tissues, particularly important during growth and repair of tissues but can also contribute to the pathology such as in tissue ischemia or cancer. The process of tumor metastasis is a complex cascade of events, including invasion, intravasation, and extravasation from the circulatory system, colonization, and finally angiogenesis at a distant site. In this chapter an attempt has been made to show the structural and biological characteristics of many snake venom proteins belonging to the snake venom VEGFs and disintegrins and reported to be able to stimulate or inhibit angiogenesis. The discovery in snake venom of these proteins has stirred growing interest because of their potential therapeutic application. Appropriate molecules could be useful in suppressing the growth of new blood vessels in tumors, or in promoting therapeutic angiogenesis during wound healing or limb ischemia.

The recently discovered snake venom VEGFs exhibit amino acid sequences sharing identities with members of the VEGF family. They were shown to strongly increase capillary permeability in mice, induce proliferation of human ECs, promote *in vitro* angiogenesis and stimulate MAP kinases. Interestingly, the biological activities of members of snake venom VEGFs were found to be at least as potent as those induced by VEGF165. However, it is important to note that there is a marked difference in the receptors specificity between VEGF165 and snake venom VEGFs. The different biological functions of snake venom VEGFs were shown to be specifically mediated through VEGFR-2 receptor signaling and, in contrast to VEGF165, studies indicated that these proteins did not interact with the others VEGF receptors VEGFR-1, VEGFR-3 and neuropilin-1. The similar structure and bioactivities of snake venom VEGFs compared to VEGF but altered receptor specificity represents a novel potentially candidate for therapeutic use.

Snake venom disintegrins are potent and selective inhibitors of tumor cell metastasis and angiogenesis as demonstrated by experimental data obtained *in vitro* and in animal models. The antiangiogenic activity *in vivo* and *in vitro* of the most studied RGD disintegrins is thought to be related to the selective blockade of the receptor integrin αvβ3 on ECs. They interfere with the anchorage-dependent survival mechanism of the vascular ECs, and the mobility of the cells. However, in a recent report, genetic ablation of the genes encoding this integrin failed to block angiogenesis and in some cases even enhanced it [28]. A more thorough understanding of the precise mechanisms of action of these inhibitors in angiogenesis is required. For the non-RGD disintegrins obtustatin and alternagin-C, their mechanism of action has been clearly outlined by their antagonism to α1β1 and α2β1, respectively. Integrins α1β1 and α2β1 were reported to provide critical support not only for EC migration but also for VEGF signal transduction in the collagen-rich matrix of skin.

Antagonism of $\alpha1\beta1$ or $\alpha2\beta1$ suppressed VEGF-driven dermal angiogenesis. Moreover, *in vivo* studies carried out by several groups clearly indicated that disintegrins are safe at clinically effective doses in animals and can be infused without detriment effect on vascular or endothelial function [82,83]. As to futur experiments, it will be interesting to look for any synergistic effects of different disintegrins having different mechanisms of action on the inhibition of angiogenesis and metastasis.

The discovery of multiple new angiogenic regulatory factors is clearly leading to a new understanding of the molecular basis of blood vessel development. Both the induction and inhibition of angiogenesis can have therapeutic benefits in various patholological conditions. Hopefully, in the coming years, we will learn more about the interesting and complicated mechanism of action of these molecules and we will develop effective applications for a number of these agents in the treatment of human disorders including coronary heart disease, critical limb ischemia or cancer.

References

[1] Folkman J, Shing Y. Angiogenesis. *J Biol Chem* 1992;267:10931-4

[2] Yancopoulos GD, Davis S, Gale NW, Rudge JS, Wiegand SJ, Holash J. Vascular-specific growth factors and blood vessel formation. *Nature* 2000;407:242-8

[3] Meredith JE, Fazelli B, Schwartz MA. The extracellular matrix as a cell survival factor. *Mol Biol Cell* 1993;4:953-61

[4] Friedlander M, Brooks PC, Shaffer RW, Kincaid CM, Varner JA, Cheresh DA. Definition of two angiogenic pathways by distinct alpha v integrins. *Science* 1995;27:1500-2

[5] Ferrara N, Henzel WJ. Pituitary follicular cells secrete a novel heparin-binding growth factor specific for vascular endothelial cells. *Biochem Biophys Res Commun* 1989;161:851-8

[6] Folkman J, Klagsbrun M. Angiogenic factors. *Science* 1987;235:442-7

[7] Carmeliet P. Mechanisms of angiogenesis and arteriogenesis. *Nat Med* 2000;6:389-95

[8] Ferrara N. Role of vascular endothelial growth factor in regulation of physiological angiogenesis. *AM J Physiol Cell Physiol* 2001;280:C1358-C1366

[9] Sheweiki D, Itin A, Soffer D, Keshet E. Vascular endothelial growth factor induced by hypoxia may mediate hypoxia-initiated angiogenesis. *Nature* 1992;359:843-5

[10] Houck KA, Ferrara N, Winer J, Cachianes G, Li B, Leung DW. The vascular endothelial growth factor family: identification of a fourth molecular species and characterization of alternative splicing of RNA. *Mol Endocrinol* 1991;5:1806-14

[11] Tischer E, Mitchell R, Hartman T *et al.* The human gene for vascular endothelial growth factor. Multiple protein forms are encoded through alternative exon splicing. *J Biol Chem* 1991;266:11947-54

[12] Houck KA, Leung DW, Rowland AM, Winer J, Ferrara N. Dual regulation of vascular endothelial growth factor bioavailability by genetic and proteolytic mechanisms. *J Biol Chem* 1992;267:26031-7

[13] Keyt BA, Berleau LT, Nguyen HV *et al.* The carboxyl-terminal domain (111-165) of vascular endothelial growth factor is critical for its mitogenic potency. *J Biol Chem* 1996;271:7788-95

[14] Ferrara N, Gerber PH, LeCouter. The biology of VEGF and its receptors. *J Nat Med* 2003;9:669-76

[15] Hattori K, Heissig B, Wu Y *et al.* Placental growth factor reconstitutes hematopoiesis by recruiting VEGFR1(+) stem cells from bone-marrow microenvironment. *Nat Med* 2002;8:841-9

[16] Luttun A, Tjwa M, Moons L *et al.* Revascularization of ischemic tissues by PlGF treatment, and inhibition of tumor angiogenesis, arthritis and atherosclerosis by anti-Flt1. *Nat Med.* 2002;8:831-40

[17] LeCouter J, Moritz DR, Li B *et al.* Angiogenesis-independent endothelial protection of liver: role of VEGFR-1. *Science* 2003;299:890-3

[18] Matsumoto T, Claesson-Welsh L. VEGF receptor signal transduction. *Sci STKE* 2001;112, RE21

[19] Karkkainen MJ, Makinen T, Alitalo K. Lymphatic endothelium: a new frontier of metastasis research. *Nat Cell Biol* 2002;4:E2-E5

[20] Soker S, Takashima S, Miao H, Neufeld G, Klagsbrun M. Neuropilin-1 is expressed by endothelial and tumor cells as an isoform-specific receptor for vascular endothelial growth factor. *Cell* 1998;92:735-45

[21] Neufeld G, Cohen T, Shraga N, Lange T, Kessler O, Herzog Y. The neuropilins: multifunctional semaphorin and VEGF receptors that modulate axon guidance and angiogenesis. *Trends Cardiovasc Med* 2002;12:13-9

[22] Rupp PA, Little CD. Integrins in vascular development. *Circ Res* 2001; 89:566-572

[23] Bouvard D, Brakebusch C, Gustafsson E *et al.* Functional consequence of integrin gene mutations in mice. *Circ Res* 2001; 89:211-23

[24] Dormand O, Ruegg C. Regulation of endothelial cell integrin function and angiogenesis by COX-2, cAMP and Protein Kinase A. *Thromb Haemost* 2003;90:577-85

[25] Brooks PC, Clark RA, Cheresh DA. Requirement of vascular integrin alpha v beta 3 for angiogenesis. *Science* 1994;264:569-571

[26] Bader BL, Rayburn H, Crowley D, Hynes RO. Extensive vasculogenesis, angiogenesis, and organogenesis precede lethality in mice lacking all alpha v integrins. *Cell* 1998;95:507-19

[27] Hynes RO. A reevaluation of integrins as regulators of angiogenesis. *Nat Med* 2002;8:918-21

[28] Reynolds LE, Wyder L, Lively JC *et al.* Enhanced pathological angiogenesis in mice lacking beta3 integrin or beta3 and beta5 integrins. *Nat Med* 2002;8:27-34

[29] Yang JT, Rayburn H, Hynes RO. Embryonic mesodermal defects in alpha 5 integrin-deficient mice. *Development* 1993;119:1093-105

[30] Kim S, Bell K, Mousa SA, Varner JA. Regulation of angiogenesis *in vivo* by ligation of integrin alpha5beta1 with the central cell-binding domain of fibronectin. *Am J Pathol* 2000;156:1345-62

[31] Senger DR, Claffey KP, Benes JE, Perruzzi CA, Sergiou AP, Detmar M. Angiogenesis promoted by vascular endothelial growth factor: regulation through alpha1beta1 and alpha2beta1 integrins. *Proc Natl Acad Sci USA* 1997;94:13612-7

[32] Pozzi A, Moberg PE, Miles LA, Wagner S, Soloway P, Gardner HA. Elevated matrix metalloprotease and angiostatin levels in integrin alpha 1 knockout mice cause reduced tumor vascularization. *Proc Natl Acad Sci USA* 2000;97:2202-7

[33] Markland FS. Snake venom and the hemostatic system. *Toxicon* 1998;36:1749-1800

[34] Stocker K. In Medical Use of Snake Venom Proteins, ed. K. F. Stocker, 1990; pp. 33-56. CRC Press, Boca Raton.

[35] Utaisincharoen P, Mackessy SP, Miller RA, Tu AT. Complete primary structure and biochemical properties of gilatoxin, a serine protease with kallikrein-like and angiotensin-degrading activities. *J Biol Chem* 1993;268:21975-83

[36] Shimokawa K, Takahashi H. Some properties of a capillary permeability-increasing enzyme-2 from the venom of *Agkistrodon caliginosus* (Kankoku-Mamushi). *Toxicon* 1993;31:1221-7

[37] Chiu HF, Chen IJ, Teng CM. Edema formation and degranulation of mast cells by a basic phospholipase A2 purified from *Trimeresurus mucrosquamatus* snake venom. *Toxicon* 1989;27:115-25

[38] Mc Lane MA, Marcinkiewicz C, Vijay-Kumar S, Wierzbicka-Patynowski I, Niewiarowski S. Viper venom disintegrins and related molecules. *Proc Soc Exptl Biol Med* 1998;219:109-19

[39] Niewiarowski S, Marcinkiewicz C, Wierzbicka-Patynowski I, Mc Lane and Calvete JJ. Structure and function of disintegrins and C-lectins : viper venom proteins modulating cell adhesion. In : A. Ménez, Editor, Perspectives in Molecular Toxinology, Wiley, New York 2002;pp 327-40

[40] Ginsberg MH, Loftus JC, Plow EF. Cytoadhesins, integrins, and platelets. *Thromb Haemost* 1988;59:1-6

[41] Miles AA, Wilhelm DL. Enzyme-like globulins from serum reproducing the vascular phenomena of inflammation. I. An activable permeability factor and its inhibitor in guinea-pig serum. *Br J Exp Pathol* 1955;36:71-81

[42] Komori Y, Nikai T, Taniguchi T, Masuda K, Sugihara H. Vascular endothelial growth factor VEGF-like heparin-binding protein from the venom of *Vipera aspis aspis* (Aspic viper). *Biochemistry* 1999;38:11769-11803

[43] Gasmi A, Abidi F, Srairi N, Oijatayer A, Karoui H, Elayeb M. Purification and characterization of a growth factor-like which increases capillary permeability from *Vipera lebetina* venom. *Biochem Biophys Res Commun* 2000;268:69-72

[44] Gasmi A, Bourcier C, Aloui Z *et al.* Complete structure of an Increasing Capillary Permeability Protein (ICPP) purified from *Vipera lebetina* venom. ICPP is angiogenic via VEGF receptor signaling. *J Biol Chem* 2002;277:29992-8

[45] Yamazaki Y, Takani K, Atoda H, Morita T. Snake venom vascular endothelial growth factors (VEGFs) exhibit potent activity through their specific recognition of KDR (VEGF receptor 2). *J Biol Chem* 2003;278:51985-8

[46] Junqueira de Azevedo IL, Farsky SH, Oliveira ML, Ho PL. Molecular cloning and expression of a functional snake venom vascular endothelium growth factor (VEGF) from the *Bothrops insularis* pit viper. A new member of the VEGF family of proteins. *J Biol Chem* 2002;276:39836-42

[47] Muller YA, Li B, Christinger HW, Wells JA, Cunningham BC, de Vos AM. Vascular endothelial growth factor: crystal structure and functional mapping of the kinase domain receptor-binding site. *Proc Natl Acad Sci U S A* 1997;94:7192-7

[48] Keyt BA, Nguyen HV, Berleau LT *et al.* Identification of vascular endothelial growth factor determinants for binding KDR and FLT-1 receptors. Generation of receptor-selective VEGF variants by site-directed mutagenesis. *J Biol Chem* 1996;271:5638-46

[49] Pan B, Li B, Russell SJ, Tom JY, Cochran AG, Fairbrother WJ. Solution structure of a phage-derived peptide antagonist in complex with vascular endothelial growth factor. *J Mol Biol* 2002;316:769-87

[50] Bjellqvist B, Hughes GJ, Pasquali Ch *et al.* The focusing positions of polypeptides in immobilized pH gradients can be predicted from their amino acid sequences. *Electrophoresis* 1993;14:1023-31

[51] Jia LG, Shimokawa K, Bjarnason JB, Fox JW. Snake venom metalloproteinases: structure, function and relationship to the ADAMs family of proteins. *Toxicon* 1996;34:1269-76

[52] Kini RM, Evans HJ. Structural domains in venom proteins: evidence that metalloproteinases and nonenzymatic platelet aggregation inhibitors (disintegrins) from snake venom are derived by proteolysis from a common precursor. *Toxicon* 1992;30:265-93

[53] Huang TF, Holt JC, Lukasiewicz H, Niewiarowski S. Trigramin. A low molecular weight peptide inhibiting fibrinogen interaction with platelet receptors expressed on glycoprotein IIb-IIIa complex. *J Biol Chem* 1987;262:16157-63

[54] Gan ZR, Gould RJ, Jacobs JW, Friedman PA, Polokoff MA. Echistatin. A potent platelet aggregation inhibitor from the venom of the viper, *Echis carinatus*. *J Biol Chem* 1988;263:19827-32

[55] Calvete JJ, Wang Y, Mann K, Schafer W, Niewiarowski S, Stewart GJ. The disulfide bridge pattern of snake venom disintegrins, flavoridin and echistatin. *FEBS Lett* 1992;309:316-20

[56] McLane MA, Vijay-Kumar S, Marcinkiewicz C, Calvete JJ, Niewiarowski S. Importance of the structure of the RGD-containing loop in the disintegrins echistatin and eristostatin for recognition of alpha IIb beta 3 and alpha v beta 3 integrins. *FEBS Lett* 1996;391:139-43

[57] Scarborough RM, Rose JW, Hsu MA *et al.* Barbourin. A GPIIb-IIIa-specific integrin antagonist from the venom of *Sistrurus m. barbouri*. *J Biol Chem* 1991;266:9359-62

[58] Calvete JJ, Schrader M, Raida M, McLane MA, Romero A, Niewiarowski S. The disulphide bond pattern of bitistatin, a disintegrin isolated from the venom of the viper *Bitis arietans*. *FEBS Lett* 1997; 416:197-202

[59] Park D, Kang I, Kim H, Chung K, Kim DS, Yun Y. Cloning and characterization of novel disintegrins from *Agkistrodon halys* venom. *Mol Cells* 1998;8:578-84

[60] Trikha M, De Clerck YA, Markland FS. Contortrostatin, a snake venom disintegrin, inhibits beta 1 integrin-mediated human metastatic melanoma cell adhesion and blocks experimental metastasis. *Cancer Res* 1994;54:4993-8

[61] Gasmi A, Srairi N, Guermazi S, Dkhil H, Karoui H, Elayeb M. Amino acid structure and characterization of a heterodimeric disintegrin from *Vipera lebetina* venom. *Biochim Biophys Acta* 2001;1547:51-6

[62] Dennis MS, Henzel WJ, Pitti RM *et al.* Platelet glycoprotein IIb-IIIa protein antagonists from snake venom: evidence for a family of platelet-aggregation inhibitors. *Proc Natl Acad Sci USA* 1989;87:2471-75

[63] Scarborough RM, Rose JW, Naughton MA *et al.* Characterization of the integrin specificities of disintegrins isolated from American pit viper venom. *J Biol Chem* 1993;268:1058-65

[64] Marcinkiewicz C, Calvete JJ, Marcinkiewicz MM *et al.* EC3, a novel heterodimeric disintegrin from *Echis carinatus* venom, inhibits alpha4 and alpha5 integrins in an RGD-independent manner. *J Biol Chem* 1999;274:12468-73

[65] Marcinkiewicz C, Calvete JJ, Vijay-Kumar S *et al.* Structural and functional characterization of EMF10, a heterodimeric disintegrin from *Eristocophis macmahomi* venom that selectively inhibits alpha 5 beta 1 integrin. *Biochemistry* 1999;38:13302-09

[66] Calvete JJ, Fox JW, Agelan A, Niewiarowski S, Marcinkiewicz C. The presence of the WGD motif in CC8 heterodimeric disintegrin increases its inhibitory effect on alphaII(b)beta3, alpha(v)beta3, and alpha5beta1 integrins. *Biochemistry* 2002;41:2014-2

[67] Shimokawa K, Jia L-G, Shannon JD, Fox JW. Isolation, sequence analysis, and biological activity of atrolysin E/D, the non-RGD disintegrin domain from *Crotalus atrox* venom. *Arch Biochem Biophys* 1998;354:239-46

[68] Eble JA , Bruckner P, Mayer U. (2003) *Vipera lebetina* venom contains two disintegrins inhibiting laminin-binding beta1 integrins. *J Biol Chem* 2003;278:26488-96

[69] Calvete JJ, Moreno-Murciano MP, Theakston RDG, Kisiel DG, Marcinkiewicz C. Snake venom disintegrins: novel dimeric disintegrins and structural diversification by disulphide bond engineering. *Biochem J* 2003;372:725-34

[70] Fujii Y, Okuda D, Fujimoto Z, Horii K, Morita T, Mizuno H. Crystal structure of trimestatin, a disintegrin containing a cell adhesion recognition motif RGD. *J Mol Biol* 2003;332:1115-22

[71] Sheu JR, Yen MH, Kan YC, Hung WC, Chang PT, Luk HN. Inhibition of angiogenesis *in vitro* and *in vivo*: comparison of the relative activities of triflavin, an Arg-Gly-Asp-containing peptide and anti-alpha(v)beta3 integrin monoclonal antibody. *Biochim Biophys Acta* 1997;1336:445-54

[72] Yeh CH, Peng HC, Huang TF. Accutin, a new disintegrin, inhibits angiogenesis *in vitro* and *in vivo* by acting as integrin alphavbeta3 antagonist and inducing apoptosis. *Blood* 1998;92:3268-76

[73] Kang IC, Lee YD, Kim DS. A novel disintegrin salmosin inhibits tumor angiogenesis. *Cancer Res* 1999;59:3754-60

[74] Kang IC, Kim DS, Jang Y, Chung KH. Suppressive mechanism of salmosin, a novel disintegrin in B16 melanoma cell metastasis. *Biochem Biophys Res Commun* 2000; 275:169-73

[75] Zhou Q, Sherwin RP, Parrish C *et al.* Contortrostatin, a dimeric disintegrin from *Agkistrodon contortrix contortrix*, inhibits breast cancer progression. *Breast Cancer Res Treat* 2000;61:249-60

[76] Yeh CH, Peng HC, Yang RS, Huang TF. Rhodostomin, a snake venom disintegrin, inhibits angiogenesis elicited by basic fibroblast growth factor and suppresses tumor growth by a selective alpha(v)beta(3) blockade of endothelial cells. *Mol Pharmacol* 2001;59:1333-42

[77] Marcinkiewicz C, Weinreb PH, Calvete JJ *et al.* Obtustatin: a potent selective inhibitor of alpha1beta1 integrin *in vitro* and angiogenesis *in vivo*. *Cancer Res* 2003;63:2020-3

[78] Senger DR, Perruzzi CA, Streit M, Koteliansky VE, de Fougerolles AR, Detmar M. The alpha(1)beta(1) and alpha(2)beta(1) integrins provide critical support for vascular endothelial growth factor signaling, endothelial cell migration, and tumor angiogenesis. *Am J Pathol* 2002; 160:195-204

[79] Mariano-Oliveira A , Coelho AL, Terruggi CH, Selistre-de-Araujo HS. Alternagin-C, a nonRGD-disintegrin, induces neutrophil migration via integrin signaling. *Eur J Biochem* 2003;270:4799-08

[80] Cominetti MR, Terruggi CH, Ramos OH *et al.* Alternagin-C, a disintegrin-like protein, induces vascular endothelial cell growth factor (VEGF) expression and endothelial cell proliferation *in vitro*. *J Biol Chem* 2004;279:18247-55

[81] Wu WB, Peng HC, Huang TF. Disintegrin causes proteolysis of beta-catenin and apoptosis of endothelial cells. Involvement of cell-cell and cell-ECM interactions in regulating cell viability. *Exp Cell Res* 2003;286:115-27

[82] Shebuski RJ, Stabilito IJ, Sitko GR, Polokoff MH. Acceleration of recombinant tissue-type plasminogen activator-induced thrombolysis and prevention of reocclusion by the combination of heparin and the Arg-Gly-Asp-containing peptide bitistatin in a canine model of coronary thrombosis. *Circulation* 1990;82:169-77

[83] Holahan MA, Mellott MJ, Garsky VM, Shebuski, RJ. Prevention of reocclusion following tissue type plasminogen activator-induced thrombolysis by the RGD-containing peptide, echistatin, in a canine model of coronary thrombosis. *Pharmacology* 1991;42:340-8

In: New Angiogenesis Research
Editor: Roberta V. Zubar, pp. 131-156

ISBN 1-59454-239-2

Chapter VII

Calcium and Angiogenesis

Luca Munaron*

Department of Animal and Human Biology, University of Torino, Italy

Abstract

The proliferation and motility of vascular endothelial cells (ECs) are critical steps in angiogenesis and are strictly controlled by different extracellular signals. Among mitogens, peptides binding to tyrosine kinase receptors (i.e. VEGFs and FGFs) are well known and released by several cell types, including ECs and tumor cells. The binding of mitogens to their specific receptors triggers intracellular signalling cascades, involving a number of messengers working in a sort of network. In particular, in this review we describe the increases of calcium levels in the cytosol, a universal, evolutionary conserved and highly versatile signal involved in the regulation of EC's proliferation and motility. Most mitogens, including angiogenic factors, generate cytosolic calcium rises through two mechanisms: entry from extracellular medium or release from intracellular organelles (mainly endoplasmic reticulum, ER). Calcium entry, the main topic of this review, can be dependent on previously IP_3-activated emptying of calcium stores (capacitative calcium entry, or CCE), or independent on it (non capacitative calcium entry, NCCE). The intracellular pathways underlying calcium responses are under investigation and recently arachidonic acid (AA) and nitric oxide (NO) metabolism have been suggested to play a key role, at least in some cell types. Even if some calcium entry blockers are under clinical trial at present with encouraging results, a better knowledge about the molecular nature of calcium channels and their intracellular regulation, together with a more detailed description of spatiotemporal dynamics of intracellular calcium events, could lead to new and more specific strategies in therapeutical approach to cancer progression and angiogenesis.

Key words: Calcium, angiogenesis, growth factors.

* Correspondence concerning this article should be addressed to Dr. Luca Munaron Department of Animal and Human Biology, University of Torino, Via Accademia Albertina 13; 10123 Torino, ITALY; phone: -390116704667; fax: -390116704692; email: luca.munaron@unito.it.

Introduction

The Control of Cell Proliferation: A Role for Calcium

Intracellular calcium signals are a highly conserved and ubiquitous mode for the control of cell survival, proliferation, motility, apoptosis, and differentiation (Berridge et al., 1998).

They are involved at different critical phases in the regulation of the complex and multistepped process of angiogenesis (Kohn et al., 1995; Patton et al., 2003).

Endothelial cells (EC) are the major actors of new blood vessels formation, and particular attention has been focused on them: during angiogenesis, ECs leave the preexisting vessel moving through the matrix, proliferate and finally stop their mitogenic activity and reorganize in a new tube; both motility and proliferation are strictly controlled by intracellular calcium dynamics, specifically modulated by extracellular agents such as vascular endothelial growth factors (VEGFs), fibroblast growth factors (FGFs), insulin like growth factors (IGFs), platelet derived growth factor (PDGF) and epidermal growth factor (EGF): in this review we will discuss in detail the mitogenic action of calcium for ECs and its role in the control of angiogenesis.

In the last decades, a relevant amount of evidence has accumulated pointing to a critical role of this ion in the control of proliferative events (Estacion and Mordan 1993; Kojima et al., 1993; Barbiero et al., 1995; Lovisolo et al., 1997; Whitaker and Larman, 2001; Munaron, 2002). Increases in cytosolic free calcium concentration are associated with the progression through the cell cycle: the exit from quiescence in early G1 phase, the G1/S transition, and other checkpoints during S and M phases (Berridge, 1995; Kahl and Means, 2003).

Calcium exerts its regulatory role by acting as a ubiquitous allosteric activator or inhibitor of several intracellular enzymes in the cytosol, organelles and nucleus. Some proteins (calcium binding proteins, CBPs), other than enzymes, interact with calcium showing different affinities and acting as calcium buffers: the effect is a limitation of free calcium diffusion in the intracellular environment. Examples are parvalbumin, calbindin-D and calretinin (Berridge et al., 2000).

Other proteins interact with the ion and regulate calcium-dependent enzymes and ion channels. The best known example is calmodulin (CaM), probably the most relevant calcium decoder for cell proliferation: it regulates, among others, the family of calcium-calmodulin dependent kinases type II (CaMKII) and several membrane channels. A great amount of data points to a direct involvement of CaMKII at several transition points during cell cycle progression (Kahl and Means, 2003: Figure 1). Calcium-dependent enzymes also mediate the activation of several nuclear factors involved in the DNA division machinery, for example cdk and cyclins (Santella, 1998).

Since the early '80s, with the development of fluorescent and luminescent calcium indicators (fura, fluo, indo, recombinant aequorin and others), a new picture of intracellular calcium homeostasis has been achieved, giving a more complex view of the dynamic behavior of this ion (Rudolf et al., 2003).

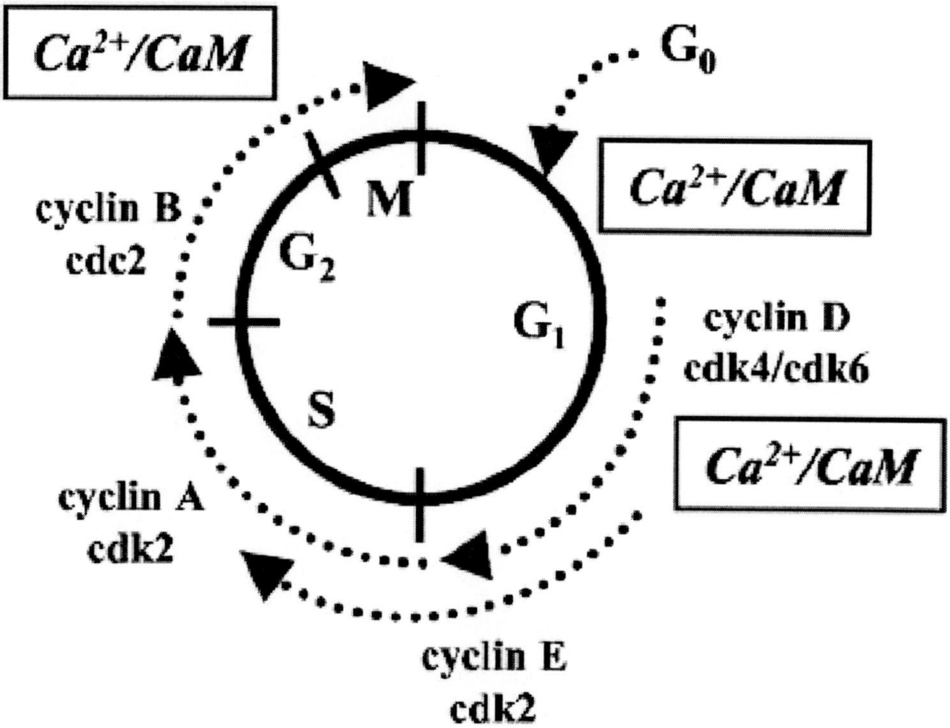

Figure 1. Cell cycle regulation by Calcium-Calmodulin (Ca/CaM) complex. Ca/CaM is required at different points: exit from G0 quiescent phase immediately after mitogenic stimulation, and later at G1/S and G2/M transitions.Modified from Kahl & Means, 2003.

Calcium Homeostasis and the Mechanisms for Calcium Signalling

Calcium concentration inside the cytosol, [Ca]c, is maintained very low (nearly 10^{-7} M in resting conditions) by active mechanisms mainly expressed in the plasmamembrane (PM) and in the membranes of endoplasmic reticulum (ER). Calcium pumps are present both in PM and in ER membranes (respectively PMCA and SERCAs) extruding the ion from the cytosol by direct energy (ATP) consumption. A secondary active calcium-extruding system, the Na-Ca exchanger, is located in the PM: it contributes to the maintenance of the resting cytosolic calcium levels and its physiological relevance differs from tissue to tissue (Hryshko and Philipson, 1997).

On the other hand, [Ca]c elevation is due to the opening of calcium channels that let the ion pass through the membranes in a passive way (following its electrochemical gradient). Calcium concentration in the extracellular medium and in ER lumen is much higher (in the μM-mM range) than [Ca]c: thus calcium entry from outside and release from ER represent the main pathways to elevate [Ca]c in all cell types.

Complessively, the dynamic steady state of calcium in the cytosol is the result of the balance between active and passive fluxes through the cell membranes and it is strictly controlled at least for two functional reasons: an informational one, because low calcium levels allow even small calcium fluxes to be a significant intracellular chemical signal, and a survival reason due to the toxic effect of prolonged and uncontrolled calcium elevations (Berridge et al., 2000).

Release from Intracellular Calcium Stores

Calcium channels in ER membranes can be activated by intracellular messengers. The $InsP_3$ receptor ($InsP_3R$) is a multimeric calcium channel that opens in a calcium-dependent fashion after binding to inositoltrisphosphate (InsP3), released into the cytosol following phospholipase C (PLC) activation by several extracellular agonists (Berridge, 1993). The InsP3-induced calcium release usually generates a very fast and short [Ca]c spike.

The ryanodine receptor (RyR) is another multimeric calcium channel modulated by calcium itself: in some models it can trigger self-sustaining intracellular calcium oscillations due to a mechanism called Calcium-Induced Calcium Release (CICR, Verkhratsky & Shmigol, 1996).

Since calcium content in ER lumen is limited, store depletion can occur rapidly and replenishment mechanisms (mainly *via* SERCAs) must be activated in order to restore initial conditions.

Calcium Entry from Outside

Calcium entry from external medium is usually mediated by calcium-permeable cationic channels in the plasmamembrane, which show varying degrees of selectivity and can support longer lasting signals, in the range of minutes or tens of minutes. It is necessary for the proliferation of several nonexcitable cell lines, including fibroblasts and ECs (Munaron, 2002).

Available evidence refers mainly to the progression through G1 and the G1/S transition. Experiments based on extracellular application of the calcium chelating agent EGTA, or of either pharmacological or inorganic blockers of mitogen-induced calcium entry, suggest that only calcium entry immediately triggered by mitogens (i.e. occurring during the first 2-4 hours of mitogen stimulation) is critical for cell cycle progression, while later calcium entry events during G1 phase are not effective (Kojima 1993; Estacion & Mordan 1993; Barbiero et al. 1995; Fiorio Pla & Munaron 2001; Antoniotti et al. 2003).

Voltage Operated Channels (VOCs)

The first informations on the structure of Ca^{2+} permeable channels have been obtained twenty years ago concerning the voltage-dependent Ca^{2+} channels (Ca_V) of the skeletal muscle (Curtis & Catterall, 1984). Additional work has shown that these channels possess the pentameric structure $\alpha 1\alpha 2\beta\gamma\delta$ (reviewed by Catterall, 2000): the $\alpha 1$ subunit alone exhibits the essential functional properties of the channel (binding sites for agonists and antagonists, voltage-sensor, ion-conducting pore), while the additional smaller subunits play a modulatory role. The Ca_V $\alpha 1$ subunit has the same structure as the α subunit of voltage-dependent Na channels and shows four homologous repeated domains (I-IV), each spanning six times the plasmamembrane (transmembrane segments are indicated as S1-S6); both N- and C-terminal regions are intracellular; cytoplasmic loops between the four domains present consensus sequences for protein kinase A-mediated phosphorylation and the binding region for the Ca^{2+}/calmodulin-mediated inactivation.

The pore region is formed by the alignment of the four aminoacidic loops between segments S5 and S6 of the four repeated domains. The S4 segment acts as a voltage sensor: its secondary structure is represented by an α-helix with a positively charged aminoacid every two hydrophobic residues; the position of this charged segment is influenced by the membrane potential and can be modulated by a depolarization, thus promoting a change in the global conformation of the channel and the opening of the pore region. Recently, this largely accepted model of VOC function has been questioned, in particular regarding the gating mechanism (Jiang et al., 2003).

Even if all Ca_V channels display this common structure, their functional features are very different, since several isoforms of $\alpha 1$ and auxiliary subunits, with splice variants, can be translated from different homologous genes. Based on electrophysiological and pharmacological studies, Ca_V channels have been classified as L-, N, P/Q-, R- and T-types: they show functional differences in activation and inactivation, single channel conductance, kinetics of channel opening, block by divalent metal ions, sensitivity to dihydropyridine compounds (Hille, 2001).

Being the first Ca^{2+} channels to be described and characterized, VOCs were the first obvious target of the search for Ca^{2+} influx pathways accounting for normal and altered proliferation. However, since most of the models used to study these processes are non excitable cells expressing relatively low levels of these channels, the data supporting this hypothesis are far from abundant, as compared with either second messenger-activated or store-activated channels.

One relevant exception may be represented by smooth muscle cells, in which Ca^{2+} VOCs are expressed at relatively high densities, and that actively proliferate in inflammation and hypertrophic growth of blood vessels and other organs; in this case, too, most of the evidence is indirect, based on the effects of VOCs blockers (see *e.g.* Yoo et al., 1997; Estacion & Mordan, 1993, Corsini et al., 1996; Mathov et al., 2001; Zhou et al., 2002).

Expression of L-type channels has been associated with long-term exposure to transforming growth factor β (TGFβ) and ensuing transformation of hepatic stellate cells (Roth-Eichhorn et al., 1999). Moreover, some transformed models appear to express relatively high levels of T-type channels (as compared to their differentiated counterparts), and some recently developed VOCs antagonists, such as mibefradil (Bertolesi et al., 2002) have an antiproliferative effect.

On the other hand, expression of T-type channels in HEK 293 cells does not increase proliferative events, thus pointing to cell-specific effects (Chemin et al., 2000). Some observations are even more conflicting: suppression of T-type channels, in many non excitable cell types, has been associated with malignant transformation by H-ras or other oncogenes (Estacion & Mordan, 1993; Chen et al., 1988; Strobeck et al., 1999). It must be considered, however, that the functional role of these channels in this context has still to be clarified.

Channels Activated Indirectly Following Receptor Activation

While Ca^{2+} VOCs open following a simple, direct stimulus such as a depolarization step, activation of voltage-independent channels needs the involvement of metabolic pathways stimulated by receptor tyrosine kinases (RTKs) or G-protein-coupled receptors (GPCRs), leading to the production of second messengers that modulate channel activity.

In spite of the variability of the mechanisms, two major pathways for the induction of calcium entry are known (Figure 2): capacitative calcium entry (CCE) is secondary to and dependent on a previously activated depletion of intracellular stores, while non capacitative entry (NCCE) is carried by store-independent calcium channels regulated by intracellular messengers released after receptor activation (Zitt et al., 2002).

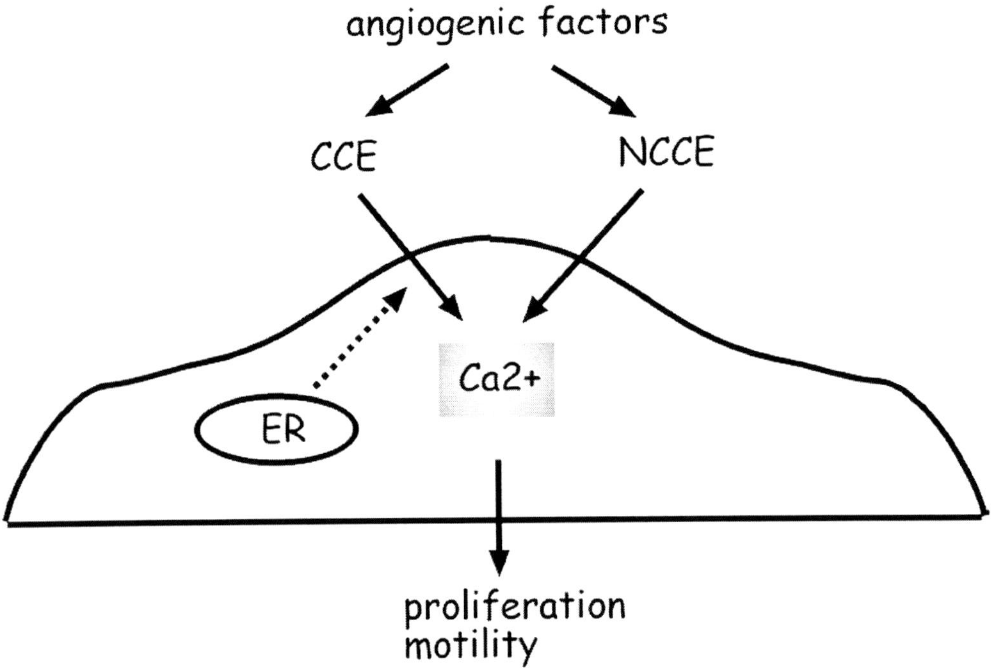

Figure 2. Simplified picture showing the main pathways involved in the activation of calcium entry by angiogenic factors. CCE: capacitative calcium entry; NCCE: non capacitative calcium entry; ER: endoplasmic reticulum.

These two types of fluxes may coexist in the same cell, in some cases depending on agonist concentration or on the expression level of the same channel (Vasquez et al., 2003). Usually low doses activate NCCE, while higher doses trigger CCE. Some Authors suggest a cross-inactivation mechanism, a sort of switch operated by the same intracellular messenger, possibly arachidonic acid (AA) (see below; Broad et al. 1999; Shuttleworth & Mignen, 2003).

CCE is the mechanism that has been more extensively associated with Ca^{2+} influx related to cell proliferation. It involves a heterogeneous class of channels, whose characterization is far from being exhaustive. The best known members are I_{crac} (Ca^{2+} release activated current) channels; even if their molecular nature is still unknown, their electrophysiological properties have been well described, mainly in blood cells. They are opened following store depletion induced by $InsP_3$ and show unique electrophysiological features, such as very low single channel conductance and high selectivity for Ca^{2+} ions over monovalent cations (Penner et al., 1993).

In leukemic T cells, block of I_{crac} caused an arrest in the G0/G1 phase (Holmuhamedov et al., 2002). Examples of CCE involvement in cell proliferation have been provided for several cell types, including basophilic leukaemia cells (Bodding, 2001), Ha-ras transformed fibroblasts (Furst et al., 2002), and bronchial smooth muscle cells (Sweeney et al., 2002).

Several other examples are related to proliferation dependent on NCCE mechanisms (see *e.g.* Magnier-Gaubil et al., 1996; Munaron, 2002; Munaron & Fiorio Pla, 2000; Fiorio Pla & Munaron, 2001); in some cases, finally, the mechanism is not specified (see *e.g.* Asano et al., 1999).

Among the second messengers proposed to play a role in NCCE activation, arachidonic acid (AA) and other lipidic molecules are the most relevant (see below). In particular, in cultured bovine aortic ECs (BAE-1), AA directly opens calcium-permeable channels independently from store depletion and promotes calcium-entry-dependent cell proliferation (Fiorio Pla & Munaron, 2001). A calcium channel whose opening is not store-dependent but induced by low concentrations of arachidonic acid has been observed in HEK293 cells (Mignen & Shuttleworth, 2000): this channel, related to I_{ARC} (arachidonate-regulated Ca^{2+} current), has not been associated with cell cycle control so far.

Plasmamembrane channels responsible for mitogen-activated calcium entry are a still elusive family of proteins: a great amount of data is available about their functional properties, but few and contradictory are evidences about their structure and physiological role.

Electrophysiological measurements using patch clamp technique (in whole cell and single cell configuration) and fluorimetric evidences using calcium-sensitive fluorescent dyes suggest that they form a heterogeneous family, showing different biophysical properties (conductance, selective permeability, kinetic behavior, modulation). Many of them are non selective cationic channels, permeable to calcium, sodium, and potassium ions. Moreover the same intracellular messenger (such as AA and NO, see below) can modulate more than one channel in the same cell type (Fiorio Pla & Munaron, 2001; Watson et al., 2004; Dedkova & Blatter, 2002).

Recent evidence points to the involvement of transient receptor potential (TRP) superfamily of channels as a relevant route of agonist-induced calcium entry.

Structure of TRP

The prototype of these channels was firstly described in mutant photoreceptors of Drosophila melanogaster (Montell & Rubin, 1989) and then several mammalian TRP homologous channels have been cloned, and now classified into six families by sequence homology (Clapham et al., 2001; Clapham, 2003). The TRP-Canonical (TRPC) family is composed by seven proteins (TRPC1-7) bearing highest homology to Drosophila TRP and is indicated also as short TRP since they are relatively short proteins (700-900 aminoacids; figure 3); the TRPV family is named based on the first member described, the vanilloid receptor, involved in pain transduction; a third group is the TRPM family, from melastatin, a long TRP homologous protein. Common architecture of TRP channels shows six transmembrane hydrophobic segments, with the loop between segments 5 and 6 forming the ion-conducting pore, intracellular N- and C- terminal domains, and ankyrin-repeats in the amino termini of TRPC and TRPV proteins; functional channels have been suggested to be homo- or heterotetramers with defined interactions between different subunits (Hofmann et al., 2002). In particular, TRPC channels have been proposed to play a role in both capacitative and non capacitative Ca^{2+} influx (reviewed in Zitt et al., 2002).

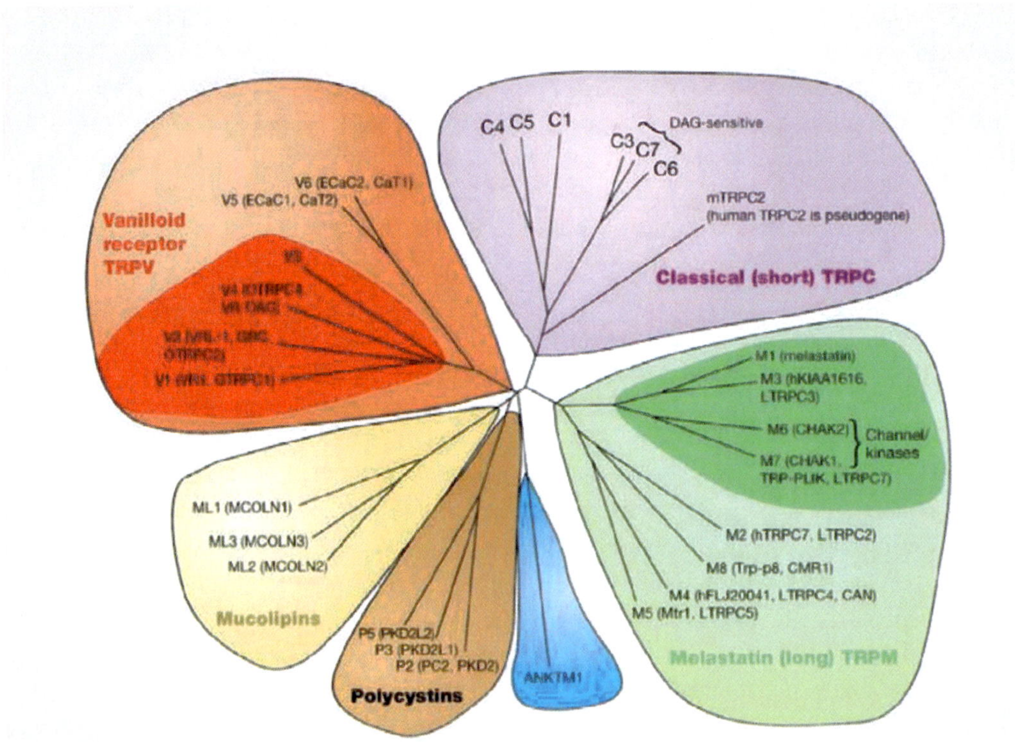

Figure 3. Mammalian TRP family tree. The evolutionary distance is shown by the total branch lengths. From Clapham, 2003.

Function of TRP

Recently cloned transient receptors potential (TRP) channels are a heterogeneous family of cationic channels, with different calcium selectivity (Zitt et al., 2002): some TRPC channels have been shown to be activated directly by intracellular messengers, including diacylglycerol (DAG) (TRP and TRPL, Chyb et al., 1999) and fatty acids including AA (TRPC3, 4, 6) (Hofmann et al., 1999; Wu et al., 2002). Moreover in an EC line endogenously expressing TRPC1, this channel seems to be involved in bFGF-induced calcium entry (Antoniotti et al., 2002). In pulmonary artery smooth muscle cells, endogenous TRPC1 channels regulate a store-dependent calcium influx critical for proliferation: basal levels of TRPC1 protein expression are significantly higher in proliferating than in growth-arrested cells (Golovina, 1999), and application of antisense oligonucleotides against TRPC1 mRNA reduces proliferation (Sweeney et al., 2002a). TRPC1 plays a role also in the proliferation control of airway smooth muscle cells (Sweeney et al., 2002b). On the contrary, down-regulation of TRPC6 has been observed in tumor mast cells during progression to malignancy with increased proliferation rate due to autocrine production of IL-3 (Buess et al., 1999).

The involvement of other calcium channels, related or unrelated to TRP channels, in mitogen-induced signalling cannot be excluded at present: for example, a calcium-permeable cationic channel with homology to the TRPC family has been characterized in Balb/c 3T3 fibroblasts and named growth-factor channel (GCR): it is activated by insulin-like growth factor (IGF-I), that induces its translocation from the intracellular pools to the plasmamembrane (Kanzaki et al., 1999).

In the next section we will review only blockers that act directly (at least partially or potentially) on Ca^{2+} channels, inhibiting Ca^{2+} influx; the huge literature on indirect blockers (*i.e.* compounds that interfere with relevant metabolic steps leading to channel opening) will not be considered here.

Calcium Channel Blockers

A great number of calcium channel blockers have been detected, with different chemical structure and variable selectivity and specificity.

They can be divided into two major groups: inorganic ions and organic molecules. This classification does not reflect a specific action of these substances, since, as we will see, many of them interfere with more than one type of channel.

Inorganic (Ionic) Blockers

Both voltage-dependent and independent Ca^{2+} channels are competitively blocked by metal ions, such as divalent transition ions (Ni^{2+}, Cd^{2+}, Co^{2+}) and lanthanides (La^{3+}, Gd^{3+}) (Hille, 2001). Given their structural simplicity, these cations have been among the first Ca^{2+} channels blockers used: they reduce Ca^{2+} influx and the related proliferation in several types of cells, both normal and transformed (Estacion & Mordan., 1993; Asano et al., 1999; Moll et al., 2002;, Kojima et al., 1988; Broad et al., 1999; Weiss et al., 2001).

Estacion and Mordan (1993) have shown that, in normal mouse fibroblasts (C3H 10T1/2 cells) primed with insulin, PDGF induced a large long-lasting Ca^{2+} increase, completely blocked by addition of 10 μM La^{3+} to the extracellular solution; moreover, La^{3+} also inhibited progression to S phase. Similar effects could be obtained also by Ni^{2+} (20 μM) and Co^{2+} (200 μM), but not Cd^{2+} (200 μM). In Balb/c 3T3 fibroblasts, IGF-I induced Ca^{2+} oscillations, dependent on extracellular Ca^{2+} and reversibly abolished by 50 μM Co^{2+}; this cation also attenuated proliferation (Kojima et al., 1988, 1992). It is worth noting that in the former case the effect was associated with a block of VOCs, in the latter to a block of voltage-independent channels. In serum-starved primary cultures of human pulmonary artery smooth muscle cells, store depletion increased capacitative Ca^{2+} influx, associated with proliferation and blocked by 0.5 mM Ni^{2+} (Golovina, 1999). In vascular smooth muscle cells (A7r5), vasopressin caused a biphasic rise in $[Ca]_c$, where the sustained phase was totally blocked by 1 mM La^{3+} or Gd^{3+}, with marked inhibitory effects on $[H^3]$ thymidine incorporation (Asano et al., 1999). In the same cells, Ca^{2+} fluxes induced by vasopressin were mediated by voltage independent channels, activated by both capacitative and non capacitative mechanisms, with different sensitivity to Gd^{3+} block: pre-treatment of A7r5 cells with 1 μM Gd^{3+} completely abolished the capacitative pathway, without affecting the non capacitative component, which could be blocked only at higher concentrations (100 μM Gd^{3+}) (Broad et al., 1999). In Muller glial cells, ATP provoked a Ca^{2+} influx, mediated by the P2Y metabotropic purinergic receptors, related to DNA synthesis and blocked by 40 μM Ni^{2+}; nickel abolished both ATP-stimulated Ca^{2+} entry and proliferation, showing the same effects as intracellular Ca^{2+} chelation by BAPTA/AM (Moll et al., 2002). In human colon carcinoma cells (HRT-18), which require Ca^{2+} for proliferation, La^{3+} inhibited both SOCE and cell proliferation (Weiss et al., 2001). In another colon carcinoma-derived cell line (Caco-2), EGF induced Ca^{2+} influx through SOC channels, related to proliferation and reduced by 25 μM La^{3+}; this ion also significantly attenuated EGF-stimulated mitogenesis (Kokoska et al., 2000).

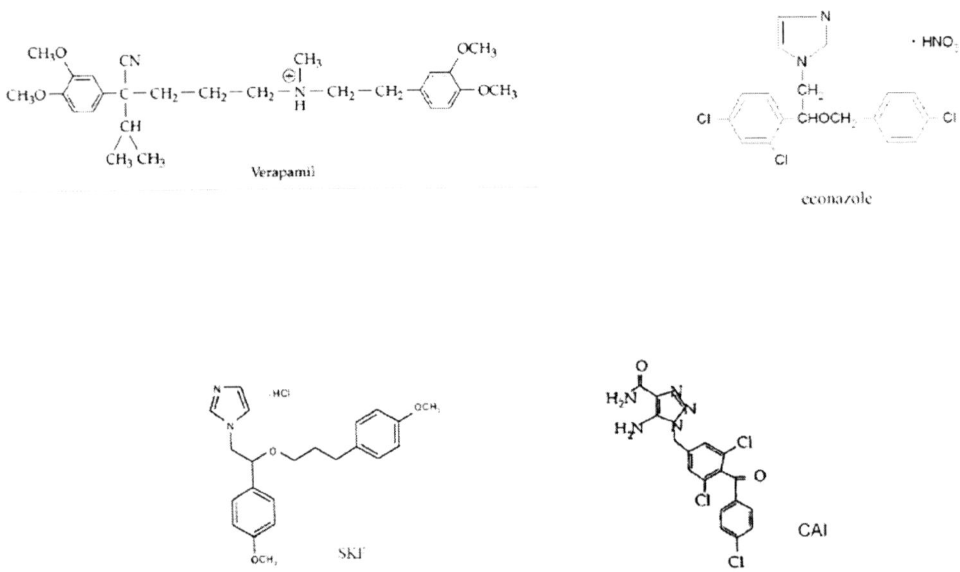

Figure 4. Structure of some widely used blockers of mitogen-activated calcium entry.

Dihydropyridines

Dihydropyridines (nifedipine and related molecules) are the most widely used blockers of L-type voltage-dependent Ca^{2+} channels, being effective in the μM range. They are usually considered to be quite specific for this class of channels, and their effects can be associated with an identified Ca^{2+} influx pathway. However, some of them (nifedipine and nicardipine) can block a voltage-insensitive Ca^{2+} influx and suppress proliferation (Willmott et al., 1996).

Evidence for the ability of such blockers to interfere with Ca^{2+} influx-dependent proliferation has been provided in several cell types, mainly vascular smooth muscle cells from normal and pathologic tissues (Yoo et al., 1997, Corsini et al., 1996; Zhou et al., 2002; Mathov et al., 2001; Kruse et al., 1994).

Other organic blockers of Ca^{2+} VOCs, associated with inhibition of proliferation, include verapamil (Yoo et al., 1997), whose selectivity of action has been extensively questioned, and mibefradil, a drug considered to be selective for T-type channels expressed in some types of cancer cells (Bertolesi et al., 2002: figure 4).

Other Organic VOCs Blockers

Carboxyamidotriazole (CAI)

Carboxyamidotriazole (CAI, L651582, NSC 609974) is a synthetic Ca^{2+} influx blocker, extensively associated with inhibitory effects on cell proliferation (Kohn et al., 1990; 1994a; 1995).

The antiproliferative effects of CAI have been ascribed to its ability to inhibit intracellular pathways involving phospholipase-Cγ $InsP_3$ and arachidonic acid release, as well as to block Ca^{2+} channels.

Early studies on muscarinic acetylcholine receptor-transfected chinese hamster ovary cells showed that 10 μM CAI inhibited receptor mediated Ca^{2+} influx in response to the muscarinic agonist carbachol, in addition to an immediate effect on arachidonic acid release and a minimal effect on inositol phoshate release. CAI inhibited proliferation and invasive properties of several tumor cell lines *in vitro*, including prostate, glioblastoma and breast-derived cell lines (Kohn et al., 1992; 1995; Moody et al., 2003). It also significantly reduced proliferation of several types of ECs (HUVECs, HAECs, BAECs) and inhibited angiogenesis induced *in vitro* by VEGF. The effect on angiogenesis is mediated by the block of calcium-mediated nitric oxide synthase (NOS) and vascular endothelial growth factor pathway (Bauer et al., 2000). In HUVECs, a reduction of NO release was observed, while no significant effect on VEGFR, PLCγ, ERK1/2, NFAT activities was detected, supporting the high specificity of the drug (Faehling et al., 2002). In BAECs, CAI partially inhibits calcium entry activated by AA, critically involved in the control of proliferation (Antoniotti et al., 2003).

Thus, the use of calcium channel inhibitors, at least in some cell types including endothelial and smooth muscle cells, suggests a role for NO and AA in the control of cell proliferation and secondarily of physiopathological processes (see below): however, the insurgence of complex feedbacks of AA and NO on calcium homeostasis renders the experimental data difficult to be clearly interpreted (Bauer et al., 2000; Faehling et al., 2002; Nilius & Droogmans, 2001; Moneer et al., 2003).

On ECs, CAI-sensitive Ca^{2+} influx has been correlated to cell adhesion, spreading, proteolysis and migration, all processes involved in tumor invasion. Endothelial cell spreading on type IV collagen, but not on type I, is specifically regulated by CAI-sensitive Ca^{2+} influx (Alessandro et al., 1998), and the expression of metalloproteinase-2 is modulated by Ca^{2+} influx and downregulated by CAI (Kohn et al., 1994b).

Inhibition of angiogenesis and metastasis has been detected in *in vivo* studies on several types of solid tumors (Kohn et al., 1992; Luzzi et al., 1999).

Administration of CAI, also in combination with other drugs, in preclinical and clinical investigations stabilized solid tumors including carcinomas and melanomas (Kohn et al., 1996; Kohn et al., 2001; Hussain et al., 2003).

Imidazole Derivatives

Imidazole derivatives, such as clotrimazole, econazole, miconazole, ketoconazole, are antimycotic drugs widely used for the treatment of yeast infections. Imidazole antimycotics are potent inhibitors of many mammalian cytochrome P450-dependent reactions. Secondary to their effects on cytochrome P450 activity, they have also been extensively used as non-specific blockers of Ca^{2+} influx (see *e.g.* Franzius et al., 1994; Graier et al., 1995; Viana et al., 1998; Gamberucci et al., 1998). Moreover, other effects on Ca^{2+} homeostasis have been described: miconazole, clotrimazole and econazole, in the μM range, promote Ca^{2+} entry in canine kidney cells (Jan et al., 1999a; 1999b; 2000); clotrimazole inhibits the activity of the sarcoplasmic reticulum Ca^{2+} pump in rabbit cardiomyocytes (Snajdrova et al., 1998).

Notably, some imidazole derivatives have been shown to affect the activity of kinases strongly involved in mitogen-induced intracellular signalling (Davies et al., 2000; Sridhar et al., 2003).

However, since it cannot be excluded that these compounds also act directly on Ca^{2+} permeable channels (as for other drugs, such as SK&F 96365 and CAI) and since they (clotrimazole in particular) are also under trial as chemotherapeutic drugs, we report here some relevant data about their effects on Ca^{2+} influx.

The compound 1-(o-Chloro-α,α-diphenylbenzyl)imidazole (clotrimazole) inhibits bradykinin-induced proliferation of smooth muscle cells and the related rise of $[Ca]_c$ (Raicu et al., 2000). The compounds 1-(2- [(4-Chlorophenyl)methoxy]-2- [2,4-dichlorophenyl]ethyl)-1H-imidazole (econazole) and (±)-cis-1-Acetyl-4-(4- [(2- [2,4-dichlorophenyl]-2- [1H-imidazol-1-ylmethyl]-1,3-dioxolan-4-yl)-methoxy]phenyl)piperazine (ketoconazole) are potential purging agents for residual leukaemia cells present in bone marrow, since proliferation of human leukaemia cells in vitro is more sensitive to these blockers than proliferation of normal hemopoietic progenitor cells; inhibition of tumoral cell proliferation by clotrimazole is ascribed to block of store operated Ca^{2+} influx (Soboloff et al., 2002). The use of clotrimazole in the treatment of proliferative disorders is being clinically tested (Benzaquen et al., 1995).

Below we will review some imidazole derivatives whose role in blocking mitogen-activated Ca^{2+} influx has been more extensively studied.

SC38249

The compound ((+-)-1,-2,3-bis- [(4-Methoxyphenyl)-methoxy]propyl)-1H-imidazole (SC38249) displays multiple actions on Ca^{2+} homeostasis, blocking both voltage-dependent and independent channels and also interfering with the activity of Ca^{2+} ATPases (Ciardo & Meldolesi, 1990). In NIH3T3 fibroblasts overexpressing the EGF receptors (EGFR-T17 cells) and lacking voltage-dependent Ca^{2+} channels, the mitogen EGF induced a biphasic rise of $[Ca]_c$, with long-lasting rhythmic fluctuations dependent on Ca^{2+} influx. SC38249 (10 μM) abolished Ca^{2+} influx and inhibited by 60% the proliferation induced by EGF. Interestingly, Ca^{2+} oscillations were paralleled by synchronous plasmamembrane hyperpolarizations due to opening of Ca^{2+}-dependent K^+ channels, blocked by charybdotoxin. Charybdotoxin induced also a minor but significant reduction (-20%) of the EGF-stimulated mitogenic effect (Magni et al., 1991). This observation is an example of how Ca^{2+} influx can be modulated not only by blocking calcium-permeable channels, but also by reducing the electrochemical gradient, thereby depolarizing the membrane potential.

SK&F 96365

The compound 1-{*ß*- [3-(4-methoxy-phenyl)propoxy]-4-methoxyphenethyl}-1*H*-imidazole hydrocloride (SK&F 96365) (Merritt et al., 1990), the best known of this class, has been widely used, and it is commonly suggested to act directly on Ca^{2+} permeable channels. However, it has been in turn classified as a specific blocker of store-operated channels (Magnier-Gaubil et al.,1996; Chaib et al., 1998), of non-store-operated ones (Kan et al., 1997; Gamberucci et al., 2002), or as a non specific blocker, acting also on VOCs (Barbiero et al.,

1995; Merritt et al., 1990). Moreover, other aspecific effects have been reported, leading to activation or block of other types of channels (Franzius et al., 1994; Schwartz et al., 1994). Independently from its specificity, it acts as an antiproliferative agent on some cell types, among them Balb-c 3T3 fibroblasts (Barbiero et al., 1995) and mammary epithelial cells (Ichikawa & Kiyohara, 2001).

LOE 908

The isoquinoline derivative (R,S)-(3,4-dihydro-6,7-dimethoxy-quinoline-1-yl)-2-phenyl-N,N-di- [2-(2,3,4-trimethoxyphenyl)ethyl]acetamide (LOE 908) is an inhibitor of receptor- and store-operated Ca^{2+} influx (Krautwurst et al., 1993; Encabo et al., 1996), largely employed by Kawanabe et al. (see *e.g.* Kawanabe et al., 2002a,b, c, 2001). In rabbit vascular smooth muscle cells, the mitogen endothelin-1 activates Ca^{2+} influx through different pathways: two types of non-selective cation channels (NSCC-1 and NSCC-2), store-operated channels (SOC) and voltage-dependent channels. Contribution of these permeation pathways to Ca^{2+} influx relevant for endothelin-induced mitogenesis can be resolved using different blockers: application of nifedipine, blocking VOCs, has a minor role on proliferation stimulated by endothelin-1, that, conversely, is completely abolished by the combination of SK&F96365 and LOE908. In these cells SK&F96365 blocks NSCC-2 and SOC channels, while LOE908 affects both types of non-selective cation channels (Kawanabe et al., 2002c). By preventing Ca^{2+} influx, LOE908 inhibits proliferation in other different experimental models, such as C6 glioma cells (Kawanabe 2002a) or A7r5 vascular smooth muscle cells stimulated with endothelin-1 (Kawanabe et al., 2001), and Chinese hamster ovary (CHO) cells overexpressing the α(1A)-adrenergic receptors treated with noradrenaline (Kawanabe 2002b).

Many more organic agents have been reported to block Ca^{2+} influx related to cell proliferation: since for most of them the data either refer to a single cell type or are not based on evidence for a direct interaction with a channel protein, they will not be treated in this section.

Calcium Signals Activated by Mitogens and Angiogenic Factors

Growth Factors

Mitogenic factors are a highly heterogeneous family of agonists, most of which act in a pleiotropic way regulating other cellular processes (survival, differentiation, motility, secretion and apoptosis). Some are peptides, such as classical growth factors, cytokines and many hormones; others are lipidic and steroid compounds: members of all these groups are able to increase [Ca]c. (Estacion & Mordan, 1997; Asano et al., 1999; Munaron, 2002; Rozengurt, 1998).

Most of the literature is related to peptidic mitogens binding to membrane receptors and in this review we focus on them, even if agonists that act by binding to intracellular receptors, such as estrogens, have been shown to be able to induce [Ca]c elevations (Improta-Brears et al., 1999).

In particular, growth factors, including some potent angiogenic factors (FGFs, EGF, PDGF, VEGFs, IGF-I), exert their effect by the interaction with intrinsic tyrosine kinase receptors (RTKs); cytokines (such as interleukins, ILs) bind to receptors associated with cytosolic TKs, and other mitogens (such as bradikinin, ATP, oxytocin, colecystokinin, many neuropeptides) act *via* G-protein-coupled receptors (GPCRs), spanning seven times the plasmamembrane (see e.g. Rozengurt 1998). While each of these classes has its peculiarities, and involves specific cascades of intracellular events, the distinction is actually not so sharp, since in many instances crosstalks between different pathways have been described and may represent a general and physiological process. Moreover, a high degree of convergence on the same effector (a channel or an enzyme) is quite usual (Gawler DJ 1998), and some signalling molecules (among them calcium signals) are well conserved and are employed by different agonists in different contexts; this finding prompts another question, i.e. how such an interwoven web of signals can be reconciled with the evidence that different factors can exert specific and unique effects on the same cellular model. We will deal with the latter issue in the last paragraph of this review.

The fact that the same effector (e.g. a calcium permeable channel) can be recruited in response to a wide repertory of extracellular signals is one of the reasons why the mechanisms involved in mitogen-induced calcium signaling are so controversial, and a sharp picture is still lacking.

Calcium rises activated after membrane receptor recruitment have been detected in virtually every type of normal and transformed cell lines, emerging as one of the most conserved responses immediately triggered in the target cells in which they exert a mitogenic activity. These signals have been observed, in many instances, also in response to the application of antibodies directed against extracellular epitopes of different receptors (Vos et al., 2000).

A striking feature of mitogen-activated calcium increase is its heterogeneity: both amplitude and time course of the response vary from cell to cell even in the same cell culture. This non-homogeneity can be ascribed to the differential expression of the receptors, the calcium channels, or the intracellular signalling machinery leading to the response. Variability can still be observed in some cell lines after serum deprivation: in these conditions most of the cells are quiescent (i.e. in G0/G1 phase), excluding a cell cycle-phase dependent effect as a major route for generating heterogeneity (Byron et al., 1992; Munaron et al. 1997; 2000) even if some mitogenic agonists can influence the expression or the functional properties of components of the signaling pathway (Golovina, 1999; Kanzaki et al., 1999).

Moreover ECs are a high heterogeneous tissue: biochemical and functional differences have been described between macro and microvascular EC lines and among ECs obtained from different tissues (Nilius & Droogmans, 2001; Ghitescu & Robert, 2002).

Increases in [Ca]c start typically after a delay of seconds. On the basis of the time course, at least four types of [Ca]c increase are detectable: a single spike due to release from intracellular stores (mainly ER), a slower and more persistent calcium signal dependent on calcium entry from the extracellular medium, a biphasic [Ca]c elevation due to the combination of the two mechanisms, and calcium oscillations.

Angiostatin, Endostatin and Calcium

A number of endogenous angiogenesis inhibitors have been found to be particularly associated with the presence of tumors: the best known are angiostatin and endostatin (Distler et al., 2003).

Angiostatins are constituted by the first three, four, or five kringle domains of the plasminogen molecule: they are released by matrix metalloproteases secreted by tumor-infiltrating macrophages.

Endostatin is a 20 kDa C-terminal fragment of collagen XVIII, probably generated by proteases and elastates activity.

Endostatin and angiostatin inhibit EC migration and proliferation, and both induce EC apoptosis. Interestingly the antiproliferative effects of angiostatin seem specific for ECs while other cell types are not affected.

Even if some studies have been performed by the analysis of acute intracellular effects of these peptides, several aspects of their mechanisms of action (including the putative membrane receptors) are unknown.

Recently calcium signalling related to angiostatin and endostatin stimulation has been described in BAECs, HMECs, and CPAECs. The response is dependent on IP3 release following PLC activation and is composed by an initial release from intracellular stores followed by a prolonged calcium entry (Jiang et al., 2001).

Another interesting observation is that prolonged exposure to endostatin attenuates acute calcium signalling in response to subsequent treatment with VEGF and FGF (Jiang et al., 2001).

Kringle domains of urokinase, another antiangiogenic endogenous factor, are also able to promote calcium increases in HUVECs but not in other cell types (Kim et al., 2003).

Arachidonic Acid, Nitric Oxide and Calcium: A Complex Interplay for Endothelial Cell Biology and Angiogenesis

Arachidonic Acid Metabolism and Calcium

In resting cells, AA is stored within the cell membrane, esterified to glycerol in phospholipids. Three enzymes (the phospholipases A2, C and D), with different sites of attack on the phospholipid backbone, mediate the deacylation reaction that releases the fatty acid (Figure 5). While PLA2 releases arachidonate in a single-step reaction, PLC and phospholipase D (PLD) do not produce AA directly; rather, they generate lipid products containing arachidonate, respectively DAG and phosphatidic acid; the latter can be metabolized to DAG by phosphatidic acid (PA) phosphatase (PA-PH). From DAG, AA can be subsequently released by diacylglycerol lipase (DAG lipase; Piomelli, 1993; Rizzo & Romero, 2002).

In mammalian cells, PLA2 is known to be present in several isoforms, recently classified in 11 groups differing in structure, intracellular localization, regulation, calcium dependence and pharmacological inhibition (Six and Dennis, 2000). One of them is the secretory PLA2 (sPLA2), a low molecular weight enzyme (14 kDa), whose activity is dependent on high calcium concentration (in the millimolar range); the cytosolic PLA2 (cPLA2, 85 kDa) is the form that has been investigated more extensively and is the enzyme stimulated mainly by growth factors through a MAPK-dependent phosphorylation on Ser-505 (Lin et al., 1993). Its activation requires also a translocation to the membrane, in order to interact with its substrate, in a calcium-dependent fashion, at the physiological Ca^{2+} levels reached after agonist stimulation (Clark et al., 1991). Another form of PLA2 (iPLA2) is Ca^{2+}-independent and its functional roles are not well characterized; recently, in a colon carcinoma cell line (Caco-2 cells), evidence has been provided for its involvement in serum-induced AA release and cell proliferation (sanchez and Moreno, 2002).

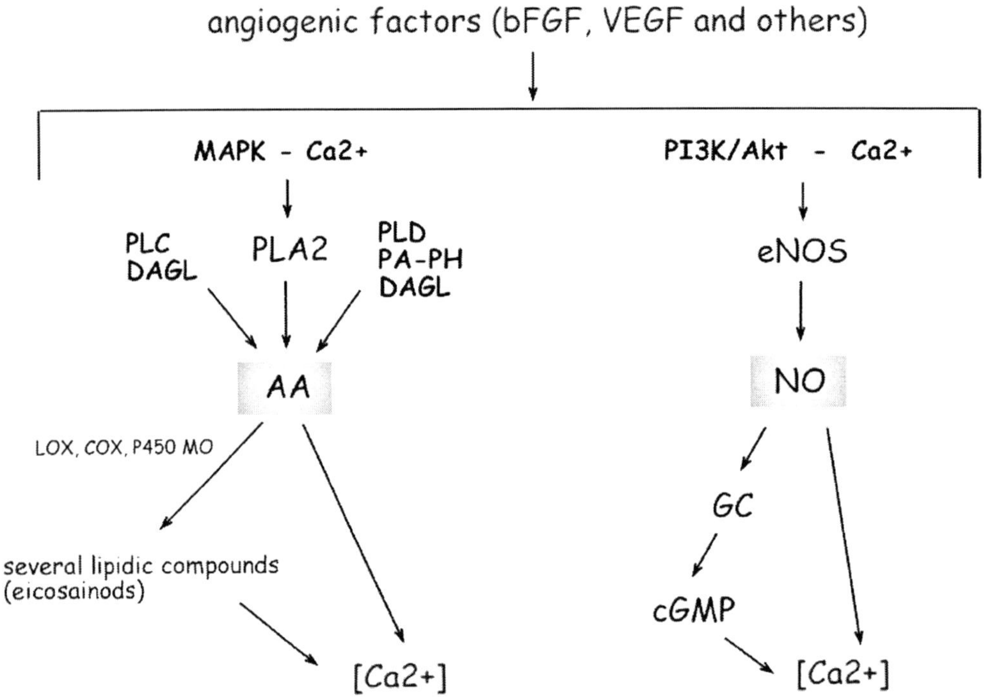

Figure 5. Arachidonic acid and Nitric Oxide metabolisms: two signal transduction pathways playing a key role in the control of calcium signalling by angiogenic factors in endothelial cells. Phospholipase D (PLD), phospholipase C (PLC), phospholipase A2 (PLA2), phosphatidic acid phosphatase (PA-PH), diacylglycerol lipase (DAG lipase), mitogen activated protein kinase (MAPK), cyclooxygenases (COX), lipoxygenases (LOX), cytocrome P450 monooxygenases (P450-MO), Guanylyl Cyclase (GC), endothelial Nitric Oxide Synthase (eNOS).

In vascular ECs, bFGF receptor activation leads to the recruitment of several adapter proteins (FRS2, Grb2) followed by the indirect activation of ras and the mitogen activated protein kinase (MAPK) cascade (Javerzat et al., 2002). MAPK triggers a series of downstream events, including the activation of phospholipase A2 (PLA2): this enzyme in turn catalyzes the hydrolysis of phospholipids at the sn-2 position, where arachidonic acid (AA) is acetylated.

AA Metabolites and Angiogenesis

Once released, free AA has different potential fates: direct regulation of several target proteins (ion channels, enzymes), diffusion outside the cell, reincorporation into phospholipids and metabolism (Piomelli, 1993). Metabolism of AA is carried out by three enzyme families: cyclooxygenases (COX), which generate prostaglandins, prostacyclins and thromboxanes, lipoxygenases (LOX), that produce leukotrienes, and cytocrome P450 monooxygenases, yielding a variety of epoxyeicosatrienoic and hydroperoxyeicosatetraenoic acids (see Figure 5).

All these compounds are collectively called eicosanoids, and act as autocrine or paracrine regulators of a variety of functions, particularly in inflammatory processes (Barrett and Bigby, 1995).

Notably, several lines of evidence suggest their involvement in the control of EC proliferation and angiogenesis progression.

In ECs from bovine adrenal cortex capillaries, AA release and the LOX pathway play a critical role in vascular cell proliferation induced by bFGF, PDGF and serum (Dethlefsen et al., 2000). In ECs isolated from bovine aorta, cPLA2 is activated by bFGF through p42 MAPK-dependent phosphorylation, triggering the release of AA (Sa et al., 1995): moreover, in the same cell type, bFGF is a potent stimulator of proliferation through the LOX pathway of AA metabolism (Fafeur et al., 1991). Therefore, in general, LOX metabolites display mitogenic activity on ECs (Nie et al., 2000), while eicosanoids produced by the cyclooxygenase pathway are considered to be predominantly involved in the stimulation of migration (Dormond et al., 2001; Sa & Fox, 1995). However, recent evidence for a role of COX metabolism in EC proliferation has been provided in BAECs (Antoniotti et al., 2003).

Some of the pathways cited above can lead to other second messengers, potentially involved in the activation of calcium-permeable channels in the plasmamembrane, notably, DAG (Hardie, 2003), and InsP3 itself (Merle et al., 1995; Distasi et al., 1998; see fig. 4): for these two messengers, up to now no clear evidence is available that the related calcium fluxes may have a mitogenic role. Moreover, for InsP3-dependent calcium channels the mechanism of activation is still debated (Zitt et al. 2001): the case is particularly sensitive, since both store-dependent and independent mechanisms have been proposed (Kiselyov et al., 1998; Ma et al., 2001).

AA and Calcium

AA itself and some of its metabolites are able to induce mitogenically-related calcium increases in fibroblasts and ECs (Munaron et al., 1997; Fiorio Pla and Munaron, 2001; Antoniotti et al., 2003).

The direct effect of AA, independent on its metabolites, has been revealed via two major strategies: the pharmacological inhibition of COX, LOX and P450 MO (using indomethacin, NDGA, econazole derivatives and other compounds, some of which highly aspecific) or the use of ETYA, an AA analogue not metabolized by the enzymes cited above, able to mimic at least partially AA-dependent calcium entry (Munaron et al., 1997).

In bovine aortic ECs (BAECs), AA induces a sustained NCCE involved in the control of proliferation: it is probably due to more than one type of calcium channels, whose molecular nature is not known (Fiorio Pla & Munaron, 2001). In the same cells, NCCE is also activated by mitogenic growth factors, including bFGF, IGF-I and (Munaron & Fiorio Pla, 2000).

Nitric Oxide Metabolism and Calcium

NO and Angiogenesis

Several lines of evidence point to a relationship between NO release and angiogenesis progression (Cooke, 2003). However, the selective role of NO in the different steps of endothelial biochemical modifications during angiogenesis (mainly proliferation) is debated.

Many angiogenic factors increase the expression of endothelial NO synthase (eNOS) and stimulate the release of endothelium-derived NO. VEGF augments the endothelial expression of NOS, and stimulates the biosynthesis of NO from cultured human umbilical venous ECs and vascular segments of rabbit thoracic aorta (Hood et al., 1998; van der Zee et al., 1997). Similarly, transforming growth factor beta (TGFß) or bFGF trigger NO release in ECs (Inoue et al. 1995; Wu et al., 1996; Tiefenbacher et al., 1997).

A number of different approaches show the global involvement of NO in angiogenesis .

Stimulation of human umbilical venous ECs in a three-dimensional gel with bFGF or VEGF triggers NO production and let them to form capillary-like structures. This process is abolished by the NOS antagonist *N*ω-nitro-l-arginine methylester (L-NAME) (Babaei et al., 1998; Papapetropoulos et al., 1997). The same effect of L-NAME is observed in the rabbit cornea, another model of angiogenesis (Ziche et al., 1997).

NO appears to affect more than one step of angiogenesis process, acting as a freely diffusible pleiotropic factor on different cell types: in particular, this ability is clearly exerted on endothelial and smooth muscle cells.

NO is an endothelial survival factor, inhibiting apoptosis (Dimmeler et al., 1999; Rossig et al., 1999): it increases proliferation of some EC types and reduces it in others (Morbidelli et al., 1996; Ziche et al., 1997; Bussolati et al., 2001).

NO also promotes endothelial migration (Ziche et al., 1994; Murohara et al., 1992), possibly via the activation of podokinesis (Noiri et al., 1995). In addition, NO enhances matrix–endothelial cell interaction by inducing the expression of αvβ3 (Murohara et al., 1992) (the ligand for the extracellular matrix protein Del-1, which is itself known to induce angiogenesis) and by increasing disruption of the extracellular matrix via the bFGF-induced upregulation of urokinase-type plasminogen activator (Ziche et al., 1997).

Intriguing evidences point to the ability of NO to act as vasodilator. Increased flow in the skeletal microcirculation has been observed to trigger endothelial cell proliferation (Hudlicka et al., 1998) and it is therefore possible that in addition to its direct effects on endothelial cell proliferation, NO may influence endothelial growth indirectly by increasing blood flow locally. Detailed mechanisms underlying this process are not known, but the effect of NO on endothelial mechanically gated calcium-permeable channels activated by shear stress could be a critical route (Yao et al., 2000; see below).

Finally, it should be noted that NO can induce the synthesis and release of VEGFfrom vascular cells, giving rise to a positive feedback (Dulack et al., 2000).

NO and Calcium

NO release is controlled by calcium elevation, due to eNOS calcium-sensitivity (Fleming & Busse, 1999; Fleming & Busse, 2003). Accordingly to its plasmamembrane association, eNOS has been proposed to be preferentially recruited by calcium entry more than by calcium release from intracellular stores in bovine aortic ECs (Koyama et al., 2002). Moreover, prolonged capacitative calcium entry strongly activates eNOS (Lin et al. 2000). On the other hand, eNOS can be activated by calcium-independent additional Dulack, such as PI3K-Akt signalling (Dimmeler et al., 1999; Fulton et al., 1999; see Fig.5).

Nitric oxide has been shown to affect calcium homeostasis in ECs in different ways. Flow induced calcium entry, mediated by mechanically-gated calcium-permeable channels, is sensitive to a protein kinase G-activated conductance in rat aortic ECs (see above; Yao et al., 2000: Yao & Huang, 2003). In porcine pulmonary artery ECs (PAECs) NO upregulates the expression of cyclic nucleotide gated channels and activates a cGMP-independent calcium entry (Zhang et al., 2002; Berkels et al., 2000). In calf pulmonary artery ECs (CPAECs), NO inhibits CCE and enhances endoplasmic reticulum uptake of calcium (Dedkova & Blatter, 2002). In these reports, NO is not explicitly associated with cell proliferation: nevertheless, due to the ability of several mitogens to release this messenger, it could play a critical role in the control of calcium signals related to proliferative processes.

Interestingly, NO has been recently suggested as a mediator of AA-induced calcium entry in smooth muscle cells and isolated mouse parotid cells (Moneer et al., 2003; Watson et al., 2004).

In conclusion the pathways leading to mitogen-induced intracellular calcium increase are calcium-dependent: some members of the phospholipase A2 (PLA2) (that release AA), PLC (releasing DAG and InsP3) and NOS families are calcium-regulated. This may establish a non-linear positive loop contributing to the complexity of the signal. Conversely, it has been shown that some receptor and cytosolic TKs are inhibited by calcium elevation, thus generating a negative feedback (Gandino et al., 1991; Epstein, 1995).

Towards Specificity

Technical Advancements in Calcium Measurements

The synthesis of fluorescent calcium-sensitive dyes, in the seventies, allowed for the first time to measure intracellular calcium signals in living cells (Takahashi et al., 1999).

Now several calcium probes are available with different spectral properties. Some of them are excited by UV light (fura-2, indo-1); a special property is their ability to allow absolute calcium measurements through the production of a calibration curve and applying a ratiometric algorithm that describe the shift of excitation or emission spectra. Ratiometric measurements avoid the problems due to the variability of the optical pathway and the biological preparation over the time. However, UV excitation generates acute and chronic toxic effects and is filtered by low quality lens in the optical pathways (Takahashi et al., 1999).

Probes excited by visible light (fluo-3, calcium greens and others) give relative calcium estimation, but show a higher emission and are not biased by UV drawbacks.

These calcium-sensitive fluorescent probes are usually introduced into the cells as inactive acetoxymethyl esters, freely permeable through the plasmamembrane and rapidly idrolysed by cytosolic esterases: the final effect is that cytosolic acidic form of the active probe is compartmentalized in the cytosol. Another approach, usually combined with patch clamp, is the introduction of the active probe directly via the patch pipette.

Improvement of calcium measurements has been recently obtained by the use of two approaches: recombinant aequorin and confocal microscopy.

Aequorin is a calcium-sensitive luminescent protein extracted from jellyfish Aequorea (Rizzuto et al., 1999). Aequorin fused with peptidic domains involved in the protein targeting allows calcium measurements in different intracellular organelles (nucleus, mitochondria, endoplasmic reticulum, Golgi membranes): in particular, this approach revealed the physiological role of mitochondria as intracellular calcium buffers associated with local microdomains in which the levels of calcium can reach high values (Pozzan et al., 2000; Rizzuto et al., 2000).

A relevant change in our view of spatiotemporal intracellular calcium dynamics has been carried by the introduction of confocal laser scanning microscopy (CLSM): calcium microdomains have been revealed in excitable and nonexcitable cells, and particular attention has been focused on the basis of the specificity of the calcium-mediated cellular response (see below).

Spatial Dynamics of Calcium Signals: From Elementary to Global Events

The improvement of confocal laser scanning microscopy (CLSM) using calcium-sensitive fluorescent dyes allowed to increase spatial resolution and revealed the existence of localized intracellular calcium signals (microdomains called blips, puffs, quarks) in different cell types, including ECs (Bootman et al., 2001; Macrez & Mironneau, 2004; Huser et al., 1997-1999): when diffusional and regenerative mechanisms are triggered, these elementary events evolve to global calcium waves involving all the cell volume, including the nucleus. Calcium microdomains have been detected in several regions: near the plasmamembrane calcium channels and close to ER releasing sites: such signals can remain localized and activate and/or recruit effectors in the vicinity. In bovine vascular ECs, focal ATP stimulation results in spatially restricted Ca release and capacitative calcium entry (Huser et al., 1997, 1999; fig.5). Mitochondria are involved in the local regulation of capacitative calcium entry and store refilling in HUVECs (Malli et al., 2003).

Caveolae, special membrane microdomains, may play a relevant role in controlling the spatial and temporal pattern of intracellular Ca signalling (Isshiki & Anderson, 1999).

Endothelial caveolae include several components of intracellular signalling such as calcium pumps, IP3 receptor-like proteins, eNOS, PLC, PKC, and both GPCR and RTKs (Goligorsky et al., 2002).

Temporal Dynamics of Calcium Signals and Gene Expression

Increased concentrations of free Ca^{2+} in the cytosol trigger arrays of both rapid and sustained events, respectively ranging in seconds/minutes and hours/days. These responses are highly variable from a cell type to another. Moreover, single cell analysis points to the existence of a variability also in the same cell population, depending on quali-quantitative differential expression of receptors, signalling molecules, calcium channels and other elements of intracellular signalling (Munaron, 2002).

The detailed mechanisms underlying the complex relationship between calcium signals with different time courses and gene activation are not known: however, some recent evidences will enable us to begin to answer this question (Dolmetsch et al., 1998; Li et al., 1998).

In T and B lymphocytes maturation and activation, the induction of a small transient spike due to calcium release from internal stores is sufficient to activate a specific pattern of signalling molecules and transcription factors such as NF-kB and JNK. However this brief calcium event fails to activate other transcription factors, notably NFAT. In resting cells the phosphorylated form of this protein is located in the cytosol: after stimulation, it is dephosphorylated by the calcium-dependent phosphatase calcineurin and translocates in the nucleus. As a result, only a long lasting calcium increase, mediated by calcium entry, is able to sustain NFAT activation (Dolmetsch et al., 1998).

DNA microarray analysis on T lymphocytes confirms these evidence providing further informations: calcium-dependent signalling mediates both gene induction and gene repression by integration of inputs from calcium store depletion, calcium entry, calcineurin activation and other downstream pathways (Feske et al., 2001).

Even if these observations have been provided on a particular and highly specialized cell type, they may be useful as a working hypothesis to be verified in other cell types, including ECs. A relevant goal could be to identify the role of calcium signals in the switch between the different events involving ECs during angiogenesis: proliferation, migration and reorganization in a new vessel.

References

Alessandro R, Masiero L, Lapidos K, Spoonster J, Kohn EC. *Biochem. Biophys. Res. Commun.* 248: 635, 1998.

Antoniotti S, Fiorio Pla A, Pregnolato S, Mottola A, Lovisolo D, Munaron L, *J. Cell. Physiol.,* 197: 370, 2003.

Antoniotti S, Lovisolo D, Fiorio Pla A, Munaron L. *FEBS Lett.*, 510: 189, 2002.

Asano M, Nakajima T, Iwasawa K, Asakura Y, Morita T, Nakamura F, Tomaru T, Wang Y, Goto A, Teruhiko T, Soma M, Suzuki S, Okuda Y. *Eur. J. Pharmacol.*, 379:199, 1999.

Babaei S, Teichert-Kuliszewska K, Monge JC, Mohamed F, Bendeck MP, Stewart DJ. *Circ Res* 82:1007, 1998.

Barbiero G, Munaron L, Antoniotti S, Baccino FM, Bonelli G, Lovisolo D. *Cell Calcium*, 18: 538, 1995.

Barrett KE, Bigby TD. *NIPS* 10:153, 1995.

Bauer KS, Cude KJ, Dixon SC, Kruger EA, Figg W. *J. Pharmacol. Exp. Ther.* 292:31, 2000.

Benzaquen LR, Brugnara C, Byers HR, Gattoni-Celli S, Halperin JA. *Nature Med.* 1:534, 1995.

Berkels R, Suerhoff S, Roesen R, Klaus W. *Microvasc. Res.*, 59:38, 2000.

Berridge MJ, Bootman MD, Lipp P. *Nature* 395: 645, 1998.

Berridge MJ. *BioEssays* 17: 491, 1995.

Berridge MJ. *Nature*. 361:315, 1993.

Bertolesi GE, Shi C, Elbaum L, Jollimore C, Rozenberg G, Barnes S, Kelly ME. *Mol. Pharmacol.* 62: 210, 2002.

Byron KL, Babnigg GG, Villereal ML. *J.Biol.Chem.* 267:108, 1992.

Bodding M. *Cell Calcium* 30:141, 2001.

Bootman MD, Lipp P, Berridge MJ. *J Cell Sci.*114:2213, 2001.

Broad LM, Cannon TR, Taylor CW. *J. Physiol.* 517:121, 1999.

Buess M, Engler O, Hirsh H, Moroni C. *Oncogene* 18:1487, 1999.
Bussolati B, Dunk C, Grohman M, Kontos CD, Mason J, Ahmed A. *Am. J Pathol.* 159:993. 2001.
Catterall WA. *Annu. Rev. Cell. Dev. Biol.* 16:521, 2000.
Chaib N, Cabre E, Metioui M, Alzola E, Dantinne C, Marino A, Dehaye JP. *Cell Calcium* 23:395, 1998.
Chemin J, Monteil A, Briquaire C, Richard S, Perez-Reyes E, Nargeot J, Lory P. *FEBS Lett.* 478:166, 2000.
Chen CF, Corbley MJ, Roberts TM, Hess P. *Science* 239:1024, 1988.
Chyb S, Raghu P, Hardie RC. *Nature*, 397: 255, 1999.
Ciardo A, Meldolesi J. Eur. *J. Pharmacol.* 188:417, 1990.
Clapham DE, Runnels LW, Strübing C. *Nature Rev.* 2:387, 2001.
Clapham DE. *Nature* 426:517, 2003.
Clark JD, Kriz RW, Ramesha CS, Sulzman LA, Lin AY, Milona N, Knopf JL. *Cell* 85:1043, 1991.
Cooke JP. *Atherosclerosis suppl.* 4:53, 2003.
Corsini A, Bonfatti M, Quarato P, Accomazzo MR, Reiteri M, Spartani A, Testa R, Nicosia S, Paletti R, Fumagalli R. J. Cardiovasc. *Pharmacol.* 28:687, 1996.
Curtis BM, Catterall WA. *Biochemistry* 23:2113, 1984.
Davies SP, Reddy H, Caivano M, Cohen P. *Biochem. J.* 351:95, 2000.
Dedkova EN, Blatter LA. *J. Physiol.* 539:77, 2002.
Dethlefsen SM, Shepro D, D'Amore PA. *Exp Cell Res* 212:262, 1994.
Dimmeler S, Fleming I, Fisslthaler B, Hermann C, Busse R, Zeiher AM. *Nature* 399:601-605, 1999.
Dimmeler S, Hermann C, Galle J, Zeiher AM. *Arterioscler Thromb Vasc Biol* 19:656, 1999.
Distasi C, Torre M, Antoniotti S, Munaron L, Lovisolo D. Eur. *J. Neurosci.* 10:2276, 1998.
Distler JH, Hirth A, Kurowska-Stolarska M, Gau RE, Distler O. Q.*J.Nucl.Med.* 47:149, 2003.
Dormond O, Foletti A, Paroz C, Ruegg C. *Nature Med* 7:1041, 2001.
Dulak J, Jozkowicz A, Dembinska-Kiec A, Guevara I, Zdzienicka A, Zmudzinska-Grochot D, et al. Arterioscler. *Thromb. Vasc. Biol.* 20:659, 2000.
Encabo A, Romanin C, Birke FW, Kukovetz WR, Groschner K. Br. *J. Pharmacol.* 119:702, 1996.
Epstein R. *Cell. Signal.* 7: 377, 1995.
Estacion M & Mordan LJ. *Cell. Signall.* 9:363, 1997.
Estacion M, Mordan LJ. *Cell Calcium* 14:439, 1993.
Faelhing M, Kroll J, Fohr KJ, Fellbrich G, Mayr U, Trischler G, Waltenberger J. *FASEB J.* 10:1805, 2002.
Fafeur V, Zhi PJ, Bohlen P. *J Cell Physiol* 149:277, 1991.
Feske S, Giltnane J, Dolmetsch R, Staudt LM, Rao A. *Nature Immunol.* 2: 316, 2001.
Fiorio Pla A & Munaron L. *Cell Calcium* 30:235, 2001.
Fleming I, Busse R. Am. J. Physiol. Regul. Integr. Comp. *Physiol.* 284:R1, 2003.
Fleming I, Busse R. *Cardiovasc Res.* 43:532, 1999.
Franzius D, Hoth M, Penner R. *Pflugers Arch.* 428:433, 1994.
Fulton D, Gratton JP, McCabe TJ, Fontana J, Fujio Y, Walsh K, Franke TF, Papapetropoulos A, Sessa WC. *Nature* 399: 597, 1999.

Fürst J, Haller T, Chwatal S, Woll E, Dartsch PC, Gschwentner M, Dienstl A, Zwierzina H, Lang F, Paulmich M, Ritter M. *Cell Physiol. Biochem.* 12:19, 2002.

Gamberucci A, Fulceri R, Benedetti A, Bygrave FL. Biochem. *Biophys. Res. Commun.* 248:75, 1998.

Gamberucci A, Giurisato E, Pizzo P, Tassi M, Giunti R, McIntosh DP, Benedetti A. *Biochem. J.* 364:245, 2002.

Gandino L, Munaron L, Naldini L, Ferracini R, Magni M, Comoglio PM. *J. Biol. Chem.*, 266:16098, 1991.

Garnier-Ravenaud S, Usson Y, Cand F, Robert-Nicoud M, Verdetti J, Faury G. Growth *Factors* 19:35, 2001.

Gawler DJ. Biochim. *Biophys. Acta*, 1448:171, 1998.

Ghitescu L, Robert M. *Microsc. Res. Tech.* 57:381-9, 2002.

Golilorsky MS, Li H, Brodsky S, Chen J. *Am J Physiol* 283:F1, 2002.

Golovina VA, Platoshyn O, Bailey CL, Wang J, Limsuwan A, Sweeney M, Rubin LJ, Yuan JX. Am. J. Physiol. *Heart Circ. Physiol.* 280:H746, 2001.

Golovina VA. *Am. J. Physiol.* 277:C343, 1999.

Graier WF Simecek S, Sturek M. *J. Physiol.* 482:259, 1995.

Hardie RC. *Annu. Rev. Physiol.*, 65:735, 2003.

Hille B. Ion channels of excitable membranes. Sinauer Associates, Inc. Sunderland, 2001.

Hofmann T, Schaefer M, Schultz G, Gudermann T. *Proc. Natl. Acad. Sci. USA* 99:7461, 2002.

Holmuhamedov E, Lewis L, Bienengraeber M, Holmuhamedova M, Ahangir A, Terzic A. *FASEB J.* 116:1010, 2002.

Hood JD, Meininger CJ, Ziche M, Granger HJ. *Am J Physiol* 274:H1054, 1998.

Hryshko LV, Philipson KD. *Basic Res Cardiol. 92 Suppl* 1:45-51, 1997.

Hudlicka O. *Microcirculation* 5:7, 1998.

Huser J, Blatter LA. *Am J Physiol.* 273:C1775, 1997.

Huser J, Holda JR, Kockskamper J, Blatter LA. *J. Physiol.* 514:101, 1999.

Hussain MM, Kotz H, Minasian L, Premkumar A, Sarosy G, Reed E, Zhai S, Steinberg SM, Raggio M, Oliver VK, Figg WD, Kohn EC. *J Clin Oncol.* 21:4356, 2003.

Ichikawa J, Kiyohara T. Cell Biochem. *Funct.* 19:213, 2001.

Improta-Brears T, Whorton R, Codazzi F, York JD, Meyer T, McDonnell DP. *PNAS* 96, 4686, 1999.

Inoue N, Venema RC, Sayegh HS, Ohara Y, Murphy TJ, Harrison DG. *Arterioscler Thromb Vasc Biol* 15:1255, 1995.

Isshiki M, Anderson RG. *Cell Calcium*, 26:201, 1999.

Jan CR, Ho CM, Wu SN, Tseng CJ. *Biochem. Biophys. Acta* 1448:533, 1999.

Jan CR, Tseng CJ, Chou KJ, Chiang HT. *Life Sci.* 66:2289, 2000.

Jan CR, Tseng CJ. *Life Sci.* 65:2513, 1999.

Javerzat S, Auguste P, Bikfalvi A. *Trends Mol. Med.* 8:483, 2002.

Jiang L, Jha V, Dhanabal M, Sukhatme VP, Alper SL. *Am. J. Physiol. Cell. Physiol.* 280:C1140, 2001.

Jiang Y, Lee A, Chen J, Ruta V, Cadene M, Chalt BT, Mc Kinnon R. *Nature* 423:33, 2003.

Kahl CR, Means AR. *Endocr. Rev.* 24:719, 2003.

Kann H, Ruan Y, Malik KU. *J. Pharmacol. Exp. Ther.* 282:113, 1997.

Kanzaki M, Zhang YQ, Mashima H, Li L, Shibata H, Kojima I. *Nat. Cell Biol.*, 1:165, 1999.

Kawanabe Y, Hashimoto N, Masaki T. *Am. J. Physiol. Cell. Physiol.* 282:C330, 2002.
Kawanabe Y, Hashimoto N, Masaki T. *Eur. J. Physiol.* 435:119, 2002.
Kawanabe Y, Hashimoto N, Miwa S, Masaki T. *Eur. J. Physiol.* 447:31, 2002.
Kawanabe Y, Okamoto Y, Hashimoto N, Masaki T. *Eur. J. Physiol.* 422:15, 2001.
Kim KS, Hong YK, Lee Y, Shin JY, Chang SI, Chung SI, Joe YA. *Exp. Mol. Med.* 35:578, 2003.
Kiselyov K, Xu X, Mozhayeva G, Kuo T, Pessah I, Mignery G, Zhu X, Birnbaumer L, Muallem S. *Nature* 396:478, 1998.
Kohn EC, Alessandro R, Spoonster J, Wersto RP, Liotta LA. *Proc. Natl. Acad. Sci. U S A* 92:1307, 1995.
Kohn EC, Felder CC, Jacobs W, Holmes KA, Day A, Freer R, Liotta LA. *Cancer Res.* 54:935, 1994.
Kohn EC, Jacobs W, Kim YS, Alessandro R, Stetler-Stevenson WG, Liotta LA. *J. Biol. Chem.* 269:21505, 1994.
Kohn EC, Jacobs W, Kim YS, Alessandro R, Stetler-Stevenson WG, Liotta LA. *J. Biol. Chem.* 269:21505, 1994.
Kohn EC, Liotta LA. *Cancer Res.* 55:1856, 1995.
Kohn EC, Liotta LA. J. Natl. *Cancer Inst.* 82:54, 1990.
Kohn EC, Reed E, Sarosy G, Christan M, Link CJ, Cole K, Figg WD, Davis PA, Jacob J, Goldspiel B, Liotta LA. *Cancer Res.* 56:569, 1996.
Kohn EC, Reed E, Sarosy GA, Minasian L, Bauer KS, Bostick-Bruton F, Kulpa V, Fuse E, Tompkins A, Noone M, Goldspiel B, Pluda J, Figg WD, Liotta LA. *Clin. Cancer Res.* 7:1600, 2001.
Kohn EC, Sandeen MA, Liotta LA. *Cancer Res.* 52:3208, 1992.
Kojima I, Matsunaga H, Kurokawa K, Ogata E, Nishimoto I. *J. Biol. Chem.* 263:16561, 1988.
Kojima I, Mogami H, Ogata E. *Am. J. Physiol.* 262:E307, 1992.
Kojima I, Mogami H, Shibata H, Ogata E. *J. Biol. Chem.* 268:10003, 1993.
Kokoska ER, Smith GS, Miller TA. *J. Gastrointest. Surg.* 4:150, 2000.
Koyama T, Kimura C, Park SJ, Oike M, Ito Y. *Life Sci.* 72:511, 2002.
Krautwurst D, Hescheler J, Arndts D, Losel W, Hammer R, Schultz G. *Mol. Pharmacol.* 43:655, 1993.
Kruse HJ, Bauriedel G, Heimerl J, Hofling B, Weber PC. *J. Cardiovasc. Pharmacol.* 24:328, 1994.
Kuwahara M, Miyaji T, Tsubone H. *Eur. J. Pharmacol.* 388:21, 2000.
Li WH, Llopis J, Whitney M, Zlokarnuk G, Tsien RY. *Nature* 392:936, 1998.
Lin LL, Wartmann M, Lin AY, Knopf JL, Seth A, Davis RJ. *Cell* 72:269, 1993.
Lin S, Fagan KA, Li KX, Shaul PW, Cooper DM, Rodman DM. *J. Biol. Chem.* 275:17979, 2000.
Lipskaia L, Lompre AM. *Biol Cell.* 96:55, 2004.
Lovisolo D, Distasi C, Antoniotti S, Munaron L. *News Physiol. Sci.* 12:279, 1997.
Luzzi KJ, Varghese HJ, McDonald IC, Kohn EC, Schmidt EE, Morris VL, Chambers AF, Groom AC. *Angiogenesis* 2:373, 1999.
Ma HT, Venkatachalam K, Li HS, Montell C, Kurosaki T, Patterson RL, Gill DL. *J. Biol. Chem.* 276:18888, 2001.
Macrez N, Mironneau J. *Curr. Mol. Med.* 4:263, 2004.
Magni M, Meldolesi J, Pandiella A. *J. Biol. Chem.* 266:6329, 1991.

Magnier-Gaubil C, Herbert JM, Quark R, Papp B, Corvazier E, Wuytack F, Levy-Toledano S, Enouf J. *J. Biol. Chem.* 271:27788, 1996.
Mathov I, Plotkin LI, Sgarlata CL, Leoni J, Bellido T. *J. Bone Miner. Res.* 16: 2050, 2001.
Merle PL, Feige JJ, Verdetti J. *J. Biol. Chem.* 270:17361, 1995.
Merritt JE, Armstrong WP, Benham CD, Hallam TJ, Jacob R, Jaxa-Chamiec, A, Leigh BK, McCarthy SA, Moores KE, Rink TJ. *Biochem. J.* 271:515, 1990.
Mignen O, Shuttleworth TJ. *J. Biol. Chem.* 275:9114, 2000.
Moll V, Weick M, Milenkovic I, Kodal H, Reichenbach A, Bringmann A. *Invest. Ophthalmol. Vis. Sci.* 43:766, 2002.
Moneer Z, Dyer JL, Taylor CW. *Biochem. J.* 370:439, 2003.
Montell C, Rubin MR. *Neuron* 2:1313, 1989.
Moody TW, Chiles J, Moody E, Sieczkiewicz GJ, Kohn EC. *Lung Cancer.* 39:279, 2003.
Morbidelli L, Chang CH, Douglas JG, Granger HJ, Ledda F, Ziche M. *Am. J. Physiol.* 270:H411, 1996.
Munaron L, Antoniotti S, Distasi C, Lovisolo D. *Cell Calcium* 22: 179, 1997.
Munaron L, Fiorio Pla A. J. *Cell. Physiol.* 185:454, 2000.
Munaron L. Int. J. *Mol. Med.* 10:671, 2002.
Murohara T, Asahara T, Takahashi T. *Circulation (Suppl)* 267:24173, 1992.
Nie D, Tang K, Diglio C, Honn KV. *Blood* 95:2304, 2000.
Nilius B, Droogmans G. *Physiol. Rev.* 81:1415, 2001.
Noiri E, Lee E, Testa J, Quigley J, Colflesh D, Keese CR, et al. *Am. J. Physiol.* 274:C236, 1998.
Papapetropoulos A, Garcia-Cardena G, Madri JA, Sessa WC. *J Clin Invest* 100:3131, 1997.
Patton AM, Kassis J, Doong H, Kohn EC. Curr. *Pharm. Des.* 9:543, 2003.
Penner R, Fasolato C, Hoth M. *Current Op. Neurobiol.* 3:368, 1993.
Piomelli D. *Curr. Op. Cell. Biol.* 5:274, 1993.
Pozzan T, Magalhães TP, Rizzuto R. *Cell Calcium* 28:279, 2000.
Raicu M, Florea S, Costache G, Popov D, Simionescu M. *Fundam. Clin. Pharmacol.* 14:477, 2000.
Rizzo MA, Romero G. *Pharmacol. Ther.* 94:35, 2002.
Rizzuto R, Bernardi P, Pozzan T. *J. Physiol.* 529: 37, 2000.
Rizzuto R, Pinton P, Brini M, Chiesa A, Filippin L, Pozzan T. *Cell Calcium* 26:193, 1999.
Rossig L, Fichtlscherer B, Breitschopf K, Haendeler J, Zeiher AM, Mulsch A, et al. *J. Biol. Chem.* 274:6823, 1999.
Roth-Eichhorn S, Eberheim A, Bode HP, Gressner AM. *J. Hepatol.* 30:612, 1999.
Rozengurt E. *J. Cell. Physiol.* 177:507, 1998.
Rudolf R, Mongillo M, Rizzuto R, Pozzan T.*Nat. Rev. Mol. Cell. Biol.* 4:579, 2003.
Ryder NM, Guha S, Hines OJ, Reber HA, Rozengurt E. *J Cell. Physiol.* 186 :53, 2001.
Sa G, Murugesan G, Jaye M, Ivashchenko Y, Fox PL. *J. Biol. Chem.* 270:2360, 1995.
Sanchez T, Moreno JJ. *J. Cell. Physiol.* 193:293, 2002.
Santella L. Biochem. *Biophys. Res. Comm.* 244:317, 1998.
Schwartz G, Droogmans G, Nilius B. *Cell Calcium* 15:45, 1994.
Shuttleworth TJ & Mignen O. *Biochem.Soc.Trans.* 31:916, 2003.
Six DA, Dennis EA. Biochim. *Biophys. Acta* 1488:1, 2000.
Snajdrova L, Xu A, Narayanan N. *J. Biol. Chem.* 273:28032, 1998.
Soboloff J, Zhang Y, Minden, M, Berger SA. *Exp. Hematol.* 30:1219, 2002.

Sridhar SS, Seymour L, Shepherd FA. *Lancet Oncol.* 4:397, 2003.
Strobeck MW, Okuda M, Yamaguchi H, Schwartz A, Fukasawa K. *J. Biol. Chem.* 274:15694, 1999.
Sweeney M, McDaniel SS, Platoshyn O, Zhang S, Yu Y, Lapp BR, Zhao Y, Thistlethwaite PA, Yuan JX. *J. Appl. Physiol.* 92:1594, 2002.
Sweeney M, Yu Y, Platoshyn O, Zhang S, McDaniel SS, Yuan JX. Am. J. Physiol. Lung Cell. Mol. *Physiol.* 283:L144, 2002.
Takahashi A, Camacho P, Lechleiter JD, Herman B. *Physiol. Rev.* 79:1089, 1999.
Tiefenbacher CP, Chilian WM. *Cardiovasc Res* 34:411, 1997.
Tiemann U, Neels P, Pohland R, Walzel H, Lohrke B. *J. Reprod. Fertil.* 116:63, 1999.
van der Zee R, Murohara T, Luo Z, Zollmann F, Passeri J, Lekutat C, et al. *Circulation* 95:1030, 1997.
Vasquez G, Wedel BJ, Trebak M, St John Bird G, Putney JW Jr. *J. Biol. Chem.* 278:21649, 2003.
Verkhratsky A & Shmigol A. *Cell Calcium* 19:1, 1996.
Viana F, de Smet H, Droogmans G, Nilius B. *Cell Calcium* 24:117, 1998.
Vos Q, Lees A, Wu ZQ, Snapper CM, Mond JJ. *Immunol.Rev.* 176: 154–170, 2000.
Watson EL, Jacobson KL, Singh JC, DiJulio DH. *Cell Signal.* 16:157, 2004.
Weiss H, Amberger A, Widschwendter M, Margreiter R, Ofner D, Dietl P. *Int. J. Cancer* 92:877, 2001.
Whitaker M and Larman MG. *Calcium and mitosis seminars in Cell & Dev. Biol.* 12:53, 2001.
Willmott NJ, Choudhury Q, Flower RJ. *FEBS Lett.* 394:159, 1996.
Wu HM, Yuan Y, McCarthy M, Granger HJ. *Am J Physiol* 271:H1087, 1996.
Wu X, Babnigg G, Zagranichnaya T, Villereal ML. *J. Biol. Chem.* 277:13597, 2002.
Yao X & Huang Y. *Trends Pharm. Sci.* 24:263, 2003.
Yao X, Kwan HY, Chan FL, Chan NW, Huang Y. *FASEB J.* 14:932, 2000.
Yoo HJ, Kozaki K, Akishita M, Watanabe M, Eto M, Nagano K, Sudo N, Hashimoto M, Kim S, Yoshizumi M, Toba K, Ouchi Y. *Atherosclerosis* 131:167, 1997.
Zhang W, Couldwell WT, Song H, Takano T, Lin JHC, Nedergaard M. *Cancer Res.* 60:5395, 2000.
Zhou X, Ono H, Ono Y, Frohlich ED. *J. Hypertens.* 20:993, 2002.
Ziche M, Morbidelli L, Choudhuri R, Zhang HT, Donnini S, Granger HJ, et al. *J Clin Invest* 99:2625, 1997.
Ziche M, Morbidelli L, Masini E, Amerini S, Granger HJ, Maggi CA, et al. *J. Clin. Invest.* 94:2036, 1994.
Ziche M, Parenti A, Ledda F, Dell'Era P, Granger HJ, Maggi CA, et al. *Circ. Res.* 80:845, 1997.
Zitt C, Halaszovich CR, Lückhoff A. *Progress Neurobiol.* 66:243, 2002.

In: New Angiogenesis Research
Editor: Roberta V. Zubar, pp. 157-170

ISBN 1-59454-239-2

Chapter VIII

The Critical Role of Inflammatory Cell Infiltration in Tumor Angiogenesis: A Target for Anti-Tumor Drug Development?

Michihiko Kuwano [1, 2,*]***, Yuji Basaki*** [2]***, Takashi Kuwano*** [3]***,***
Nakao Shintaro [3]***, Shinji Oie*** [2]***, Yusuke N. Kimura*** [1]***,***
Teruhiko Fujii [1] ***and Mayumi Ono*** [2, 3]
[1]Kurume University, Fukuoka, Center for Innovative Cancer Therapy
[2]Kyushu University, Fukuoka, Station-II for Collaborative Research
[3]Kyushu University, Fukuoka, Department of Medical Biochemistry, Graduate School of Medical Science

Abstract

Inflammatory responses are often associated with acquisition of malignant characteristics in various human tumors. In this article, we focus on the idea that inflammatory angiogenesis is a critical component of tumor progression. Inflammatory angiogenesis may confer a specific microenvironment on each tumor, resulting in characteristic formation of stroma in the tumor. In particular, we suggest a critical role of macrophage infiltration in the tumor stroma in the development of angiogenesis by presenting experimental angiogenesis models in response to IL-1β and other inflammatory cytokines. We also discuss the anticancer therapeutic potential of molecular targets or cells appearing during the inflammatory angiogenesis.

---

* Send correspondence to Michihiko Kuwano, M.D., Ph.D. Center for Innovative Cancer Therapy, Kurume University, Kurume, Fukuoka, 830-0011, Japan; E-mail: michik@med.kurume-u.ac.jp.

Introduction

Since the first proposal that cancer is chronic inflammation by Dr. Virchow in 1863, the relationship between inflammation and cancer has often been disputed for almost one and half centuries. The appearance of a single precancerous cell with a mutated oncogene/ oncosuppressor gene, together with proliferation of cancer cells alone does not provide sufficient conditions to cause malignant tumor, because stroma components of cancer are essential for malignant tumor progression [1]. Inflammation in the tumor microenvironment enhances not only cell proliferation in the tissue injury during wound healing but also progression of cancer, injury without healing [2, 3]. Plausible mechanisms underlying the causal relationship between inflammation and cancer have recently been presented [1, 4]. Inflammation and tumor could be intercorrelated through hemangiogenesis [5] and lymphangiogenesis [6] (Figure 1). The mechanism for lymphangiogenesis as well as hemangiogenesis is now being investigated at the molecular basis [6]. Here we seek to give insight into the functional relationship between inflammation and cancer from the standpoint of angiogenesis.

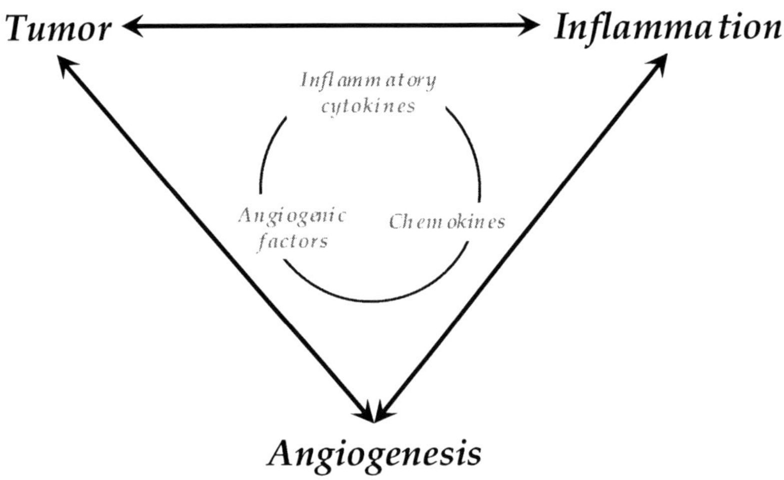

Figure 1. Inflammatory responders including inflammatory cells, cytokines and chemokines closely associated with angiogenesis greatly affect the stromal microenvironment in each malignant tumor. Cancer cells that produce abundant pro-inflammatory cytokines can induce activation of stromal cells including inflammatory cells to potentiate angiogenesis, resulting in the promotion of tumor growth and acquisition of various malignant characteristics.

Inflammatory Cells are the Main Components of Tumor Stroma

In the inflammatory response, wound healing is a self-limiting angiogenesis: neutrophils are the first recruited effector cells, and monocytes/ macrophages next migrate to the site of tissue injury in response to chemotactic cytokines. Once activated, monocytes produce various proangiogenic cytokines such as vascular endothelial growth factor (VEGF), tumor necrosis factor-α (TNF-α), interleukin-1α/β (IL-1α/β), IL-6, as well as extracellular matrices-degrading enzymes such as matrix metalloproteinases (MMPs) and plasminogen activators (PAs), and switch on angiogenesis, resulting in healing the injury site. On the other hand, during the inflammatory responses in malignant tumors, tumor cells produce various cytokines and chemokines that attract leukocytes such as neutrophils, dendritic cells, monocytes/ macrophages, eosinophils, mast cells and lymphocytes, which also produce various cytokines, proteases, reactive oxygen species. Of these inflammatory components, infiltration of monocytes/ macrophages appears to play key roles in the development of tumor and its acquisition of malignant characteristics. Macrophage infiltration is often associated with poor prognosis of cancer patients with breast cancer, cervical cancer, lung cancer, bladder cancer, glioma and melanoma [7 - 10]. Monocytes recruited by monocyte chemotactic protein-1 (MCP-1) are educated by the tumor environment, and these tumor educated macrophages, called tumor-associated macrophages (TAMs), are thought to support tumor progression and metastasis [4]. TAMs produce VEGF-A, VEGF-C and VEGF-D, IL-8, TNF-α, IL-1α/β, transforming growth factor-β (TGF-β), arachidonate metabolites and proteases, resulting in promotion of angiogenesis as well as lymphangiogenesis [11 - 13].

Angiogenesis by Inflammatory Cytokines through Augmentation of Potent Angiogenic Factors and Cyclooxygenase-2

Of various inflammatory cytokines, IL-1α and β, members of the IL-1 family, induce their signals through interaction with type I and type II IL-1 receptor, and IL-1 receptor antagonist (IL-1Ra) antagonizes (Figure 2). Expression of this signaling by IL-1 is often up-regulated and associated with pathological conditions of rheumatoid arthritis, septic shock, graft-versus-host disease, arteriosclerosis, asthma, adult T cell leukemia, multiple myeloma and many other tumor types, and angiogenesis is also closely associated with pathological conditions in these diseases. Concerning the direct involvement of IL-1α/β in tumor development, Voronov et al recently reported that IL-1α and β are required for development of angiogenesis and tumor in an experimental animal model [14]. Angiogenesis is markedly diminished in both IL-1α - and IL-1β -knockout mice, and tumor angiogenesis is much less abolished in IL-1β knockout mice than that in IL-1α knockout mice (Table 1). IL-1β promotes growth and invasion of cancer as well as angiogenesis in animal models with concomitant enhanced production of VEGF, IL-8, MMPs and adhesion molecules [15, 16] (see also Figure 3). IL-1α promotes angiogenesis *in vitro* as well as *in vivo* through up-regulation of VEGF, IL-8 and other angiogenesis-related factors [7, 10]. Although IL-1α and IL-1β share their receptor, type I IL-1 receptor, Song et al have recently proposed differential effects of IL-1α and IL-1β on tumorigeniciy patterns, invasiveness and angiogenesis [18 - 20] (Table 1). Acquisition of malignant characteristics of invasion, metastsis, and angiogenesis thus appears to be mediated through these inflammatory cytokines, suggesting a close linkage between cancer and inflammation. Overexpression of IL-1α in highly invasive fibrosarcoma cells results in a marked loss of tumor development with activation of antitumor immunological effector mechanism whereas IL-1β overproduction in fibrosarcoma cells results in enhancement of angiogenesis as well as enlargement, invasion and metastasis of tumor [18]. IL-1α thus reduces tumorigenicity by inducing antitumor immunity together with tumor suppression in the host, and IL-1β promotes invasiveness and angiogenesis of tumor.

Members of the IL-1 family

Receptors: Type I IL-1R and type II IL-1R

Agonists: IL-1α and IL-1β

Receptor antagonist: IL-1 receptor antagonist (IL-1Ra)

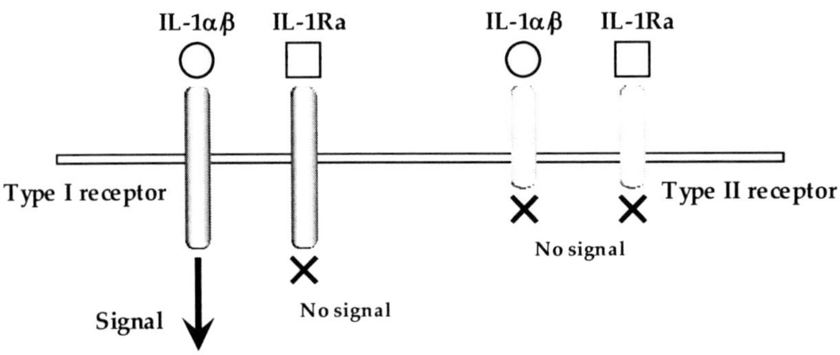

Figure 2. IL-1α and IL-1β induce their signaling through interaction with type I IL-1 receptor. The IL-1 family consists of IL-1 receptors type I (IL-1RI) and Type II (IL-1RII), receptor agonists IL-1α and IL-1β, and IL-1 receptor antagonist (IL-1Ra). IL-1α and IL-1β are produced as inactive precursors, pro-IL-1α and pro-IL-1β, respectively. Pro-IL-1α is cleaved by calpains and pro-IL-1β is cleaved by caspase-1 to generate mature forms. The binding of IL-1α and IL-1β to IL-1RI transduces the signal whereas binding to IL-1RII does not. IL-1Ra binds to both IL-1RI and IL-1RII without signal transduction and abrogates the association of IL-1α and IL-1β to the receptor.

Inflammation induces up-regulation of various angiogenesis-related factors. Treatment with TNF-α of vascular endothelial cells and cancer cells results in a marked induction of VEGF, bFGF, IL-8 and PA through activation of Sp-1, AP-1, hypoxia response element, NF-κB and other regulatory elements [21 - 23]. TNF-α or IL-1α also enhances production of VEGF, IL-8, bFGF and MMPs from cancer cells and endothelial cells, resulting in a switch of angiogenesis through autocrine/ paracrine controls [9, 12, 13] (Figure 3). On the other hand, α4 integrins that are counter-receptors for VCAM-1 are expressed on the surface of vascular endothelial cells [24], expression of α4 integrin and VCAM-1/ soluble VCAM-1 by TNF-α induces angiogenesis in the corneas of mice through p38 and FAK signaling pathways [25]. Expression of soluble VCAM-1 is also dramatically enhanced in vascular endothelial cells by IL-4 or IL-13 derived from mast cells [26, 27]. In addition, Kaneko et al have recently demonstrated that the binding of VEGF receptor to its ligand transduces signals through integrin-linked kinase associated with the integrin β chain in human endothelial cells, suggesting that integrin-mediated signals also cooperate with VEGF receptor in vascular endothelial cells to induce angiogenesis [28]. Taken together, these facts suggest that inflammatory cytokines-induced angiogenesis is mediated through enhanced production of angiogenesis regulatory factor and activation of various adhesion and integrin molecules by the cytokines.

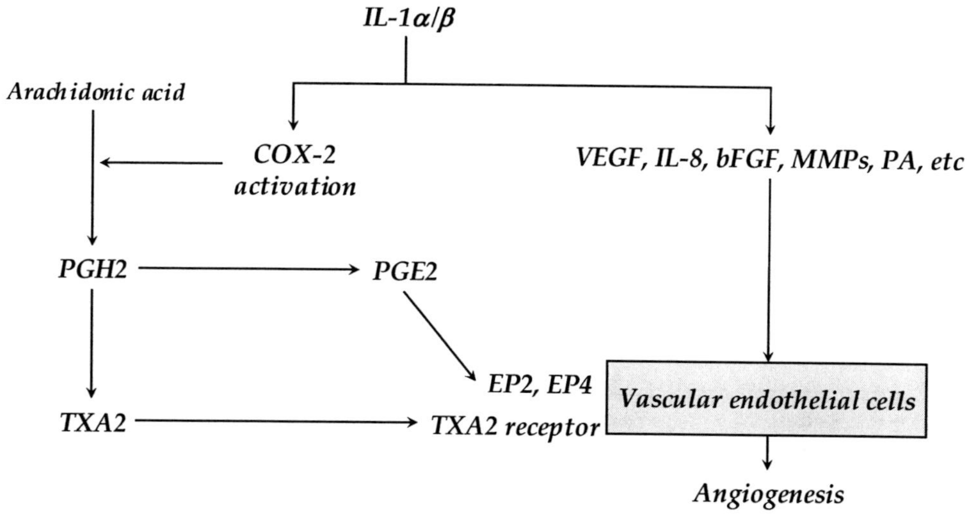

Figure 3. Angiogenesis by IL-1α/β is mediated through dual pathways: induction of angiogenesis-related factors and COX-2 activation. IL-1 stimulates induction of angiogenesis-related factors such as VEGF, IL-8, bFGF, MMPs and PA from vascular endothelial cells and other cell types. These factors co-operatively activate vascular endothelial cells resulting in angiogenesis. On the other hand, IL-1 induces angiogenesis through the activation of COX-2 in vascular endothelial cells and other cell types. PGE2 and TXA2 are expected to induce angiogenesis autocrine control. Recent study also demonstrates that PGF2 and TXA2 stimulate production of some angiogenesis-related factors, resulting in angiogenesis.

Table 1. The specific roles of IL-1α and IL-1β in various malignant characteristics of tumor including angiogenesis.

Experimental conditions	Findings	References
Tumor growth and angiogenesis by melanoma cells in IL-1α or IL-1β-knockout mice	• IL-1β is more closely associated with tumor growth and tumor angiogenesis than IL-1α	Voronov et al [14]
Lung cancer cell line expressing IL-1β	• Tumor growth and metastasis as well as angiogenesis are markedly enhanced by IL-1β	Yano et al [15] Saijo et al [16]
Mouse fibrosarcoma cells expressing IL-1α and IL-1β	• IL-1α reduces tumorigenicity by antitumor Immunity • IL-1β promotes invasiveness and tumor angiogenesis	Song et al [18]
Hepatic metastasis by IL-1α gene transfection in melanoma cell and effect of IL-1 receptor antagonist on tumor growth and metastasis	• IL-1α increases tumor cell adhesion to endothelial cell and VCAM-1 expression • IL-1α enhances melanoma hepatic metastasis	Anasagasti et al [19] Vidal-Vanaclocha et al [20]

On the other hand, cyclooxygenases (COXs) play a key role in tumor angiogenesis [29], probably in close association with inflammation. Of the two COXs, COX-1 and COX-2 that convert arachidonic acid to prostaglandins, the COX-2 can be induced by a variety of proinflammatory cytokines and growth factors. In a model of human familiar adenomatous polyps using mice with a targeted mutation in the APC tumor suppressor gene (Apc-knockout mice), polyp formation is markedly reduced in Apc/COX-2-knockout mice [30], and Seno et al have further reported that stromal expression of COX-2 is required for induction of VEGF and tumor angiogenesis [31]. Tumor growth as well as angiogenesis can be suppressed by COX-2 inhibitors when cancer cells express COX-2 [32]. The primary prostanoids, prostaglandin E2 (PGE2), PGF2α, PGD2, PGI2 and thromboxane A2 (TXA2) mediate angiogenesis, partly through modulation of VEGF levels in response to these prostanoids. VEGF levels are markedly decreased in tumors in the COX-2-knock out mice, suggesting that a close link between COX-2 and VEGF in tumor angiogenesis [33]. Concerning the possible role of COX-2 in tumor angiogenesis, COX-2 expression is elevated not only in cancer cells but also in microvasculatures, various infiltrating blood cell types and fibroblasts in the tumor stroma [29]. COX-2-expressing cancer cells form larger tumors than cancer cells that lack COX-2 expression [34]. However, it remains unclear whether COX-2 activity is directly involved in the up-regulation of the VEGF gene. Chang et al have also reported up-regulation of both VEGF and EP1, 2, 4 receptors in COX-2-transgenic mammary tissue, and PGE2 mostly stimulates expression of this potent angiogenic factor, VEGF, in mammary tumor cells [35]. In the tumor angiogenesis, PGE2-EP3 signaling also regulates tumor-angiogenesis and tumor growth [36].

A recent study by Kuwano et al demonstrated a close association of COX-2 activity with inflammatory cytokine IL-1β-induced angiogenesis *in vitro* and *in vivo* [37]. In their study, EP2, 4 agonists and TXA2 receptor agonist themselves induce angiogenesis in mouse corneas, and IL-1β-induced angiogenesis is inhibited by an EP4 antagonists and a TXA2 receptor antagonist. Moreover, IL-1β-induced angiogenesis is markedly abrogated in COX-2-knockout mice, and this angiogenesis was only partly blocked by co-administration of a VEGF receptor tyrosine kinase inhibitor [37]. From these findings, one can expect that inflammatory cytokine-induced angiogenesis is mediated through dual pathways: up-regulation of angiogenesis-regulated factors and also prostanoids produced by COX-2 (Figure 3).

Inflammatory Angiogenesis and Macrophage Infiltration are Essential for Development of Malignant Tumors Including Multiple Myeloma

Tumor growth and metastasis of solid tumor are dependent on hemangiogenesis and lymphangiogenesis [6,38]. Angiogenesis also appears to play a critical role during development of multiple myeloma [39]. Concerning the development of multiple myeloma, the bone marrow microenvironment includes both cytokines and growth factor, and also physical interaction with stroma cells and extracellular matrices. In this microenvironment, the interaction of multiple myeloma cells with various stromal cells types plays a key role in the pathogenesis of multiple myeloma [40]. Born marrow-related angiogenesis increases in multiple myeloma with malignancy progression [41, 42]. Bone marrow-related angiogenesis is thus expected to promote expansion of the multiple myeloma mass by inducing plasma cell proliferation. Moreover, high bone marrow angiogenesis is an adverse prognostic factor in multiple myeloma [43, 44]. Multiple myeloma cells produce and secrete potent angiogenic factors, MMPs and PAs in their microenvironment with a concomitant appearance of cytokines recruiting inflammatory cells such as mast cells, monocytes/ macrophages and neutrophils [39]. Formation of a network system by multiple myeloma cells and various stroma cells might promote angiogenesis in the multiple myeloma environment. Moreover, IL-6, a key enzyme for tumor growth for multiple myeloma cells, affects production of the potent angiogenic factor VEGF [45]. Other cytokines, TNF-α and IL-1, also stimulate expression of VEGF and other angiogenesis-related factors such as IL-8, bFGF in various cell types [10, 22, 23], and VEGF production by multiple myeloma cells is also elevated by these inflammatory cytokines [46, 47]. Thus, angiogenesis is expected to play a key role in acquirement of pathological characteristics during tumor progression in multiple myeloma cells [37] as well as in other solid tumor types [38, 48]. Inflammatory cytokines are thus expected to be implicated in angiogenesis not only during solid tumor development but also during multiple myeloma development (Figure 4). This inflammatory network systems operating in multiple myeloma are also expected to function in other solid tumor types.

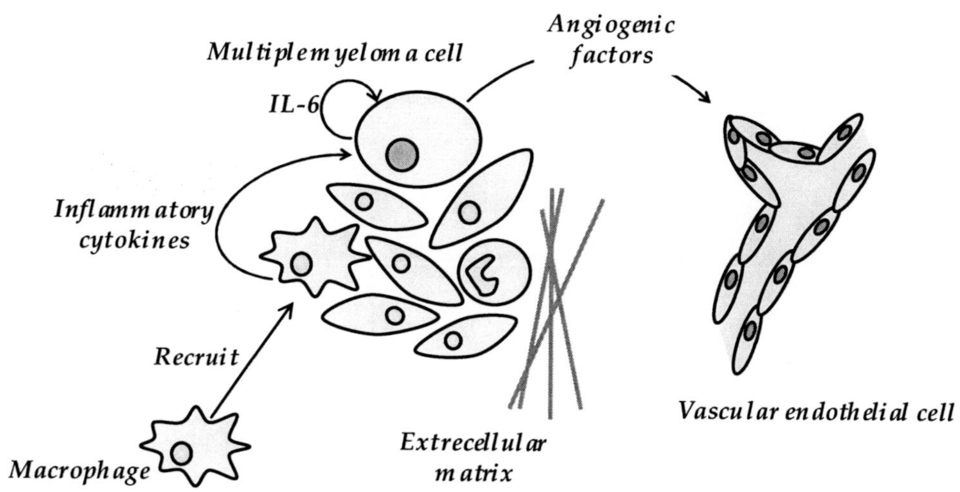

Figure 4. Multiple myeloma form a network near bone marrow through interaction with various inflammatory cell types. Angiogenesis plays a critical role in stroma formation for multiple myeloma through interaction of multiple myeloma cells with various stroma cell types and cytokines.

Monocytes and macrophages are expected to play critical roles in malignant tumor progression [1, 4]. In various inflammatory responses, macrophages play a key role in providing an environment that stimulates cell migration, survival and proliferation of cancer cells and various stromal cell types by producing angiogenic factors, growth factors, cytokines and proteases [1, 4]. In particular TAMs are a significant component of inflammatory infiltrates in tumors, and TAMs derived from monocytes are mainly recruited in response to MCP-1 and other chemokines resulting in tumor progression. Since the first clinical evidence indicating an association of macrophage infiltration with invasive breast cancer [7], many other studies also demonstrate that infiltration of TAMs is often closely associated with survival or prognosis in many tumor types, suggesting a role of TAMs in tumor progression and metastasis. The close correlation of the abundance of TAMs in tumor stroma and poor prognosis appears to be due to at least in part to angiogenesis [1, 12]. In keeping with this notion, TAMs produce various proangiogenic factors (VEGF, bFGF, PDGF, HGF angiopoetin-1 and 2, IL-8, thymidine phosphorylase), inflammatory cytokines (TNF-α, IL-1), proteases (PA, MMP-7 and MMP-9), and NO [4, 11 - 13] (Figure 5). Infiltration of abundant COX-2-positive cells, including macrophages and neutrophils, is recognized near neovasculatures that are evident in cornea by IL-1β [13]. TAMs also express VEGF-C and D as well as VEGF receptor 3 (VEGFR-3), suggesting that TAMs could modulate not only hemangiogenesis but also lymphangiogenesis [11]. A recent study by Cursiefen et al demonstrated that VEGF-A recruitment of monocyte/ macrophages plays a crucial role in induction of inflammatory angiogenesis by supplying signals essential for both hemangiogenesis and lymphyangiogenesis [49]. TAMs are thus implicated in the formation of blood vessels and lymphatic vessels by alteration of the local balance of proangiogenic factors during tumor development.

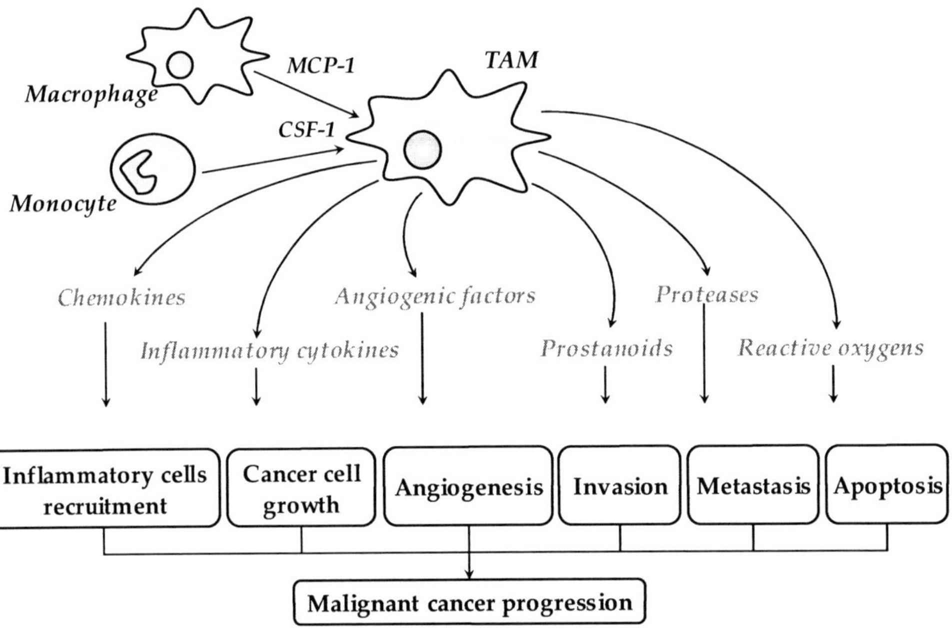

Figure 5. Tumor-associated macrophages (TAMs) have pro-tumorigenic and pro-angiogenic functions through formation of a complex network system of various cell types in the tumor stroma. Monocytes/ macrophages are recruited to the malignant tumor area by chemotactic cytokines, such as MCP-1, secreted by tumor. The soluble colony-stimulating factor (CSF-1), abundant molecule in the tumor microenvironment, transforms infiltrated macrophages to TAMs: CSF-1 has two forms both soluble CSF-1 (sCSF-1) and cell-surface CSF-1. TAMs are expected to promote recruitment of inflammatory cells, tumor growth, angiogenesis, invasion, metastasis and apoptosis by production of various factors.

Therapeutic Potential of Anticancer Drugs by Targeting Inflammatory Angiogenesis and TAMs

The significant contribution of COX-2 in cancer promotion has been demonstrated in a model of human familiar adenomatous polyps. Inhibitors of COXs may therefore reduce cancer risk. Representative drugs developed by targeting inflammation are both COX-1- and COX-2-targeting agents such as aspirin and nonsteroidal anti-inflammatory drugs (NSAIDs) that reduce colon cancers risk and also prevent breast, lung, esophagus and stomach cancer [50, 51]. There have been many clinical trials of NSAIDs not only for familial adenomatous polyposis and sporadic colorectal neoplasia but also for cancer of breast esophagus, stomach, pancreas, ovarian, urinary tract, prostate and other organs [50]. Aspirin and other NSAIDs may provide protection against cancer in gastrointestinal tract. However, the effects of NSAIDs on cancers outside the gastrointestinal tract remain to be investigated.

COX-2 contributes to angiogenesis in inflammatory diseases and malignant tumors [29], and the expression in both cancer cells and multiple cell types in the tumor environment may play an important role in tumor progression and angiogenesis through production of angiogenic eicosanoids, and angiogenic factors. COX-2 expression is apparently up-regulated in multiple cell types including macrophages that are infiltrated in neovasculatures developed by IL-1β in mouse corneas [37]. COX-2 inhibitors, as well as NSAIDs, may limit tumor growth, invasion and metastasis through inhibition of angiogenesis in some tumor types. Chang et al reported that COX-2 overexpression in the mammary glands of transgenic mice induces tissue specific tumorigenic transformation with angiogenesis in the stromal tissues of mammary glands [35]. Up-regulation of angiogenesis factor genes in COX-2-transgenic mice can be inhibited by treatment with indomethacin, an inhibitor of COX-2-induced prostanoid synthesis. Moreover, a COX-2-specific inhibitor, Celecoxib, can markedly reduce tumor growth and angiogenesis which are partly mediated through PGE2-EP1, 2, 4 receptor pathway in tumor in COX-2-transgenic mice [35].

TNF-α, a proinflammatory cytokine as well as IL-1α/β, mediates downstream signaling in inflammation. Antibody developed against TNF-α shows therapeutic efficacy in rheumatic disease [52]. Since these inflammatory cytokines play important roles in angiogenesis in inflammatory diseases and cancer [40, 53], drugs targeting TNF-α and IL-1α/β may be effective in anticancer treatment. For example, thalidomide which is now approved to treatment of Hansen's disease and multiple myeloma, affects production of various cytokines, in particular, TNF-α from monocytic cells in culture. Development of thalidomide derivatives that potently inhibit TNF-α production have marked antiangiogenesis activity [59], suggesting a close link between TNF-α and angiogenesis. D'Amato et al reported antiangiogenesis activity by thalidomide in a rabbit corneal angiogenesis model using bFGF [55]. However, further studies have reported disputed findings. Thalidomide-induced antitumor effects in mice appear not to be due to a decrease of VEGF level [56]. Thalidomide shows pleiotropic effects such as increase of T cells and activation of NK cell [57], inhibition of IFN-γ production [58], inhibition of αVβ3 integrin expression [59] and interaction with DNA [60], suggesting that its teratogenic activity and antitumor activity are mediated through complex mechanisms. Further investigations are required to understand at the molecular basis how thalidomide could induce antitumor effects in some malignant tumor types.

TAMs, the main components of tumor microenvironment, are expected to potentiate tumor progression together with other many immunity-related cells such as neutrophils and mast cells, and one of their pleiotropic responses is induction of angiogenesis in the tumor environment. TAMs, along with mast cells and neutrophils, promote tumor progression and metastasis by production of angiogenic factors, proteases, growth factors and cytokines, resulting in formation of tumor stroma characteristics for each malignant cancer [1, 4]. If continuous inflammation due to persistent infection and other irritants play a critical role in tumor progression, TAMs hold promise as target cells of intrinsic importance for the development of antiangiogenesis and antitumor drugs. One approach for the anti-inflammatory and antitumor strategy could be developed by targeting proteases such as PAs, MMPs, inflammation cytokines, COXs, growth factors, and inflammatory cytokines. Another approach is to target TAMs and other pronounced inflammatory cells by either blocking cell migration of inflammatoty cells such as TAMs, neutrophlis and mast cells, or killing the TAMs themselves. We need further study to understand which molecular targets or which tumor-associated inflammatory cells should be aimed at to develop antitumor drugs.

Acknowlegements

This study was supported by grant-in-aid for cancer research of Ministry of Education, Culture, Sport and Scientific Technology, Japan (M. K., M. O.). We also thank editorial helps for Naomi Shinbaru. The authors are also indebted to Prof. J. Patrick Barron of the International Medical Communications Center of Tokyo Medical University for his review of this manuscript.

References

[1] Coussens LM, and Werb Z. Inflammation and cancer. *Nature*. 2002, 420: 860-867.

[2] Balkwill F. and Mantovani A. Inflammation and cancer: back to Virchow? *Lancet*. 2001, 357: 539-545.

[3] Dvorak HF. Tumors: wounds that do not heal. Similarities between tumor stroma generation and wound healing. *N Engl J Med*. 1986, 315: 1650-1659.

[4] Pollard JW. Tumour-educated macrophages promote tumour progression and metastasis. *Nat Rev Cancer*. 2004, 4: 71-78.

[5] Carmeliet P. Angiogenesis in health and disease. Nat Med. 2003, 9: 653-660.

[6] Baldwin ME, Stacker SA, and Achen MG. Molecular control of lymphangiogenesis. *Bioessays*. 2002, 24: 1030-1040.

[7] Leek RD, Lewis CE, Whitehouse R, Greenall M, Clarke J, and Harris AL. Association of macrophage infiltration with angiogenesis and prognosis in invasive breast carcinoma. *Cancer Res*. 1996, 56: 4625-4629.

[8] Toi M, Ueno T, Matsumoto H, Saji H, Funata N, Koike M, and Tominaga T. Significance of thymidine phosphorylase as a marker of protumor monocytes in breast cancer. *Clin Cancer Res*. 1999, 5: 1131-1137.

[9] Nishie A, Ono M, Shono T, Fukushi J, Otsubo M, Onoue H, Ito Y, Inamura T, Ikezaki K, Fukui M, Iwaki T, and Kuwano M. Macrophage infiltration and heme oxygenase-1

expression correlate with angiogenesis in human gliomas. *Clin Cancer Res.* 1999, 5: 1107-1113.

[10] Torisu H, Ono M, Kiryu H, Furue M, Ohmoto Y, Nakayama J, Nishioka Y, Sone S, and Kuwano M. Macrophage infiltration correlates with tumor stage and angiogenesis in human malignant melanoma: possible involvement of TNFalpha and IL-1alpha. *Int J Cancer.* 2000, 85: 182-188.

[11] Schoppmann SF, Birner P, Stockl J, Kalt R, Ullrich R, Caucig C, Kriehuber E, Nagy K, Alitalo K, and Kerjaschki D. Tumor-associated macrophages express lymphatic endothelial growth factors and are related to peritumoral lymphangiogenesis. *Am J Pathol.* 2002, 161: 947-956.

[12] Ono M, Torisu H, Fukushi J, Nishie A, and Kuwano M. Biological implications of macrophage infiltration in human tumor angiogenesis. *Cancer Chemother Pharmacol.* 1999, 43: 69-71.

[13] Kuwano M, Fukushi J, Okamoto M, Nishie A, Goto H, Ishibashi T, and Ono M. Angiogenesis factors. *Intern Med.* 2001, 40: 565-572.

[14] Voronov E, Shouval DS, Krelin Y, Cagnano E, Benharroch D, Iwakura Y, Dinarello CA, and Apte RN. IL-1 is required for tumor invasiveness and angiogenesis. *Proc Natl Acad Sci U S A.* 2003, 100: 2645-2650.

[15] Yano S, Nokihara H, Yamamoto A, Goto H, Ogawa H, Kanematsu T, Miki T, Uehara H, Saijo Y, Nukiwa T, and Sone S. Multifunctional interleukin-1beta promotes metastasis of human lung cancer cells in SCID mice via enhanced expression of adhesion-, invasion- and angiogenesis-related molecules. *Cancer Sci.* 2003, 94: 244-252.

[16] Saijo Y, Tanaka M, Miki M, Usui K, Suzuki T, Maemondo M, Hong X, Tazawa R, Kikuchi T, Matsushima K, and Nukiwa T. Proinflammatory cytokine IL-1 beta promotes tumor growth of Lewis lung carcinoma by induction of angiogenic factors: in vivo analysis of tumor-stromal interaction. *J Immunol.* 2002, 169: 469-475.

[17] Salven P, Hattori K, Heissig B, and Rafii S. Interleukin-1alpha promotes angiogenesis in vivo via VEGFR-2 pathway by inducing inflammatory cell VEGF synthesis and secretion. *FASEB J.* 2002, 16: 1471-1473.

[18] Song X, Voronov E, Dvorkin T, Fima E, Cagnano E, Benharroch D, Shendler Y, Bjorkdahl O, Segal S, Dinarello CA, and Apte RN. Differential effects of IL-1 alpha and IL-1 beta on tumorigenicity patterns and invasiveness. *J Immunol.* 2003, 171: 6448-6456.

[19] Anasagasti MJ, Alvarez A, Martin JJ, Mendoza L, and Vidal-Vanaclocha F. Sinusoidal endothelium release of hydrogen peroxide enhances very late antigen-4-mediated melanoma cell adherence and tumor cytotoxicity during interleukin-1 promotion of hepatic melanoma metastasis in mice. *Hepatology.* 1997, 25: 840-846.

[20] Vidal-Vanaclocha F, Alvarez A, Asumendi A, Urcelay B, Tonino P, and Dinarello CA. Interleukin 1 (IL-1)-dependent melanoma hepatic metastasis in vivo; increased endothelial adherence by IL-1-induced mannose receptors and growth factor production in vitro. *J Natl Cancer Inst.* 1996, 88: 198-205.

[21] Okamura K, Sato Y, Matsuda T, Hamanaka R, Ono M, Kohno K, and Kuwano M. Endogenous basic fibroblast growth factor-dependent induction of collagenase and interleukin-6 in tumor necrosis factor-treated human microvascular endothelial cells. *J Biol Chem.* 1991, 266: 19162-19165.

[22] Ryuto M, Ono M, Izumi H, Yoshida S, Weich HA, Kohno K, and Kuwano M. Induction of vascular endothelial growth factor by tumor necrosis factor alpha in human glioma cells. Possible roles of SP-1. *J Biol Chem.* 1996, 271: 28220-28228.
[23] Yoshida S, Ono M, Shono T, Izumi H, Ishibashi T, Suzuki H, and Kuwano M. Involvement of interleukin-8, vascular endothelial growth factor, and basic fibroblast growth factor in tumor necrosis factor alpha-dependent angiogenesis. *Mol Cell Biol.* 1997, 17: 4015-4023.
[24] Massia SP, and Hubbell JA. Immobilized amines and basic amino acids as mimetic heparin-binding domains for cell surface proteoglycan-mediated adhesion. *J Biol Chem.* 1992, 267: 10133-10141.
[25] Nakao S, Kuwano T, Ishibashi T, Kuwano M, and Ono M. Synergistic effect of TNF-alpha in soluble VCAM-1-induced angiogenesis through alpha 4 integrins. *J. Immunol.*, 2003, 170: 5704 - 5711.
[26] Fukushi J, Morisaki T, Shono T, Nishie A, Torisu H, Ono M, and Kuwano M. Novel biological functions of interleukin-4: formation of tube-like structures by vascular endothelial cells in vitro and angiogenesis in vivo. *Biochem Biophys Res Commun.* 1998, 250: 444-448.
[27] Fukushi J, Ono M, Morikawa W, Iwamoto Y, and Kuwano M. The activity of soluble VCAM-1 in angiogenesis stimulated by IL-4 and IL-13. *J Immunol.* 2000, 165: 2818-2823.
[28] Kaneko Y, Kitazato K, and Basaki Y. Integrin-linked kinase regulates vascular morphogenesis induced by vascular endothelial growth factor. *J. Cell Sci.*, 2004, 117: 407-415.
[29] Gately S, and Kerbel R. Therapeutic potential of selective cyclooxygenase-2 inhibitors in the management of tumor angiogenesis. *Prog Exp Tumor Res.* 2003, 37: 179-92.
[30] Oshima M, Dinchuk JE, Kargman SL, Oshima H, Hancock B, Kwong E, Trzaskos JM, Evans JF, and Taketo MM. Suppression of intestinal polyposis in Apc delta716 knockout mice by inhibition of cyclooxygenase 2 (COX-2). *Cell.* 1996, 87: 803-809.
[31] Seno H, Oshima M, Ishikawa TO, Oshima H, Takaku K, Chiba T, Narumiya S, and Taketo MM. Cyclooxygenase 2- and prostaglandin E(2) receptor EP(2)-dependent angiogenesis in Apc(Delta716) mouse intestinal polyps. *Cancer Res.* 2002, 62: 506-511.
[32] Sawaoka H, Tsuji S, Tsujii M, Gunawan ES, Sasaki Y, Kawano S, and Hori M. Cyclooxygenase inhibitors suppress angiogenesis and reduce tumor growth in vivo. *Lab Invest.* 1999, 79: 1469-1477.
[33] Williams CS, Tsujii M, Reese J, Dey SK, and DuBois RN. Host cyclooxygenase-2 modulates carcinoma growth. *J Clin Invest.* 2000 , 105: 1589-1594.
[34] Tsujii M, Kawano S, Tsuji S, Sawaoka H, Hori M, and DuBois RN. Cyclooxygenase regulates angiogenesis induced by colon cancer cells. *Cell.* 1998, 93: 705-716.
[35] Su JL, Shih JY, Yen ML, Jeng YM, Chang CC, Hsieh CY, Wei LH, Yang PC, and Kuo ML. Cyclooxygenase-2 induces EP1- and HER-2/Neu-dependent vascular endothelial growth factor-C up-regulation: a novel mechanism of lymphangiogenesis in lung adenocarcinoma. *Cancer Res.* 2004, 64: 554-564.
[36] Amano H, Hayashi I, Endo H, Kitasato H, Yamashina S, Maruyama T, Kobayashi M, Satoh K, Narita M, Sugimoto Y, Murata T, Yoshimura H, Narumiya S, and Majima M.

Host prostaglandin E(2)-EP3 signaling regulates tumor-associated angiogenesis and tumor growth. *J Exp Med*. 2003, 197: 221-232.

[37] Kuwano T, Nakao S, Yamamoto H, Tsuneyoshi M, Yamamoto T, Kuwano M, and Ono M. Cyclooxygenase 2 is a key enzyme for inflammatory cytokine-induced angiogenesis. *FASEB J*. 2004, 18: 300-310.

[38] Hanahan D, and Folkman J. Patterns and emerging mechanisms of the angiogenic switch during tumorigenesis. *Cell*. 1996, 86: 353-364.

[39] Ria R, Roccaro AM, Merchionne F, Vacca A, Dammacco F, and Ribatti D. Vascular endothelial growth factor and its receptors in multiple myeloma. *Leukemia*. 2003, 17: 1961-1966.

[40] Hideshima T, Chauhan D, Hayashi T, Podar K, Akiyama M, Gupta D, Richardson P, Munshi N, and Anderson KC. The biological sequelae of stromal cell-derived factor-1alpha in multiple myeloma. *Mol Cancer Ther*. 2002, 1: 539-544.

[41] Vacca A, Ribatti D, Roncali L, Ranieri G, Serio G, Silvestris F, and Dammacco F. Bone marrow angiogenesis and progression in multiple myeloma. *Br J Haematol*. 1994, 87: 503-508.

[42] Vacca A, Ribatti D, Presta M, Minischetti M, Iurlaro M, Ria R, Albini A, Bussolino F, and Dammacco F. Bone marrow neovascularization, plasma cell angiogenic potential, and matrix metalloproteinase-2 secretion parallel progression of human multiple myeloma. Blood. 1999, 93: 3064-3073.

[43] Sezer O, Niemoller K, Eucker J, Jakob C, Kaufmann O, Zavrski I, Dietel M, and Possinger K. Bone marrow microvessel density is a prognostic factor for survival in patients with multiple myeloma. *Ann Hematol*. 2000, 79: 574-577.

[44] Iwasaki T, Hamano T, Ogata A, Hashimoto N, Kitano M, and Kakishita E. Clinical significance of vascular endothelial growth factor and hepatocyte growth factor in multiple myeloma. *Br J Haematol*. 2002, 116: 796-802.

[45] Dankbar B, Padro T, Leo R, Feldmann B, Kropff M, Mesters RM, Serve H, Berdel WE, and Kienast J. Vascular endothelial growth factor and interleukin-6 in paracrine tumor-stromal cell interactions in multiple myeloma. *Blood*. 2000, 95: 2630-266.

[46] Pulkki K, Pelliniemi TT, Rajamaki A, Tienhaara A, Laakso M, and Lahtinen R. Soluble interleukin-6 receptor as a prognostic factor in multiple myeloma. Finnish Leukaemia Group. *Br J Haematol*. 1996, 92 : 370-374.

[47] Neufeld G, Cohen T, Gengrinovitch S, and Poltorak Z. Vascular endothelial growth factor (VEGF) and its receptors. *FASEB J*. 1999, 13: 9-22.

[48] Risau W. Mechanisms of angiogenesis. *Nature*. 1997, 386: 671-674.

[49] Cursiefen C, Chen L, Borges LP, Jackson D, Cao J, Radziejewski C, D'Amore PA, Dana MR, Wiegand SJ, and Streilein JW. VEGF-A stimulates lymphangiogenesis and hemangiogenesis in inflammatory neovascularization via macrophage recruitment. *J Clin Invest*. 2004, 113: 1040-1050.

[50] Baron JA, and Sandler RS. Nonsteroidal anti-inflammatory drugs and cancer prevention. *Annu Rev Med*. 2000, 51: 511-523.

[51] Garcia-Rodriguez LA, and Huerta-Alvarez C. Reduced risk of colorectal cancer among long-term users of aspirin and nonaspirin nonsteroidal antiinflammatory drugs. *Epidemiology*. 2001, 12: 88-93.

[52] Shanahan JC, and St Clair W. Tumor necrosis factor-alpha blockade: a novel therapy for rheumatic disease. *Clin Immunol*. 2002, 103: 231-242.

[53] Majumdar S, Lamothe B, and Aggarwal BB. Thalidomide suppresses NF-kappa B activation induced by TNF and H2O2, but not that activated by ceramide, lipopolysaccharides, or phorbol ester. *J Immunol.* 2002, 168: 2644-2651.

[54] Hashimoto Y. Structural development of synthetic retinoids and thalidomide-related molecules. *Cancer Chemother Pharmacol.* 2003, 1: 16-23.

[55] D'Amato RJ, Loughnan MS, Flynn E, and Folkman J. Thalidomide is an inhibitor of angiogenesis. *Proc Natl Acad Sci U S A.* 1994, 91: 4082-4085.

[56] Neben K, Moehler T, Kraemer A, Benner A, Egerer G, Ho AD, and Goldschmidt H. Response to thalidomide in progressive multiple myeloma is not mediated by inhibition of angiogenic cytokine secretion. *Br J Haematol.* 2001, 115: 605-608.

[57] Davies FE, Raje N, Hideshima T, Lentzsch S, Young G, Tai YT, Lin B, Podar K, Gupta D, Chauhan D, Treon SP, Richardson PG, Schlossman RL, Morgan GJ, Muller GW, Stirling DI, and Anderson KC. Thalidomide and immunomodulatory derivatives augment natural killer cell cytotoxicity in multiple myeloma. *Blood.* 2001, 98: 210-216.

[58] Meierhofer C, Dunzendorfer S, and Wiedermann CJ. Theoretical basis for the activity of thalidomide. *BioDrugs.* 2001, 15: 681-703.

[59] Stephens TD, Bunde CJ, and Fillmore BJ. Mechanism of action in thalidomide teratogenesis. *Biochem Pharmacol.* 2000, 59: 1489-1499.

[60] Parman T, Wiley MJ, and Wells PG. Free radical-mediated oxidative DNA damage in the mechanism of thalidomide teratogenicity. *Nat Med.* 1999, 5: 582-585.

In: New Angiogenesis Research
Editor: Roberta V. Zubar, pp. 171-188

ISBN 1-59454-239-2

Chapter IX

Contrast-Enhanced Dynamic Computed Tomography for the Prevalence of Tumor Angiogenesis in Lung Cancer: A Prospective Study

Ukihide Tateishi*[*]*, Hiroaki Onaya, Mitsuo Satake and Noriyuki Moriyama
Division of Diagnostic Radiology, National Cancer Center Hospital, Tokyo, Japan

Abstract

Purpose

Diagnostic strategies based on imaging studies for tumor angiogenesis in lung cancer are complex. The aim of the present study was to evaluate the prevalence of VEGF-related tumor angiogenesis in lung cancer using contrast-enhanced dynamic computed tomography (CT).

Materials and Methods

In a prospective study, we enrolled 135 patients with suspected lung cancer on conventional CT scan. Patients underwent contrast-enhanced CT prior to operation to obtain CT measurements of maximum attenuation value (MAV) and arterial perfusion value (APV). CT was performed on multidetectors using axial four-slice modes (four images per gantry rotation) or sixteen-slice modes (sixteen images per gantry rotation).

[*] Correspondence concerning this article should be addressed to Ukihide Tateishi, MD, PhD, Division of Diagnostic Radiology, National Cancer Center Hospital, 5-1-1, Tsukiji, Chuo-Ku, 104-0045, Tokyo, Japan. Phone:+81-3-3542-2511; E-mail: utateish@ncc.go.jp. (This work was supported in part by grant for Scientific Research Expenses for Health and Welfare Programs, Foundation for the Promotion of Cancer Research, and 2nd-term Comprehensive 10-year Strategy for Cancer Control.)

All patients received iodinated nonionic contrast material (300 mgI/ml) intravenously at a rate of 3.0 ml/sec for a total of 100 ml by autoinjector. Examinations were performed during breath holding at full suspended inspiration for 20 seconds per sequential scan. The acquisition time was 0.5 seconds per section, and the tube current was 120 kVp between 150 and 200 mA. The scan delay was set at 0, 40, and 120 seconds after injection of contrast material. Images were reconstructed with 2 mm slice thickness using a standard algorithm without edge enhancement at a display window width of 350 Hounsfield Unit (HU) and a window center of 40 HU. All patients underwent surgical resection which was comprised of wedge resection, partial resection, lobectomy, or pneumonectomy. The time interval between CT examination and surgery ranged from 0 to 16 days. Tumor tissue specimens were fixed with 10 % buffered formalin and were embedded in paraffin. The sections were incubated with rabbit polyclonal antibody to the N-terminus of VEGF (5 μg/ml; anti-VEGF rabbit IgG affinity purified). Two reviewers, masked with respect to the results of pathological diagnosis, assessed the CT images independently. The CT measurements of MAV and APV were compared between VEGF-positive and -negative tumors.

Results

A statistically significant difference was found in MAV (HU) between VEGF-positive and -negative tumors (82.4±16.9, 52.3±13.4, $P<0.0001$). A significant difference was also found in APV between VEGF-positive and -negative tumors (6.32±1.53, 3.91±1.12, $P<0.0001$). The receiver operative curve (ROC) analysis revealed the preoperative distinction of VEGF-positive and -negative tumors in both MAV (Az: 0.936±0.023) and APV (0.917±0.025). Subclassification into histologic subtypes revealed that both MAV and APV were significantly higher in VEGF-positive adenocarcinomas and squamous cell carcinomas than those in VEGF-negative ones ($P<0.0001$). The patients with VEGF-positive tumors were significantly more likely to be associated with nodal involvement ($P<0.05$). In patients with n1 and n2 disease, both mean MAV and APV were significantly higher in VEGF-positive tumors than those in VEGF-negative tumors ($P<0.0001$).

Conclusion

Increased CT measurements of tumor enhancement and arterial perfusion are predictive indicators of VEGF-related tumor angiogenesis in lung cancer that can be elicited by incorporating either CT measurement in contrast-enhanced CT into existing imaging protocols for preoperative evaluation.

Introduction

In the last decade, a great deal has been revealed regarding vascular endothelial growth factor (VEGF)-related tumor angiogenesis in lung cancer and has been summarized in an evidence-based description that includes diagnostic algorithms, prognostic relevance, and treatment protocols. Multiple studies have generally been accepted-that is, in approximately 60-80% of surgically treated lung cancers, a relationship between VEGF-positive tumors and adverse prognosis has been found [1-8].

Recent imaging studies based on contrast-enhanced dynamic protocols can help in detection and quantification of tumor angiogenesis [9-15]. At the most basic and qualitative level, early tumor enhancement on contrast-enhanced dynamic imaging studies is directly related to tumor angiogenesis in a number of tumor types. The underlying biological principle is that VEGF-related tumor angiogenesis in lung cancer is reflected by pathophysiologic changes in pulmonary vasculature, including circulation of bronchial and pulmonary arteries. The bronchial arterial blood flow, receiving low cardiac output compared with pulmonary arterial blood flow, is of significant importance for both tumor hemodynamics and angiogenesis in lung cancer. However, the exact hemodynamic mechanism by which VEGF contributes to the development of increased vascularity in lung cancer remains to be established.

Retrospective studies based on VEGF revealed that tumor angiogenesis was correlated with poor prognosis, including higher rates of lymph node metastases and poor patient survival rates in lung cancer [16-19]. Thus, it is expected that accurate imaging techniques for quantifying tumor angiogenesis may provide important prognostic information prior to therapy. However, imaging techniques such as contrast-enhanced dynamic imaging studies are relatively complex and preclude their generalized use in preoperative evaluations of lung cancer.

Preliminary results of contrast-enhanced dynamic computed tomography (CT) scans of lung cancer demonstrate early and arterial-phase CT image to aid in detecting the early enhancement associated with VEGF-related tumor angiogenesis [20]. Previous studies of contrast-enhanced dynamic CT analysis from our laboratory have shown that VEGF-positive lung cancer demonstrates a greater maximum attenuation value compared with VEGF-negative tumors [21]. Studies such as those designed in contrast-enhanced dynamic CT are invaluable for evaluating angiogenesis of lung cancer in the clinical setting.

To further evaluate the findings for VEGF-related tumor angiogenesis on contrast-enhanced dynamic CT, we have performed the first prospective study in our institution. The aim of the present study was to assess VEGF-related tumor angiogenesis prospectively using contrast-enhanced dynamic CT as the reference method in non-selected patients with highly suspected lung cancer at a single institution.

Materials and Methods

Patients

We recruited 212 consecutive patients with highly suspected lung cancer from ongoing preoperative evaluation of tumor angiogenesis in lung cancer and the value of contrast-enhanced dynamic CT scan to detect VEGF-related tumor angiogenesis between October, 2001 and June, 2002.

To determine the eligibility for the study, patients underwent unenhanced conventional CT scans. Patients with nodular lesions which had ill-defined and/or spiculated margins on unenhanced CT images were eligible for the study. Patients with nodular lesions which showed well-defined, smooth margins, or an absence of growth over two years were excluded from this study.

Clinical records were available for review from all patients. Clinical histories of cases to identify any underlying medical conditions, and the presence or absence of symptoms were also reviewed. Our institutional review board confirmed its approval and informed consent for review of patient records and images.

All patients underwent surgical resection which was comprised of wedge resection, partial resection, lobectomy, or pneumonectomy. Complete resection or sampling of mediastinal or hilar lymph nodes was performed in all patients with lung cancer. These included high and low ipsilateral paratracheal, subcarinal, and inferior pulmonary ligament lymph nodes and any other suspicious lymph nodes identified at surgery.

Procedures

CT was performed on a multidetector scanner (Aquilion V-detector, Toshiba Medical Systems, Tokyo, Japan) using axial four-slice modes (four images per gantry rotation) or sixteen-slice modes (sixteen images per gantry rotation). All patients received iodinated nonionic contrast material (300 mgI/ml) intravenously at a rate of 3.0 ml/sec for a total of 100 ml by autoinjector (Autoenhance A-250, Nemoto Kyorindo, Tokyo, Japan). Examinations were performed after deep inspiration with a single breath-hold for 20 seconds per sequential scan. The acquisition time was 0.5 seconds per section, and the tube current was 120 kVp between 150 and 200 mA. The scan delay was set at 0, 40, and 120 seconds after injection of contrast material. Images were reconstructed with 2 mm slice thickness using a standard algorithm without edge enhancement at a display window width of 350 Hounsfield Unit (HU) and a window center of 40 HU. Hard-copy images were photographed at window settings for lung (center, -600 HU and width, 2,000 HU) and mediastinum (center, 40 HU and width, 350 HU). The time interval between CT examination and surgery ranged from 0 to 16 days.

A dedicated workstation (Alatoview, Toshiba Medical Systems, Tokyo, Japan) was used for the quantitative analysis of each CT image. The regions of interest (ROI) were chosen on the basis of the best tumor delineation on CT images. Time-attenuation curves were created with circular ROI drawn over the tumor, thoracic aorta (or left subclavian artery if the aorta was not included in the section), and pulmonary artery as selected and their mean values were obtained. The ROI was drawn as large as possible to minimize noise but with care in order to avoid partial volume effect. The diameter of the ROI was 100 % of the diameter of tumors by using this criterion. If the proper scan level was not attained because of inadequate respiration, the image was eliminated from the data analysis. The maximum attenuation value of the time-attenuation curve (MAV) was defined as the peak attenuation minus the baseline of precontrast attenuation. The intra-observer variability was less than 5 HU in the ROI setting, which did not affect the data analysis. The arterial perfusion value (APV) was determined with the following equation: $APV=MAV/[AUC \times \rho t]$, where AUC is the area under the arterial time attenuation curve, MAV is maximum attenuation value of the time attenuation curve, and ρt is the density of the tissue of interest, which is considered to be 1.0 g/ml [22].

Tumor tissue specimens were fixed with 10 % buffered formalin and embedded in paraffin. Five-micron sections of the tumoral largest diameter were mounted on silanized slides, dewaxed with xylene, and then dehydrated with ethanol. The sections were pretreated in 10 mM citrate buffer (pH 6.0) for 15 minutes at room temperature before the immunohistochemical staining to retrieve the antigen. To block endogenous peroxidase activity, the sections were incubated with 0.3 % hydrogen peroxidate for 15 minutes at room temperature. To suppress nonspecific binding, the sections were incubated with 1.5 % non-immune goat serum for 20 minutes. The sections were incubated with rabbit polyclonal antibody to the N-terminus of VEGF (5 μg/ml; anti-VEGF rabbit IgG affinity purified; IBL, Japan) of which the antibody was raised overnight at room temperature against a synthetic peptide corresponding to the amino acid residues of human VEGF. After being washed with phosphate-buffered solution (PBS), the sections were incubated with avidine-biotin-peroxidase complex (Histofine, Nichirei, Japan) for 30 minutes and washed once more with PBS. The sections were finally incubated with 3,3-diaminobenzidine (Simplestain DAB, Nichirei, Japan). Negative controls were carried out by omitting the primary antibody and by substituting the primary antibody with an irrelevant antibody. No significant immunohistochemical reaction occurred in the control sections. Counterstaining was performed with hematoxylin. VEGF expression was judged by two pathologists. No statistical differences were seen in the VEGF evaluations (r=0.82; $p<0.0001$) between the two observers.

Statistical Analysis

Differences in baseline characteristics between patients with VEGF-positive and -negative lung cancer were analyzed by using unpaired *t* tests for continuously distributed variables. Pearson's χ^2 tests were applied as indicated in the results. P values less than 0.05 were considered statistically significant. Additionally, the performance of contrast-enhanced dynamic CT scans in indicating VEGF-positivity in lung cancer was compared and analyzed by using receiver operating characteristic (ROC) curves. The *Az* value, the area under the ROC curve, was also calculated. The rate of agreement between two observers was established. The weighted Kappa statistic was used to calculate the agreement beyond the chance. Kappa values larger than zero were considered to indicate a positive correlation; value of 0-0.20, poor agreement; 0.21-0.40, fair agreement; 0.41-0.60, moderate agreement; 0.61-0.80, good agreement; 0.81-1.00, excellent agreement. All statistical analyses were performed with the SPSS 11.0 statistical software program for Windows (SPSS Inc, Chicago, IL).

Results

The initial cohort was 212 patients, 140 men and 72 women, with a median age of 67.2 years (range 42-88 years). Of these, 7 patients (3%) had previous anaphylactic reactions to iodinated nonionic contrast agent and were excluded from the baseline study population. In 8 patients (4%), contrast-enhanced dynamic CT was not interpretable because of misregistration. Fifty patients (24%) who underwent contrast-enhanced CT examination had lesions with attenuation of air, which were not applicable for data analysis and were excluded. Twelve patients (7%) who were diagnosed as having inflammatory lesions (n=11, 5%) and primary pulmonary lymphoma (n=1, 0.5%) were also excluded. Thus, a total of 135 patients (64% of cohort) with lung cancer were eligible for the present study. Their clinical data are summarized in Table 1. The mean age at presentation was 66.3 years. The male to female ratio was approximately 8:5.

No patients received any therapy before surgery, including chemotherapy. The tumor size measured on pathologic specimens ranged from 10 to 57 mm (mean 24.7 mm) in diameter. The pathologic diagnoses of lung cancer were stage IA (n=72, 53%), IB (n=14, 10%), IIA (n=28, 21%), IIB (n=14, 10%), and IIIA (n=7, 5%), and whole pathologic specimens were available. Among the 135 patients, 93 (69%) had adenocarcinoma, 29 (21%) had squamous cell carcinoma, nine (7%) had large cell neuroendocrine carcinoma (LCNEC), three (2%) had adenosquamous cell carcinoma, one (0.7%) had pleomorphic carcinoma, and one (0.7%) had mucoepidermoid carcinoma.

Table 1. Demographics of the patients.

	VEGF-positive	VEGF-negative	Total
Gender (male/female)	56/42	26/11	82/53
Age (years)	66.7±7.4	66.0±9.1	66.3±8.6
range (years)	50-84	42-83	42-84
Height (cm)	159.8±8.4	161.2±8.4	160.2±8.4
Weight (kg)	57.9±10.2	56.5±10.3	57.5±10.2
BSA (m2)	1.59±0.16	1.57±0.18	1.58±0.17
Histology			
Ad	71	21	92
Sq	18	11	29
LCNEC	6	3	9
Adsq	1	2	3
others	2	0	2

Note - BSA=Body surface areas. Ad=Adenocarcinoma, Sq=Squamous cell carcinoma, LCNEC=Large cell neuroendocrine carcinoma. Adsq=Adenosquamous carcinoma. Others contain pleomorphic carcinoma (n=1) and mucoepidermoid carcinoma (n=1).

Both observers read 135 of the available contrast-enhanced dynamic CT investigations independently. Agreement was present for 121 patients (90%); but the observers disagreed in four patients with solid tumors with cystic components. This disagreement resulted in a Kappa value of 0.78, which is generally thought to be a moderate standard for a diagnostic test.

The time attenuation curves were obtained by contrast-enhanced dynamic CT in all patients (Table 2 and 4). A statistically significant difference was found in MAV between VEGF-positive and -negative tumors (82.4±16.9, 52.3±13.4, $P<0.0001$). A significant difference was also found in APV between VEGF-positive and -negative tumors (6.32±1.53, 3.91±1.12, $P<0.0001$). The ROC analysis revealed the preoperative distinction of VEGF-positive and -negative tumors in both MAV and APV. No significant difference was found in the *Az* value between MAV and APV ($P=0.17$).

Subclassification into histologic subtypes revealed that both MAV and APV were significantly higher in VEGF-positive adenocarcinomas than those in VEGF-negative ones ($P<0.0001$, Tables 2 and 4). Likewise, in squamous cell carcinoma, both values were significantly higher in VEGF-positive tumors compared with VEGF-negative tumors

(*P*<0.0001, Table 2 and 4). In LCNEC, there was no significant difference in both values between VEGF-positive and -negative tumors (*P*=0.14 and 0.12, Table 2 and 4). The results of ROC analysis and comparisons of the *Az* values are shown in Tables 3 and 5, respectively.

Table 2. The MAV of VEGF-positive and -negative tumors based on histological subclassification.

	VEGF-positive	VEGF-negative	P Value
Total (n)	98	37	
MAV (HU)	82.4±16.9 (50.3-157.0)	52.3±13.4 (20.8-82.6)	<0.0001
Ad (n)	71	21	
MAV (HU)	82.6±16.3 (50.3-155.4)	52.5±16.3 (20.8-82.6)	<0.0001
Sq (n)	18	11	
MAV (HU)	79.8±9.7 (58.3-92.8)	52.1±7.5 (42.5-70.4)	<0.0001
LCNEC (n)	6	3	
MAV (HU)	89.3±36.4 (61.0-157.0)	51.9±16.2 (36.0-68.3)	0.14
Adsq (n)	1	2	
MAV (n)	68.9	46.5, 54.8	NA
Others (n)	2	0	
MAV (HU)	79.5, 93.0	NA	NA

Table 3. Results of the ROC analysis in the distinction of MAV between VEGF-positive and -negative tumors.

	Az Value
Ad	0.917±0.034
Sq	0.985±0.019
LCNEC	0.889±0.123

Nodal involvement was seen in 35 patients (26%). Of these, 28 patients (21%) had n1 disease and five (5%) had n2 (Table 6). Compared with the n0 group, no significant difference was found in the mean MAV and APV of patients with n1 and n2 disease. The patients with VEGF-positive tumors were significantly more likely to be associated with development of n1 or n2 disease, which was seen in 30 of 35 patients (86%) as compared with 5 of 32 patients (16%) with VEGF-negative tumors (OR=2.8; 95% CI, 1.0 to 7.7; *P*<0.05). In patients with n1 and n2 disease, both mean MAV and APV were significantly higher in VEGF-positive tumors than those in VEGF-negative tumors (*P*<0.0001, Table 7 and 8).

Table 4. The APV of VEGF-positive and -negative tumors based on histological subclassification.

	VEGF-positive	VEGF-negative	P Value
Total (n)	98	37	
APV	6.32±1.53 (3.81-12.8)	3.91±1.14 (1.69-6.11)	<0.0001
Ad (n)	71	21	
APV	6.30±1.55 (3.81-12.8)	3.86±1.22 (1.69-6.11)	<0.0001
Sq (n)	18	11	
APV	5.96±1.13 (4.08-8.31)	3.90±0.95 (2.68-5.21)	<0.0001
LCNEC (n)	6	3	
APV	7.14±2.41 (4.74-11.4)	4.38±1.68 (2.68-6.04)	0.12
Adsq (n)	1	2	
APV	6.72	2.99, 4.52	NA
Others (n)	2	0	
APV	7.05, 7.82	NA	NA

Table 5. Results of the ROC analysis in the distinction of APV between VEGF-positive and -negative tumors.

	Az Value
Ad	0.915±0.034
Sq	0.919±0.050
LCNEC	0.833±0.162

Table 6. The difference of nodal status between VEGF-positive and -negative tumors.

	n0	n1	n2
VEGF-positive tumors	68 (50)	23 (17)	7 (5)
VEGF-negative tumors	32 (24)	5 (4)	0

Note.- The number of the parentheses are percentages.

Table 7. The relationship between MAV and nodal status in VEGF-positive and -negative tumors.

	VEGF-positive	VEGF-negative	P Value
n0 (n)	68	32	
MAV (HU)	86.9±16.8 (64.8-157.0)	53.2±14.1 (20.8-82.6)	<0.0001
n1 or n2 (n)	30	5	
MAV (HU)	72.1±12.1 (50.3-99.1)	46.4±4.88 (40.7-52.0)	<0.0001

Table 8. The relationship of APV and nodal status in VEGF-positive and -negaive tumors.

	VEGF-positive	VEGF-negative	P Value
n0 (n)	68	32	
APV	6.55±1.60 (4.08-12.8)	4.03±1.16 (1.69-6.11)	<0.0001
n1 or n2 (n)	30	5	
APV	5.79±1.23 (4.08-8.31)	3.11±0.49 (2.84-3.99)	<0.05

Discussion

The purpose of this study was to evaluate VEGF-related tumor angiogenesis prospectively using contrast-enhanced dynamic CT in non-selected patients with highly suspected lung cancer. Tumor angiogenesis is a heterogeneous process that varies widely in pattern and distribution from one patient to another. In designing outcome measures for this study, we included CT measurements of the entire MAV and APV within the tumor. Both MAV and APV act as global measures of sectioned tumor slices and are relatively insensitive to regional changes; potentially missing the micro-focus of tumor thrombus or necrosis. When stratified by histologic subclassification, our results showed that there was no significant difference in MAV or APV between VEGF-positive and -negative tumors in LCNEC compared with those of adenoarcinoma or squamous cell carcinoma. Necrotic features identified more frequently in LCNEC compared with other histologic subtypes affected data processing of CT measurements in our study.

The bronchial arterial blood flow is of significant importance for tumor angiogenesis in lung cancer. The bronchial arteries arise from the thoracic aorta and lead to the lung tissue in normal subjects. Besides supplying peribronchial blood flow, they finally form bronchopulmonary anastomoses along the alveoli, which are usually destructed in the tissue of lung cancer patients. In our study, two different CT measurements were evaluated, both in VEGF-positive and -negative tumors.

Methodological differences between MAV and APV are affected by individual cardiac output of the patient. In contrast, two CT measurements represented similar study results in the distinction of VEGF-positive and -negative tumor or the presence of nodal involvement in lung cancer. These results may be because the bronchial arterial blood flow receives only 3-5 % of cardiac output compared with systemic blood flow.

Tumor vascularity is more likely to increase in lung cancer that is characterized by high microvessel counts on microscopic observations. To investigate tumor vascularity in the clinical setting, various protocols of contrast-enhanced dynamic incremental CT were performed [23-26]. Although the relationship between pathologic microvessel count and CT measurements remains to be fully elucidated, maximum attenuation of lung cancer has been clearly implicated. To determine the relationship between vascular densities of lung cancer, assessed by contrast-enhanced dynamic incremental CT and enhancement, Yamashita and coworkers studied 18 patients with lung cancer [27]. CT measurement of maximum attenuation, defined as a ROI within a tumor, was positively related to microvessel density counted using pathologic specimens (r=0.77), as well as to the distribution of elastic fibers in the tumoral interstitium (P=0.04). The authors concluded that enhancement characteristics of lung cancer on contrast-enhanced dynamic incremental CT correlated with the increase in microvessels and the elastic properties of lung cancer. However, this study has only demonstrated retrospective results involving small sample sizes and an independent association between CT measurement and vascular density is obscure. Similarly, the primary endpoint of contrast-enhanced dynamic incremental CT analysis in lung cancer has not been clarified.

In previous studies, CT measurement of maximum attenuation of lung cancer only required a single collection of attenuation values within a few minutes after injection of contrast media using a single slice helical CT scanner [23-27]. However, little attention has been paid to detect earlier enhancement of the tumor in the clinical setting. In the present study, scan delay was settled at 40 seconds after injection of contrast media in order to reduce the first pass effect by the pulmonary artery and to obtain similar effects by bronchial artery. Resolution of scanning time was improved to be faster using four-slice or sixteen slice modes with 0.5 second per one rotation. Long scan delay may be caused by the inaccurate CT measurement, because maximum attenuation of the tumor reflects indirect diffusion of contrast media to the extravascular intersticum of the tumor. CT measurement of maximum attenuation obtained by a short scan delay setting should be compared with microvessel densities within tumors. Therefore, to investigate tumor angiogenesis with special reference to microvessel counting, rapid scanning with a short scan delay is needed and may have considerable implications for assessing tumor angiogenesis in lung cancer.

We found that CT measurements of MAV and APV on contrast-enhanced dynamic CT were predictive indicators of VEGF-related tumor angiogenesis. The MAV as well as APV were greater in VEGF-positive tumors compared to VEGF-negative tumors. This is in agreement with the description of microvessel densities in areas of surgical specimens regardless of histologic subtypes [20] as well as the finding of a significant accumulation in tumor area in a correlation study of contrast-enhanced dynamic CT compared with 18-Fluctodeoxyglucose (FDG)-PET imaging [28].

Common to most immunohistochemical studies of VEGF-related tumor angiogenesis, the proportion of VEGF-positive lung cancer is apparently greater compared with VEGF-negative ones [1-8]. The problems of matching between VEGF-positive and -negative lung cancer cannot be overlooked. Nevertheless, the possibility of a difference between VEGF-positive and -negative lung cancer, as judged by MAV or APV, has been mirrored in previous studies [20,21].

In this study, we demonstrated that CT measurements of MAV or APV were associated with VEGF-related tumor angiogenesis in lung cancer. Although we investigated with rabbit polyclonal antibody to the N-terminus of VEGF, the effect may contain four VEGF subtypes (eg, VEGF 121, 165, 189, and 206) as a whole. Also noted is that there are various gene products derived from these VEGF subtypes, each showing different activity.

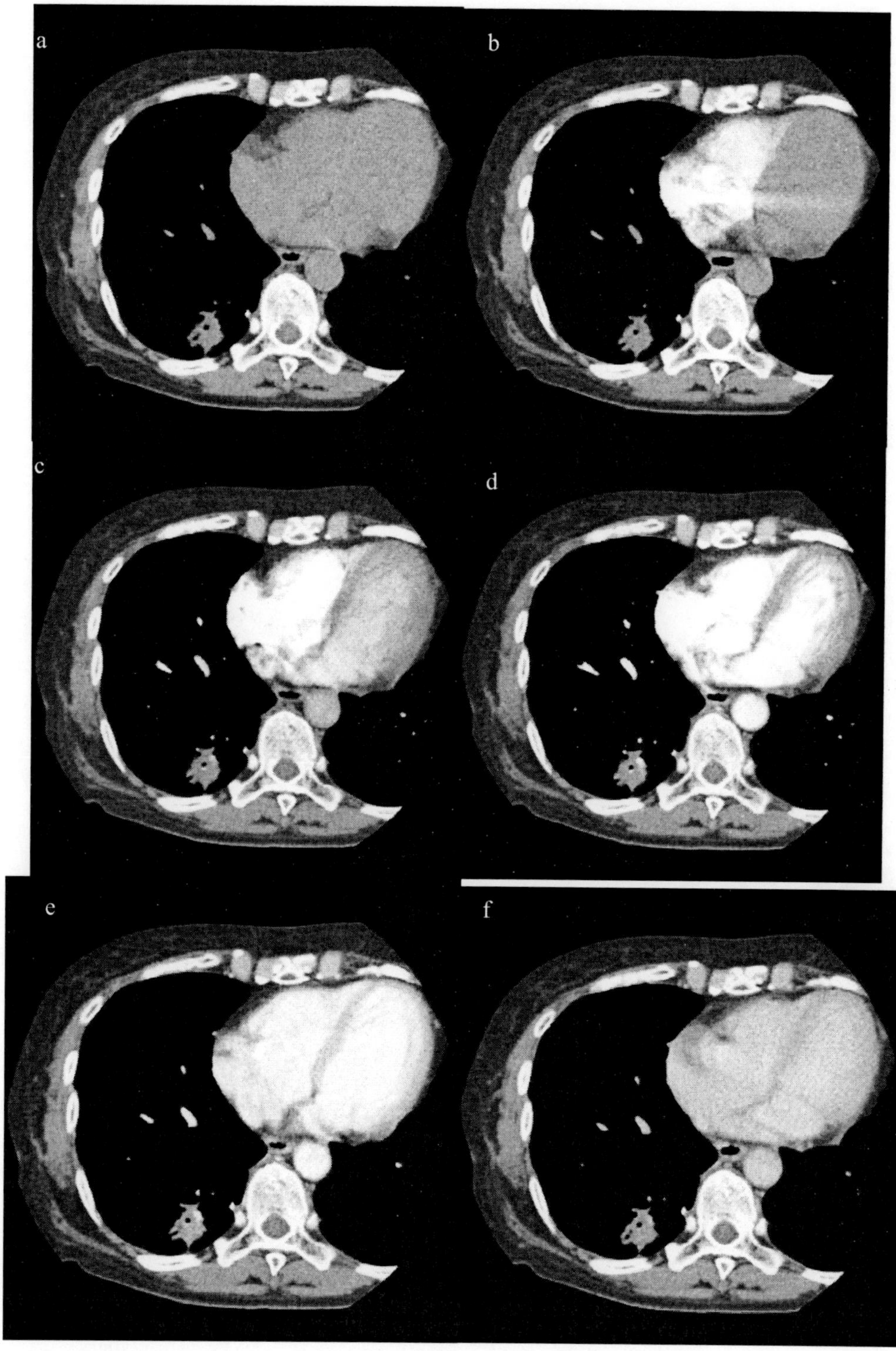

Figure 1. Images depict stage IA lung adenocarcinoma in a 59-year-old woman. (a-f) Sequential transverse contrast-enhanced dynamic CT images obtained with a scan delay of (a) 0, (b) 10, (c) 15, (d) 20, (e) 55, and (f) 120 seconds reveal MAV of 85 HU 55 seconds after administration of contrast material (APV: 6.51).

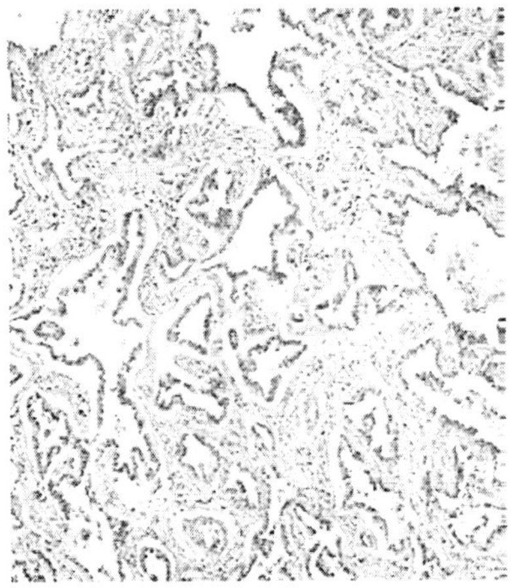

Fig 1 (g) Photomicrograph shows papillary growth of tumor cells consistent with lung adenocarcinoma (Hematoxylin-eosin stain; original magnification, ×100).

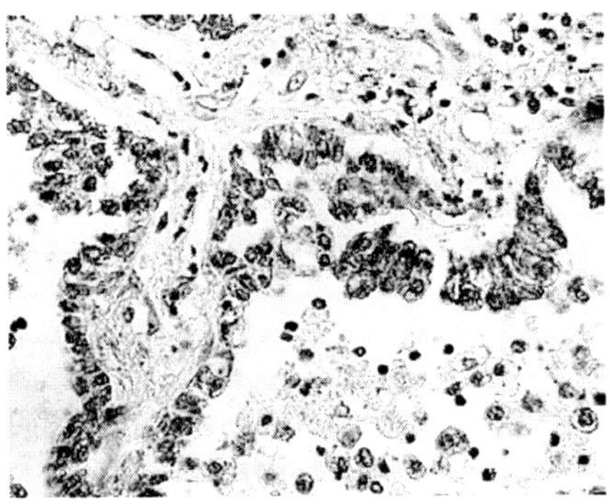

Fig 1 (h) Immunohistochemical staining of anti-vascular endothelial growth factor (anti-VEGF) antibody is shown (original magnification, ×200).

The findings of our study are needed to evaluate whether it is relevant to clinical practice. Considering a couple of methodologic issues, the evaluation of contrast-enhanced dynamic CT scans to detect maximum attenuation is not quite as straightforward as it seems. In addition, the data obtained by the ROI setting of lung cancer, do not allow any judgment about whether there is interobserver agreement or not. More importantly, the partial volume effect can affect the degree of observer agreement between CT measurements. The precise CT measurements need to be tested in a different population. The possibility of T measurements to predict VEGF-positivity using a cut-off derived from the same population should be tested.

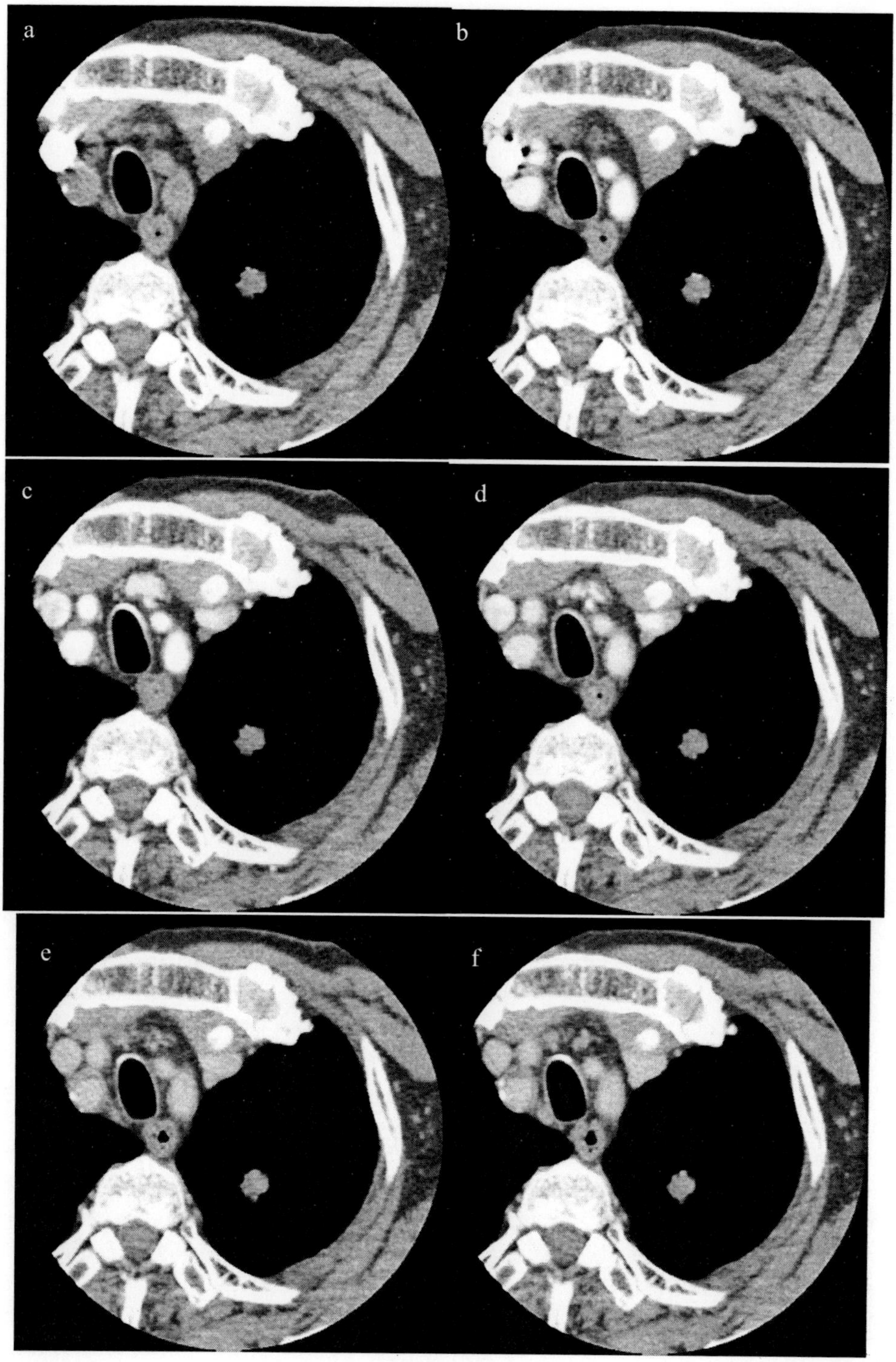

Figure 2. Images depict stage IA lung squamous cell carcinoma in a 60-year-old man. (a-f) Sequential transverse contrast-enhanced dynamic CT images obtained with a scan delay of (a) 5, (b) 15, (c) 20, (d) 45, (e) 60, and (f) 120 seconds reveal MAV of 65 HU 45 seconds after administration of contrast material (APV: 5.92).

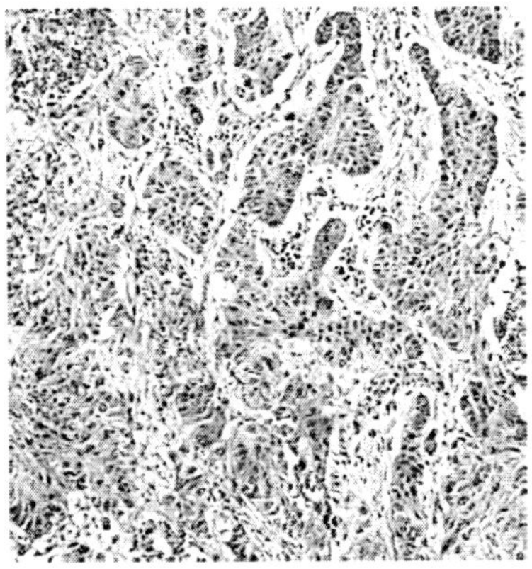

Fig 2 (g) Photomicrograph shows tumor cells consistent with lung squamous cell carcinoma (Hematoxylin-eosin stain; original magnification, ×100).

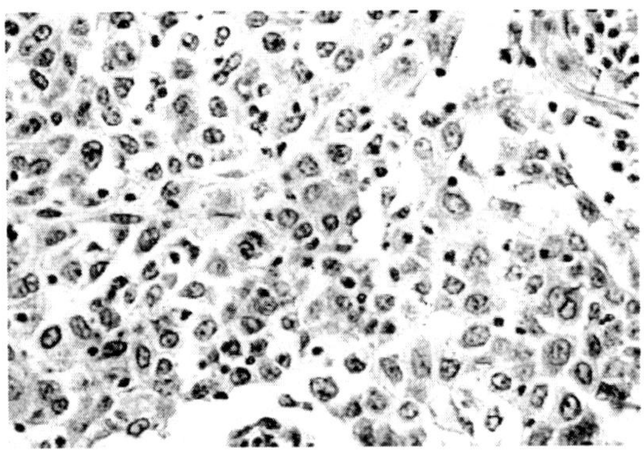

Fig 2 (h) Immunohistochemical staining of anti-vascular endothelial growth factor (anti-VEGF) antibody is shown (original magnification, ×200).

Our results may provide helpful information in the assessment of treatments [30] that target VEGF-related tumor angiogenesis (eg, SU5416). This is considered the final goal of the study. However, we have not yet established confident criteria to evaluate treatment effects by anti-VEGF agents. In addition, only a few phase I studies which included anti-VEGF agent-based chemotherapy [31-33] for lung cancer were performed in our country. Unfortunately, it is difficult to evaluate therapeutic effects in a randomized study using our methodology.

CT measurement of arterial perfusion, in agreement with others, suggests that APV may be useful clinically and may be complementary to conventional contrast-enhanced CT studies in assessing the perfusion status of the tumor during treatment [29]. Also, it has been reported that CT measurement of standardized arterial perfusion may have positive correlation with standardized uptake value (SUV) of 18-FDG-PET imaging in lung cancer [22]. Indeed, and in agreement with previous studies [28], we have shown that SUV detected by 18-FDG-PET imaging correlates with microvessel densities calculated by in vitro immunohistochemical surveys. This correlation is in agreement with the line of previous investigation, demonstrating that angiogenesis is associated with increased glucose metabolism in lung cancer, thus suggesting SUV of 18-FDG-PET imaging may be regulated by vascular supply or arterial blood flow within the tumor. This must be substantiated further by in vivo 18-

FDG-PET imaging in large population, which would confirm that APV values distinguish stable from contrast-enhanced dynamic CT examinations as an independent multivariate predictor of outcome. Although we found a significant association between VEGF-related tumor angiogenesis and CT measurement of arterial perfusion, it does not perfectly reflect their complementary values in the vascular physiology of the tumor.

In contrast to previous reports, the prevalence of proven lung cancer in this study sample was higher than expected [23-26]. The reasons for this may be that first there was selection bias introduced through screening surgically curative patients with highly suspicious lung cancer, second that the analyses of CT measurements were based on CT densitometry of only solid lesions with soft-issue attenuation and no adjustment was possible for lesions with air attenuation to analyze (ie, bronchioloalveolar carcinoma), which would tend to underestimate the prevalence of pseudo tumors with air attenuation (ie, focal inflammatory process), and third there has been a recent surgical trend toward more intensive management of lesions with air attenuation (ie, pure ground-glass attenuation), which may also have reduced the prevalence of suspicious lung cancer.

The patients studied here are typical of those with surgically treatable lung cancer. They were less elderly, were associated with a localized disease, had no impaired function of other organs, and did not require any medication for symptom control. Despite this typical clinical profile and clinically characteristic respectable lung cancer, a significant majority of the eligible patients for anti-VEGF agents-based chemotherapy were associated with extended disease. Presumably, this extended disease is due to distant metastasis as the extra-pulmonary manifestations on imaging studies (ie, magnetic resonance imaging of the brain). The presence of extended disease does not raise the possibility that some of the diagnostic benefits we have shown with CT measurements of MAV or APV could be only achieved by examining primary or secondary intrathoracic lesions with soft-tissue attenuation to detect. There is substantial literature to support evaluation of therapeutic effects of the whole body in patients with the extended diseases [34-36]. It can sometimes achieve an overall therapeutic effect. However, not all investigators have demonstrated diagnostic results based on molecular analysis of tumor angiogenesis.

Finally, more sensitive measures of tumor angiogenesis such as biomarkers for angiogenetic receptors or gene products might provide insight into tissue modulation that has not advanced to the level detectable by contrast-enhanced dynamic CT. The role of contrast-enhanced dynamic CT in VEGF-related tumor angiogenesis in lung cancer is currently being assessed in a clinical trial comparing it with 18-FDG-PET imaging [28]. If this trial shows a diagnostic benefit from contrast-enhanced dynamic CT, then comparative studies of 18-FDG-PET/CT imaging versus 18-FDG-PET imaging alone will be required to define their relative diagnostic efficacies and to compare their cost/benefit ratios. In addition, the reproducibility of contrast-enhanced dynamic CT is also relatively complicated by variability in the anatomic changes of the cancer itself, and has the potential to evaluate tissue changes at the local and regional levels. Misregistration of the tumor may be a cause of less reproducible characteristics in contrast-enhanced dynamic CT. Considering the heterogeneity of tumor processes in lung cancer, further investigation into quantitative contrast-enhanced dynamic CT scans at the regional level is also warranted.

The findings of the current study suggest that the significant predictor provided by contrast-enhanced dynamic CT examinations may have important potential as a predictor of tumor angiogenesis in patients with lung cancer.

References

[1] Fontanini G, Vignati S, Boldrini L, Chiné S, Silvestri V, Lucchi M, et al. Vascular endothelial growth factor is associated with neovascularization and influences progression of non-small cell lung carcinoma. *Clin Cancer Res* 1997; 76:1041-1045.

[2] Han H, Silverman JF, Santucci TS, Macherey RS, d'Amato TA, Tung MY, et al. Vascular endothelial growth factor expression in stage I non-small cell lung cancer correlates with neoangiogenesis and a poor prognosis. *Ann Surg Oncol* 2001; 8:72-79.

[3] Yamazaki K, Abe S, Takekawa H, Sukoh H, Watanabe N, Ogura S, et al. Tumor angiogenesis in human lung adenocarcinoma. *Cancer* 1994; 74:2245-2250.

[4] Mattern J, Koomagi R, Volm M. Vascular endothelial growth factor expression and angiogenesis in non-small cell lung carcinomas. *Int J Cancer* 1995; 6:1059-1062.

[5] Mattern J, Koomagi R, Volm M. Association of vascular endothelial growth factor expression with intratumoral microvessel density and tumor cell proliferation in human epidermoid lung carcinoma. *Br J Cancer* 1996; 73:931-934.

[6] Yano T, Tanikawa S, Fujie T, Masutani M, Horie T. Vascular endothelial growth factor expression and neovascularization in non-small cell lung cancer. *Eur J Cancer* 2001; 36:601-609.

[7] Ohta Y, Endo Y, Tanaka M, Shimizu J, Oda M, Hayashi Y, et al. Significance of vascular endothelial growth factor messenger RNA expression in primary lung cancer. *Clin Cancer Res* 1996; 2:1411-1416.

[8] Fontanini G, Boldrini L, Chiné S, Pisaturo F, Basolo F, Calcinai A, et al. Expression of vascular endothelial growth factor mRNA in non-small cell lung carcinomas. *Br J Cancer* 1999; 79:363-369.

[9] Schlemmer HP, Merkle J, Grobholz R, Jaeger T, Michel MS, Werner A, Rabe J, van Kaick G. Can pre-operative contrast-enhanced dynamic MR imaging for prostate cancer predict microvessel density in prostatectomy specimens? *Eur Radiol.* 2004 Feb;14(2):309-17.

[10] Tekes A, Kamel IR, Szarf G, Chan TY, Schoenberg MP, Bluemke DA. Carcinosarcoma of the urinary bladder: dynamic contrast-enhanced MR imaging with clinical and pathologic correlation. *AJR Am J Roentgenol.* 2003 Jul;181(1):139-42.

[11] Hulka CA, Edmister WB, Smith BL, Tan L, Sgroi DC, Campbell T, Kopans DB, Weisskoff RM. Dynamic echo-planar imaging of the breast: experience in diagnosing breast carcinoma and correlation with tumor angiogenesis. *Radiology.* 1997 Dec;205(3):837-42.

[12] Su MY, Cheung YC, Fruehauf JP, Yu H, Nalcioglu O, Mechetner E, Kyshtoobayeva A, Chen SC, Hsueh S, McLaren CE, Wan YL Correlation of dynamic contrast enhancement MRI parameters with microvessel density and VEGF for assessment of angiogenesis in breast cancer. *J Magn Reson Imaging.* 2003 Oct;18(4):467-77.

[13] Daldrup-Link HE, Rydland J, Helbich TH, Bjornerud A, Turetschek K, Kvistad KA, Kaindl E, Link TM, Staudacher K, Shames D, Brasch RC, Haraldseth O, Rummeny EJ. Quantification of breast tumor microvascular permeability with feruglose-enhanced MR imaging: initial phase II multicenter trial. *Radiology.* 2003 Dec;229(3):885-92.

[14] Kwak BK, Shim HJ, Park ES, Kim SA, Choi D, Lim HK, Park CK, Chung JW, Park JH Hepatocellular carcinoma: correlation between vascular endothelial growth factor level

and degree of enhancement by multiphase contrast-enhanced computed tomography *Invest Radiol.* 2001 Aug;36(8):487-92.

[15] Tuncbilek N, Karakas HM, Altaner S. Dynamic MRI in indirect estimation of microvessel density, histologic grade, and prognosis in colorectal adenocarcinomas. *Abdom Imaging.* 2004 Jan 28

[16] Yuan A, Yang PC, Yu CJ, Lee YC, Yao YT, Chen CL, et al. Tumor angiogenesis correlates with histologic type and metastasis in non-small cell lung cancer. *Am J Respir Crit Care Med* 1995; 152:2157-2162.

[17] Fontanini G, Bigini D, Vignati S, Basolo F, Mussi A, Lucchi M, et al. Microvessel count predicts metastatic disease and survival in non-small cell lung cancer. *J Pathol* 1995; 177:57-63.

[18] Macchiarini P, Fontanini G, Hardin MJ, Squartini F, Angeletti CA. Relation of neovascularization to metastasis of non-small cell lung cancer. *Lancet* 1992; 340:146-146.

[19] Ohta Y, Watanabe Y, Murakami S, Oda M, Hayashi Y, Nomomura A, et al. Vascular endothelial growth factor and lymph node metastasis in primary lung cancer. *Br J Cancer* 1997; 76:1041-1045.

[20] Tateishi U, Kusumoto M, Nishihara H, Nagashima K, Morikawa T, Moriyama N. Contrast-enhanced dynamic computed tomography for the evaluation of tumor angiogenesis in patients with lung carcinoma. *Cancer.* 2002 Aug 15;95(4):835-42.

[21] Tateishi U, Nishihara H, Watanabe S, Morikawa T, Abe K, Miyasaka K Tumor angiogenesis and dynamic CT in lung adenocarcinoma: radiologic-pathologic correlation. *J Comput Assist Tomogr.* 2001 Jan-Feb;25(1):23-7.

[22] Miles KA, Griffiths MR, Fuentes MA. Standardized perfusion value: universal CT contrast enhancement scale that correlates with FDG PET in lung nodules. *Radiology.* 2001 Aug;220(2):548-53.

[23] Zhang M, Kono M. Solitary pulmonary nodules: Evaluation of blood flow patterns with dynamic CT. *Radiology* 1997; 205:471-478.

[24] Yamashita K, Matsunobe S, Tsuda T, Nemoto T, Matsumoto K, Miki H, et al. Solitary pulmonary nodule: preliminary study of evaluation with incremental dynamic CT. *Radiology* 1995; 194:399-405.

[25] Swensen SJ, Morin RL, Schueler BA, Brown LR, Cortese DA, Pairolero PC, et al. Solitary pulmonary nodule: CT evaluation of enhancement with iodinated contrast material – a preliminary report. *Radiology* 1992; 182:343-347.

[26] Swensen SJ, Brown LR, Colby TV, Weaver AL. Pulmonary nodules: CT evaluation of enhancement with iodinated contrast material. *Radiology* 1995; 194:393-398.

[27] Yamashita K, Matsunobe S, Takahashi R, Tsuda T, Matsumoto K, Miki H, et al. Small peripheral lung carcinoma evaluated with incremental dynamic CT: radiologic-pathologic correlation. *Radiology* 1995; 196:401-408.

[28] Tateishi U, Nishihara H, Tsukamoto E, Morikawa T, Tamaki N, Miyasaka K. Lung tumors evaluated with FDG-PET and dynamic CT: the relationship between vascular density and glucose metabolism. *J Comput Assist Tomogr.* 2002 Mar-Apr;26(2):185-90.

[29] Fuentes MA, Keith CJ, Griffiths M, Durbridge G, Miles KA. Hepatic haemodynamics: interrelationships between contrast enhancement and perfusion on CT and Doppler perfusion indices. *Br J Radiol.* 2002 Jan;75(889):17-23.

[30] Strawn LM, McMahon G, App H, Schreck R, Kuchler WR, Longhi MP, Hui TH, Tang C, Levitzki A, Gazit A, Chen I, Keri G, Orfi L, Risau W, Flamme I, Ullrich A, Hirth KP, Shawver LK. Flk-1 as a target for tumor growth inhibition. *Cancer Res.* 1996 Aug 1;56(15):3540-5.

[31] Gossmann A, Helbich TH, Kuriyama N, Ostrowitzki S, Roberts TP, Shames DM, van Bruggen N, Wendland MF, Israel MA, Brasch RC. Dynamic contrast-enhanced magnetic resonance imaging as a surrogate marker of tumor response to anti-angiogenic therapy in a xenograft model of glioblastoma multiforme. *J Magn Reson Imaging.* 2002 Mar;15(3):233-40.

[32] Checkley D, Tessier JJ, Wedge SR, Dukes M, Kendrew J, Curry B, Middleton B, Waterton JC. Dynamic contrast-enhanced MRI of vascular changes induced by the VEGF-signalling inhibitor ZD4190 in human tumour xenografts. *Magn Reson Imaging.* 2003 Jun;21(5):475-82.

[33] Morgan B, Thomas AL, Drevs J, Hennig J, Buchert M, Jivan A, Horsfield MA, Mross K, Ball HA, Lee L, Mietlowski W, Fuxuis S, Unger C, O'Byrne K, Henry A, Cherryman GR, Laurent D, Dugan M, Marme D, Steward WP. Dynamic contrast-enhanced magnetic resonance imaging as a biomarker for the pharmacological response of PTK787/ZK 222584, an inhibitor of the vascular endothelial growth factor receptor tyrosine kinases, in patients with advanced colorectal cancer and liver metastases: results from two phase I studies. *J Clin Oncol.* 2003 Nov 1;21(21):3955-64.

[34] Fontanini G, Vignati S, Bigini D, Mussi A, Lucchi M, Chiné S, et al. Recurrence and death in non-small cell lung carcinomas: a prognostic model using pathological parameters, microvessel count, and gene protein products. *Clin Cancer Res* 1996; 2:1067-1075.

[35] Takanami I, Tanaka F, Hashizume T, Kodaira S. Vascular endothelial growth factor and its receptor correlates with angiogenesis and survival in pulmonary adenocarcinoma. *Anticancer Res* 1997; 17:2249-2252.

[36] Volm M, Koomagi R, Mattern J. Vascular endothelial growth factor and basic fibroblast growth factor in primary lung carcinomas and the incidence metastasis. *Int J Oncol* 1996; 9:711-714.

In: New Angiogenesis Research
Editor: Roberta V. Zubar, pp. 189-196

ISBN 1-59454-239-2

Chapter X

Angiogenesis in Gynecological Cancers

Jiro Fujimoto*[*], Hiroshi Toyoki, Eriko Sato, Hideki Sakaguchi and Teruhiko Tamaya

Department of Obstetrics and Gynecology, Gifu University School of Medicine, Japan

Abstract

Specific expression manner of main angiogenic factors and the linked angiogenic transcription factor was studied in each gynecological cancer to create new strategies of anti-angiogenic therapy in order to avoid recruitment of alternative pathways as a form of tolerance.

Key words: angiogenesis, cervical cancers, ovarian cancers, endometrial cancers, VEGF, thymidine phosphorylase, IL-8, basic FGF, ETS-1

Introduction

Angiogenesis is essential for development, growth and advancement of solid tumors [1]. The manner of advancement specific to each tumor is critical to patient prognosis. In uterine cervical cancers, lymph node metastasis, recognized as common metastasis, is critical to patient prognosis. In uterine endometrial cancers, myometrial invasion and dedifferentiation, recognized as a common advancement manner, is a reliable indicator of poor patient prognosis. In ovarian cancer, peritoneal dissemination as a common advancement manner is a drastic event that leads to poor patient prognosis.

When the cluster of cancer cells is smaller than 2 mm in diameter, angiogenesis does not occur. However, when the cluster size reaches 2 mm, angiogenesis inevitably occurs. Thereafter, a new capillary network is rapidly formed to nourish and grow the tumors.

[*] Correspondence concerning this article should be addressed to Jiro Fujimoto, Department of Obstetrics and Gynecology, Gifu University School of Medicine 1-1 Yanagido, Gifu City 501-1193, Japan. Phone +81 58 230 6349;Fax +81 58 230 6348. E-mail: jf@cc.gifu-u.ac.jp.

Therefore, attaining a diameter of 2 mm is critical to the manner of tumor growth [1]. Unfortunately, when a secondarily spread lesion has been discovered, its size is usually already larger than 2 mm in diameter. This means angiogenesis in the lesion has already begun, and the manner of angiogenesis that accompanies advancement is informative to know how each tumor's characteristics are linked to patient prognosis. Therefore, we have studied the expression manner of angiogenic factors and one transcription factor for angiogenesis in gynecological cancers.

Concept of Tumor Angiogenesis

Neovascularization involves two concepts, vasculogenesis and angiogenesis. Vasculogenesis is formation of vascular plexus by differentiation from hemangioblasts to endothelial cells without any existing vascular system. For example, primary vascular plexus is formed from hemangioblasts in fetuses by the process of vasculogenesis. Angiogenesis is formation of new capillary from existing capillary. Angiogenesis occurs in tumors, and supports growth and advancement of tumors.

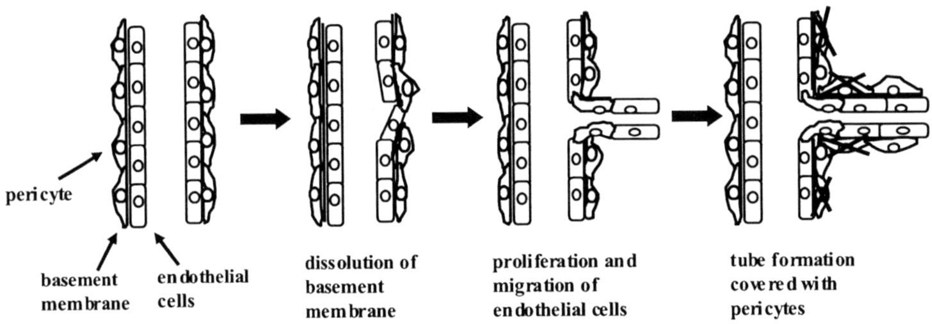

Fig. 1. Process of angiogenesis in tumors.

Fig. 1 shows the detailed process of angiogenesis in tumors. Angiogenic factors from tumors induce and activate matrix metalloproteinase, plasminogen activator, collagenase, and other enzymes in endothelial cells. The enzymes dissolve the basement membrane of endothelial cells, after which the endothelial cells proliferate and migrate under the influence of angiogenic factors. Angiogenic factors induce production of integrins in the endothelial cells. The endothelial cells then form immature capillary tubes. In normal tissue, the capillary is matured upon being covered with pericytes. However, the pericyte-covering layer of capillaries in tumors, consisting of fewer cells than normal with inferior function, is not very good. Therefore, the unique point is that cancer cells can easily invade to and from the immature capillary, as shown in Fig. 1.

Tumor Angiogenesis Specific to Gynecological Cancers

If there is a positive correlation between microvessel density in tumors and the target factor levels, it is plausible that the target factor is an angiogenic factor. The microvessel density is evaluated by counting microvessels using immunohistochemical staining for CD31, CD34 or factor VIII-related antigen specific to the endothelial cells. The angiogenic factors basic fibroblast growth factor (bFGF), thymidine phosphorylase (TP), vascular endothelial growth factor (VEGF) and interleukin (IL)-8 are the main angiogenic factors in gynecological cancers. A brief introduction for each of them follows: Basic FGF expressed in cancer and stromal cells works on basic angiogenesis. VEGF expressed in cancer cells translocates to endothelial cells to work on sensitive angiogenesis. TP expressed in stromal cells works on specific angiogenesis with enzymatic activity. IL-8 secreted from macrophages works on angiogenesis associated with cancer cell invasion. Following are the details of the working manner of the various angiogenic factors and one mediator that are closely related with the advancement manner of the different gynecological cancers.

In uterine cervical cancers, the main manner of angiogenesis is shown in Fig. 2. Basic FGF levels increase with advancement regardless of histological type. However, the correlation between bFGF levels and poor patient prognosis is not so clear. Therefore, bFGF might be associated with basic angiogenesis to drive uterine cervical cancers in growth and secondary spreading [2]. Among the subtypes of VEGF, the populations of $VEGF_{165}$ and $VEGF_{121}$ are dominant in uterine cervical cancers. The levels of $VEGF_{165}$ and $VEGF_{121}$ are remarkably higher in advanced stage adenocarcinomas of the cervix than in other cases. Thus, the elevation of $VEGF_{165}$ and $VEGF_{121}$ might contribute to the relatively late advancement via angiogenic activity in advanced adenocarcinomas of the cervix [3]. IL-8 levels correlate with microvessel and infiltrated macrophage counts and the localization of IL-8 is similar to that of CD68 specific to macrophages. The prognosis of patients with high IL-8 was extremely poor. Consequently, IL-8 can be regarded as a prognostic indicator as an angiogenic factor supplied from macrophages in uterine cervical cancers [4].

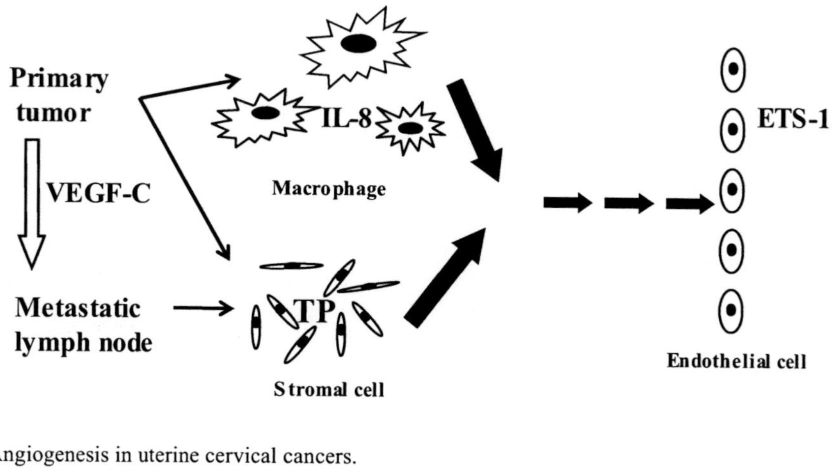

Fig. 2. Angiogenesis in uterine cervical cancers.

TP has a wide range of expression and is highly expressed in uterine cervical cancers regardless of clinical stage. The prognosis of patients with high TP in primary tumors is worse than in those with low TP. Hence, it is apparent that TP in uterine cervical cancers plays a role of basic angiogenesis in all processes of advancement of uterine cervical cancers [5]. Furthermore, TP remarkably increased in 8 of 40 metastatic lymph node lesions of uterine cervical cancers. The prognosis of the patients with high TP in metastatic lymph node lesions was extremely poor. Therefore, TP expressed in stromal cells appears to contribute to the advancement of metastatic lymph nodes after the establishment of metastasis, and is recognized as a prognostic indicator [6]. Incidentally, VEGF-C expressed in cancer cells directly contributes to lymph node metastasis in uterine cervical cancers as a non-angiogenic factor [7]. TP and VEGF-C expressions in metastatic lymph node are keys to evaluating patient prognosis and to building new strategies of anti-angiogenic therapy. In addition, serum TP in patients with uterine cervical cancers reveals positive correlations with clinical stage and tumor size and with the advancement indicators lymph node metastasis, parametrial involvement, and vessel permeation in both squamous cell carcinomas and adenocarcinomas. Serum TP level is recognized as a novel tumor marker regardless of histopathological type of the uterine cervical cancer [8].

ETS-1 levels correlate with microvessel density in uterine cervical cancers and the localization of ETS-1 is similar to that of vascular endothelial cells. Among the angiogenic factors, ETS-1 levels correlate with the TP and IL-8 levels. Furthermore, the prognosis of patients with high ETS-1 was extremely poor. ETS-1 is a prognostic indicator as an angiogenic mediator in uterine cervical cancers [9]. This linkage is important for developing a new strategy of anti-angiogenic therapy to suppress angiogenic signal transduction processes.

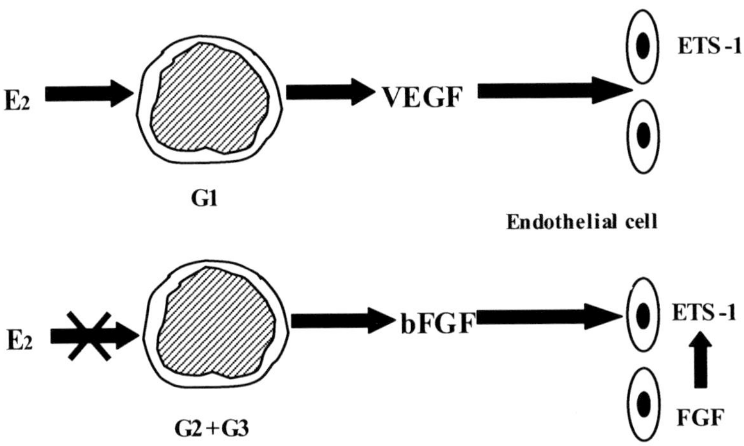

Fig. 3. Angiogenesis in uterine endometrial cancers.

Fig. 3 shows the main manner of angiogenesis in uterine endometrial cancers. Because endometrial cancers conserve hormone dependency in growth and in angiogenic potential, angiogenesis is very complicated. VEGF levels are higher in order of histopathological differentiation: normal uterine endometrium (NE) > well differentiated (G1) > moderately differentiated (G2) and poorly differentiated (G3). They are also lower in order of the advancement of clinical stages: NE > stage I > stage II > stages III and IV. Thus, it may be concluded that VEGF contributes to the early process of advancement with a high degree of differentiation via angiogenic activity [10]. In G1 endometrial cancer cells, estrogen transiently induces VEGF expression. The transient upregulation of VEGF is considered to be logical, as the upstream of VEGF gene conserves estrogen-responsive elements. Therefore, it is natural that VEGF expression should be downregulated with advancement and dediffentiation in uterine endometrial cancers. Furthermore, progestins (progesterone, medroxyprogesterone acetate [MPA] and 17 alpha-hydroxyprogesterone) suppress the estrogen-induced events. Therefore, in the clinical setting, progestins could suppress VEGF-related angiogenic potential, which contributes to tumor growth in the early stage of uterine endometrial cancers that conserve estrogen dependency [11].

TP levels are highest in G1 endometrial cancers with invasion to ≤ half the myometrium (B) and in stage 1 in all uterine endometrial cancers. Hence, it is apparent that the active availability of TP contributes to the acceleration of angiogenic activity in the early process of invasion of G1 endometrial cancers [12]. In the normal menstrual cycle, TP levels in uterine endometrium do not alter during the proliferative phase prior to ovulation. They are then temporarily low after ovulation, but increase remarkably through the late secretory phase. Therefore, it is clear that TP expression depends upon changes in sex steroid levels [13,14]. In G1 endometrial cancer cells, estradiol induces TP expression, and the estrogen-induced expression is increased approximately two-fold by progesterone and by its metabolite, 17alpha-hydroxyprogesterone, but not by MPA. Therefore, the endogenous steroids progesterone and 17alpha-hydroxyprogesterone induce TP-related angiogenic potential, but the synthetic steroid MPA does not, and the failure of TP induction by MPA is the great merit of anti-angiogenic treatment with MPA for uterine endometrial cancers [15].

IL-8 levels correlate with microvessel and infiltrated macrophage counts and the localization of IL-8 is similar to that of CD68 specific to macrophages. IL-8 levels are increased during myometrial invasion from stage Ia to stages Ib through IV. Consequently, we can say that IL-8 supplied from infiltrated macrophages acts as an angiogenic switch in myometrial invasion in stage I uterine endometrial cancers [16]. Basic FGF level is highest in G3 and stage III-IV in all uterine endometrial cancers. Since lethal lesions are mostly confined to endometrial cancers of G3 and stages III-IV, we can conclude that the increase in bFGF leads to angiogenesis, and contributes to the acceleration of growth and secondary spreading [17]. In addition, O-(chloroacetyl-carbamoyl) fumagillol (TNP-470; AGM-1470) as an anti-angiogenic agent reduces bFGF levels in G3 endometrial cancer cells regardless of hormone dependency [18]. ETS-1 levels correlate with microvessel density and the localization of ETS-1 is similar to that of vascular endothelial cells. ETS-1 levels tend to increase with advancement. Furthermore, ETS-1 levels correlate with VEGF levels in G1 and with bFGF levels in G2 and G3 endometrial cancers. Therefore, it is clear that ETS-1 links to VEGF in G1, and to bFGF in G2 and G3 endometrial cancers to mediate angiogenesis [19]. In addition, ETS-1 levels increase in the proliferative phase, reach a peak during peri-ovulation, decrease in the secretory phase, and correlate with VEGF levels in the proliferative phase. Thus, it can be seen that ETS-1 is an angiogenic mediator in uterine endometrium linked to VEGF in the proliferative phase by estrogen [20,21].

In ovarian cancers, the main manner of angiogenesis is shown in Fig. 4. $VEGF_{165}$ levels in ovarian cancers are higher than in normal ovaries regardless of histopathological type or clinical stage, and correlate with poor patient prognosis [22]. Increased VEGF levels from the primary tumor to the peritoneal disseminated lesion of ovarian cancers were found in 8 of 30 cases. The 24-month survival rate of the patients with increased VEGF levels from the primary tumor to the peritoneal disseminated lesion was extremely poor. Therefore, we can conclude that VEGF is a key signal in growth and advancement of peritoneal dissemination as a prognostic indicator [23]. ETS-1 levels correlate with microvessel density and the localization of ETS-1 is similar to that of vascular endothelial cells. ETS-1 levels increase with the progression of ovarian cancers, and correlate with poor patient prognosis and VEGF expressions [24]. Furthermore, the prognosis of the patients with increased ETS-1 levels from the primary tumor to the peritoneal was extremely poor, and ETS-1 was linked to VEGF expression. Hence, it may be concluded that ETS-1 linked to VEGF acts as an angiogenic mediator in primary tumors and especially in peritoneal disseminated lesions, and is directly related to patient prognosis of ovarian cancers [25].

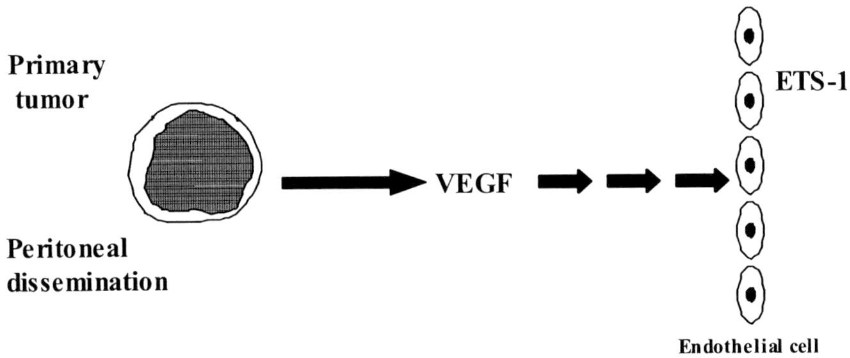

Fig. 4. Angiogenesis in ovarian cancers.

Conclusion

Each gynecological cancer conserves specific expression manners of angiogenic factors and the angiogenic transcription factor ETS-1 to promote specific secondary spreading. The keys to creating new strategies of anti-angiogenic therapy are: (1) overexpression of TP linked to ETS-1 in metastatic lymph nodes of uterine cervical cancers; (2) signal switching from VEGF to bFGF linked to ETS-1 with dedifferentiation; and (3) overexpression of VEGF linked to ETS-1 in peritoneal dissemination of ovarian cancers. We are looking forward to proceeding with clinical trials of anti-angiogenic agents in advanced-stage patients and after curative resection of gynecological cancers.

References

[1] Folkman J: Tumor angiogenesis. *Adv Cancer Res* 1985;43:175-203

[2] Fujimoto J, Ichigo S, Hori M, Ichigo S, Tamaya T: Expression of basic fibroblast growth factor and its mRNA in advanced uterine cervical cancers. *Cancer Lett* 1997;111:21-26

[3] Fujimoto J, Sakaguchi H, Hirose R, Ichigo S, Tamaya T: Expression of vascular endothelial growth factor (VEGF) and its mRNA in uterine cervical cancers. *Br J Cancer* 1999;80:827-833

[4] Fujimoto J, Sakaguchi H, Aoki I, Tamaya T: Clinical implications of expression of interleukin 8 related to angiogenesis in uterine cervical cancers. *Cancer Res* 2000;60:2632-2635

[5] Fujimoto J, Sakaguchi H, Hirose R, Ichigo S, Tamaya T: The expression of platelet-derived endothelial cell growth factor in uterine cervical cancers. *Br J Cancer* 1999;79:1249-1254

[6] Fujimoto J, Sakaguchi H, Hirose R, Wen H, Tamaya T: Clinical implication of expression of platelet-derived endothelial cell growth factor (PD-ECGF) in metastatic lesions of uterine cervical cancers. *Cancer Res* 1999;59:3041-3044

[7] Fujimoto J, Toyoki H, Sato E, Sakaguchi H, Tamaya T: Clinical implication of expression of vascular endothelial growth factor-C in metastatic lymph nodes of uterine cervical cancers. *Br J Cancer* (in press)

[8] Fujimoto J, Sakaguchi H, Aoki I, Tamaya T: The value of platelet-derived endothelial cell growth factor as a novel predictor of advancement of uterine cervical cancers. *Cancer Res* 2000;60:3662-3665

[9] Fujimoto J, Aoki I, Toyoki H, Khatun S, Tamaya T: Clinical implications of ETS-1 related to angiogenesis in uterine cervical cancers. *Ann Oncol* 2002;13:1598-1604

[10] Fujimoto J, Ichigo S, Hirose R, Sakaguchi H, Tamaya T: Expressions of vascular endothelial growth factor (VEGF) and its mRNA in uterine endometrial cancers. *Cancer Lett* 1998;134:15-22

[11] Fujimoto J, Sakaguchi H, Hirose R, Ichigo S, Tamaya T: Progestins suppress estrogen-induced expression of vascular endothelial growth factor (VEGF) subtypes in uterine endometrial cancer cells. *Cancer Lett* 1999;141:63-71

[12] Fujimoto J, Ichigo S, Sakaguchi H, Hirose R, Tamaya T: Expression of platelet-derived endothelial cell growth factor (PD-ECGF) and its mRNA in uterine endometrial cancers. *Cancer Lett* 1998;130:115-120

[13] Fujimoto J, Ichigo S, Sakaguchi H, Hirose R, Tamaya T: Expression of platelet-derived endothelial cell growth factor in uterine endometrium during the menstrual cycle. *Mol Hum Reprod* 1998;4:509-513

[14] Fujimoto J, Sakaguchi H, Hirose R, Tamaya T: Expression of platelet-derived endothelial cell growth factor (PD-ECGF) related to angiogenesis in ovarian endometriosis. *J Clin Endocrinol Metab* 1999;84:359-362

[15] Aoki I, Fujimoto J, Tamaya T: Effects of various steroids on platelet-derived endothelial cell growth factor (PD-ECGF) and its mRNA expression in uterine endometrial cancer cells. *J Steroid Biochem Mol Biol* 2003;84:217-222

[16] Fujimoto J, Aoki I, Khatun S, Toyoki H, Tamaya T: Clinical implications of interleukin-8 related to myometrial invasion with angiogenesis in uterine endometrial cervical cancers. *Ann Oncol* 2002;13:430-434

[17] Fujimoto J, Hori M, Ichigo S, Tamaya T: Expression of basic fibroblast growth factor and its mRNA in uterine endometrial cancers. *Invas Metast* 1995;15:203-210

[18] Fujimoto J, Hori M, Ichigo S, Hirose R, Sakaguchi H, Tamaya T: Plausible novel therapeutic strategy of uterine endometrial cancer with reduction of basic fibroblast

growth factor secretion by progestin and O-(chloroacetyl-carbamoyl) fumagillol (TNP-470; AGM-1470). *Cancer Lett* 1997;113:187-194

[19] Fujimoto J, Aoki I, Toyoki H, Khatun S, Tamaya T: Clinical implications of ETS-1 related to angiogenesis in uterine endometrial cancers. Ann Oncol 2002;13:1605-1611

[20] Fujimoto J, Aoki I, Toyoki H, Khatun S, Sato E, Tamaya T: Expression of ETS-1 related to angiogenesis in uterine endometrium during the menstrual cycle. *J Biomed Sci* 2003;10:320-327

[21] Sakaguchi H, Fujimoto J, Aoki I, Toyoki H, Khatun S, Sato E, Tamaya T: Expression of E26 transformation specific (ETS-1) related to angiogenesis in ovarian endometriosis. *Fertil Steril* (in press)

[22] Fujimoto J, Sakaguchi H, Hirose R, Ichigo S, Tamaya T: Biologic implications of the expression of vascular endothelial growth factor subtypes in ovarian carcinoma. *Cancer* 1998;83:2528-2533

[23] Fujimoto J, Sakaguchi H, Aoki I, Khatun S, Tamaya T: Clinical implications of the expression of vascular endothelial growth factor in metastatic lesions of ovarian cancers. *Br J Cancer* 2001;85:313-316

[24] Khatun S, Fujimoto J, Toyoki H, Tamaya T: Clinical implication of expression of ETS-1 related to angiogenesis in ovarian cancers. *Cancer Sci* 2003;94:769-773

[25] Fujimoto J, Aoki I, Toyoki H, Khatun S, Sato E, Sakaguchi H, Tamaya T: Clinical implications of expression of ETS-1 related to angiogenesis in metastatic lesions of ovarian cancers. *Oncology* (in press)

In: New Angiogenesis Research
Editor: Roberta V. Zubar, pp. 197-217

ISBN 1-59454-239-2

Chapter XI

Angiogenesis as Discriminating Aspect Between Melanoma and Uncertain Melanocytic Lesions: An Immunohistochemical Study

Oriana Simonetti*, Guendalina Lucarini[1], Graziella Biagini[1] and Annamaria Offidani
Clinic of Dermatology, [1]Institute of Normal Human Morphology, Università Politecnica delle Marche, Ancona, Italy

Abstract

Background

Vascular Endothelial Growth Factor (VEGF) an endothelial cell mitogen, plays a crucial role in physiological and pathological angiogenesis. The regulation of the mechanism leading to tumour angiogenesis is complex and depends on multiple and interactive factors between cells and extracellular matrix. Extracellular proteolysis has been implicated in many of these processes in particular those belonging to matrix metalloproteinases, including the 72 kDa gelatinase A/type IV collagenase (MMP-2) and the 92 kDa gelatinase B/type IV collagenase (MMP-9). In particular MMP-9 was recently discovered as a key regulator of angiogenesis.

Methods

We assessed the immunohistochemical expression of VEGF and metalloproteinases MMP-2 and MMP-9 in paraffin-embedded biopsy specimens of malignant melanomas

* Correspondence concerning this article should be addressed to Dr. Oriana Simonetti, Clinica Dermatologica, Ospedale Regionale "Umberto I" Via Conca 60020 Torrette (Ancona), Italy. Tel: +39 71 5963494; E-mail: orisimonetti@libero.it. o.simonetti@ao-umbertoprimo.marche.it.

(18 invasive melanomas and 10 in situ melanomas), dysplastic nevi with architectural disorder and cytological atypia of melanocytes, Spitz nevi, and compound or predominantly intradermal ordinary benign melanocytic nevi.

Results

We observed strong cytoplasmatic staining for VEGF in melanoma cells in as many as 77% of primary invasive melanomas, whereas only 25% of the in situ melanomas exhibited a detectable immunoreactivity for VEGF. Interestingly no immunoreactivity was shown by any nevi; Spitz nevi, in particular, showed a negative immunoreactivity to VEGF.

Invasive melanomas and in situ melanomas displayed co-expression of MMP-2 and MMP-9, although to a variable extent. In particular high MMP-2 staining was observed in 14 out of 18 invasive melanomas, and strong MMP-2 expression was also observed in 60% of in situ melanomas, while the residual 40% showed a moderate level of positivity. Similarly to VEGF no MMP-9 immunostaining was observed in tissue sections from benign, Spitz and atypical nevi. Conversely we found a positive correlation between VEGF and MMP-9 in melanomas ($r=0.37$, $p<0.05$), and this correlation was highly significant in invasive melanomas ($p<0.001$).

Conclusions

On the basis of our data, which show that malignant melanocytic tumors display a strong VEGF expression whereas benign melanocytic proliferations show no immunoreactivity for VEGF and MMP-9, VEGF could also be used as a discriminating factor between malignant melanoma and uncertain lesions and MMP-9 could be considered an important regulator of angiogenesis.

Key words: Melanoma, naevi, immunohistochemistry, VEGF, MMP-2, MMP-9

Introduction

Human malignant melanoma is a highly metastatic tumour [1-2] of increasing incidence. Cutaneous melanoma may develop de novo from normal melanocytes or from potential precursor lesions, such as atypical dysplastic nevi or congenital nevi [3-4] The series of events by which a putatively normal cell develops into a metastatic cancer cell have been designated as tumor progression, the mechanisms of which are not well defined in malignant melanoma. Crucial events in tumor progression include the ability of the tumor to grow, to cross mechanical and molecular barriers of invasion, to escape immune surveillance, and to disseminate [2]. Early steps in this progression require tumor proliferation and the formation of new vascular channels to sustain tumor growth and provide it with a gateway through which it enters the circulation and metastasizes to distant sites [5-6]. Angiogenesis is a complex multistep process involving extravasation of plasma proteins, degradation of extracellular matrix, endothelial cell migration and proliferation, and capillary tube formation [7]. Positive regulators of angiogenesis include, but are not limited to, the vascular endothelial growth factor (VEGF), basic fibroblast growth factor (FGF) and its relative, interleukin 8 (IL-

8), placental growth factor (PIGF), transforming growth factor-B (TGF-B), platelet-derived endothelial growth factor (PDEGF) [7-9]. A number of endogenous negative regulators have been described including trombospondin-1 and 2, angiostatin, endostatin, vasostatin, and VEGF [9-11]. It appears that in normal tissue, vascular quiescence is maintained by the dominant influence of endogenous angiogenesis inhibitors over angiogenic stimuli. Therefore it was postulated that tumor angiogenesis is a consequence of a balance shift in favour of the angiogenic inducers and/or downregulation of inhibitors [9] . Often the tumor-associated angiogenesis occurs during the radial growth phase of melanoma, without competence for metastasis, and may result in the development of the vertical growth phase with metastatic competence and a worse clinical prognosis [12-13]. The factors that lead to this specific pattern of spread are largely unknown, but it has been hypothesized that melanoma cells must undergo progressive phenotypic changes to develop the ability to form a vertical growth phase and spread to the dermal lymphatic bed, to the regional lymph nodes, and to distant metastatic sites [14] The development of the ability to express proangiogenic factors is likely to be one of the phenotypic changes that allow melanoma cells to spread and grow in the regional lymph nodes. It has been found that many angiogenic factors are expressed by melanoma cells including IL-8 [15-16], platelet-derived endothelial cell growth factor (PD-ECGF) [17], basic fibroblast growth factor (bFGF) [18], and vascular endothelial growth factor (VEGF) [19]. Among the numerous chemical mediators, VEGF or vascular permeability factor is believed to be one of the most potent stimulators of endothelial activation and proliferation. VEGF is a heparin-binding dimeric polypeptide which, because of differential splicing, can be found in six different isoforms encoding proteins of 121, 145, 165, 183, 189 and 206 aminoacids [20-21]. It also exerts a number of important biological actions on endothelial cells; it increases the permeability of microvessels to circulating macromolecules [20-22] and acts as a selective endothelial cell mitogen by binding to the specific plasma membrane receptor Flt-1 and Flt-1/KDR on endothelial cells [23-24].VEGF is markedly upregulated in many tumors and its expression has been shown to correlate with malignancy [22, 25]. In addition VEGF alters endothelial cell gene expression, inducing increased production of tissue factor and several proteases, which include interstitial collagenase and both the urokinase-like and tissue plasminogen activators [26-27]. On the other hand investigations have demonstrated that both endothelial cell serine protease [27 -29] and Metalloproteinases (MMPs) [30-31] can contribute to angiogenesis through subendothelial basement membrane degradation, endothelial cell migration, and the formation of a newly formed vasculature. The coinduction of plasminogen activator and procollagenase by VEGF suggests that serine and metalloproteinases cooperate in producing the matrix degradation necessary for vessel sprouting [26]. Moreover the transformation from non-invasive to invasive carcinomas is a complex and multistep processes, including detachment of cancer cells from a primary site, invasion into surrounding tissue through breakdown matrix, spreading through lymphatic or blood circulation and finally proliferation in a distant organ. Degradation and remodelling of the extracellular matrix (ECM) and basement membranes are necessary to allow malignant cells to migrate from the primary location. The role of several groups of proteases in tumor cell invasion and metastases have been extensively discussed [31-35]. Actually matrix metalloproteinases activity represent a key element in the multistage process of tumor invasion and metastasis [31, 36-37]. MMP are expressed in an inactive, or zymogen form, and activity depends on extracellular activation of enzymes requiring cleavage of the cystein-containing pro-enzyme region that contacts the zinc atom in the active catalytic site [38]. Regulation of MMP activity is dependent upon gene expression, enzyme activation and the presence of inhibitors [39]. Basal production of metalloproteinases is typically low or absent and requires inducing factors, such as cytokine, growth factor, or contact with components of the extracellular matrix in order to increase their expression [40]. Among the MMP family members, the 72 kDa gelatinase A/type IV collagenase (MMP-2) and the 92 kDa gelatinase B/type IV collagenase (MMP-9) [31, 36-37] are thought to play a critical role in regulating cell migration and proliferation during cancer cell invasion, basement remodelling and angiogenesis. Part of the influence of MMPs, including MMP-2 and MMP-9, was mediated by their effect on VEGF and the angiopoietin family [41]. In particular MMP9 is implicated in promoting angiogenesis since expression of MMP-9 has been associated with this process in a number of systems. [42-44] The objective of this study was to evaluate the immunohistochemical expression of VEGF and metalloproteinases 2 and 9 in benign cutaneous melanocytic lesions and in lesions representing different stages of progression to malignant melanoma.

Material and Methods

All tissues used in this study were obtained from the archives of the Pathology Department. Biopsy specimens obtained at surgery were fixed in 10% buffered formalin and embedded in paraffin. The diagnoses were made on haematoxylin and eosin-stained sections, but Fontana-Masson staining and immunoistochemical staining with S-100, NSE and HMB-45 antibodies was also performed in selected cases. The diagnoses were based on the usual criteria. [45] The formalin fixed, paraffin embedded melanocytic lesions represented 18 primary invasive malignant melanomas (PIMM) with invasion (Clark's) levels IV (seven Breslow thickness > 1,5-3; eleven Breslow thickness > 3), none of which presented regression areas, 10 malignant melanoma in situ (MMIS), 9 atypical (dysplastic) melanocytic nevi with architectural disorder and cytological atypia of melanocytes (AN), 6 Spindle and epithelioid cell (Spitz) nevi (SN), and 10 ordinary benign melanocytic nevi (BMN) either compound or predominantly intradermal.

Immunohistochemistry

For immunohistochemistry conventional 4 μm thick histological sections were obtained with a microtome from the selected blocks and mounted on slides pre-treated with poly-l-lysine (Sigma Chemicals, St Louis, MO, USA). The slides were then de-paraffined and re-hydrated in a gradient of ethanol and xylene . To better unmask the antigenic sites, sections were incubated with a solution of TUF (Target Unmasking Fluid; Alexis, Biochemical) for 10 min. at 90° C. After washing in H2O and then in Tris buffer solution the sections were incubated overnight at 4°C with the monoclonal antibody anti-VEGF (dil. 1:200, Santa Cruz, CA) and the polyclonal antibodies anti MMP-2 (dil. 1:400) and anti MMP-9 (dil. 1:500; kindly manufactured by Stetler Stevenson, NIH, Bethesda, MD). The incubations with the antibodies were carried out in a humidified atmosphere.The antibodies were linked to an alkaline phosphatase anti-alkaline phosphatase (APAAP) catalyzed reaction (Kit Dako, SpA Italy), being washed troughly with PBS between all stages in the procedure. The APAAP technique was used according to Cordell et al. [46]. For visualization of the antibodies sections were incubated with the substrate Fas red (Dako SpA, Italy) , yelding a red end product at the site of the target antigen. The sections were finally counterstained with Mayer's haematoxylin , dehydrated and mounted in glycerol-gelatin (Dako SpA, Italy). Each series included appropriate negative control sections omitting the primary antibody. Fetal renal tissue seved as positive control.

The immunohistochemical expression of the antibodies studied was scored by two independent observers (L.G. & S.O.) and evaluated by light microscopy-observing 10 fields for each sample at 250X magnification and identifying zone representatives. If 1% or more of the cells showed a positive immunoreaction, the tumour was considered to be positive. We evaluated particular immunohistochemical expression of the positive cells as following: negative: no cell stained; low: 1-10% cells stained; moderate: 15-30% cells stained; high: more of 40% cells stained.

Statistical Analysis

Correlation between VEGF and MMP-9 was assessed by linear regression analysis. A P-value<5% denoted the presence of a statistically significant difference.

Results

VEGF

VEGF immunostaining was found in the cytoplasm of the melanocytic cells and endothelial cells of the observed samples.

No VEGF immunoreactivity was detected in the cells of ordinary benign melanocytic nevi, atypical melanocytic nevi (Fig.1) and Spitz nevi (Fig.2). While it was observed in endothelial cells of microvessels in all samples.

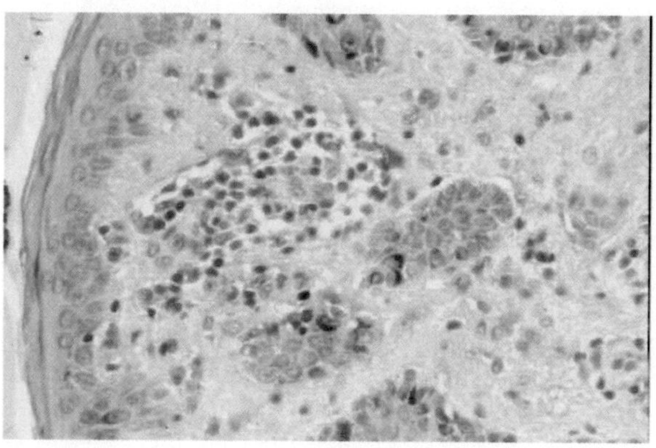

Fig. 1. Dysplastic compound nevus: no vascular endothelial growth factor immunohistochemical expression is observed (alkaline phosphatase- antialkaline phosphatase technique, x400).

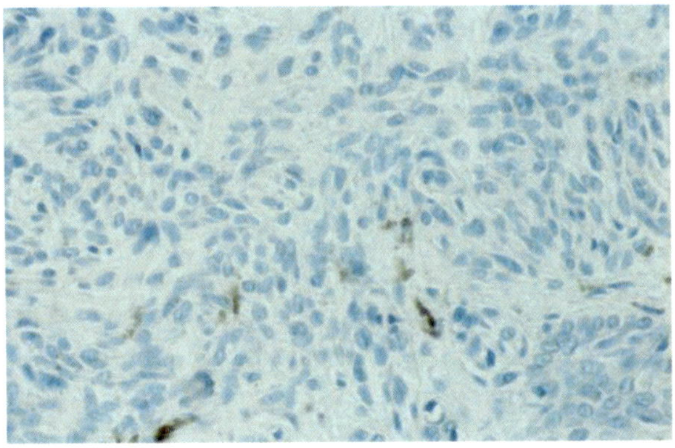

Fig. 2. Spitz nevus shows no Vascular Endothelial Growth Factor immunolocalization (alkaline phosphatase-antialkaline phosphatase technique, x200).

A moderate percentage (15-30%) of melanoma cells were detected in five out of ten melanoma in situ (Fig.3), whereas in the other five a faint immunopositivity could be scored. Few host response cells were positive to VEGF .

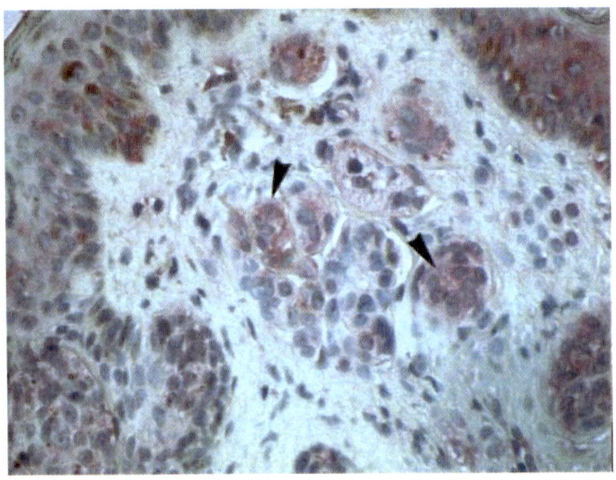

Fig.3. Melanoma in situ: Vascular Endothelial Growth Factor immunopositivity is observd (arrowheads alkaline phosphatase-antialkaline phosphatase technique, x400).

A high cytoplasmatic tumor cell staining was observed in fourteen out of the 18 invasive melanoma (Fig.4). The others exhibited a faint immunopositivity. Focal cytoplasmic VEGF staining was observed in tumor infiltrating inflammatory cells in all samples examined.

Metalloproteinases

MMP-2 and MMP-9 expression was found in the cytoplasm of melanocytic cells.

Normal skin showed no immunostaining for the antibodies against MMP-2 and MMP-9.

While moderate or faint MMP-2 expression was observed in ordinary benign melanocytic nevi and typical junctional melanocytic nevi. In nevic cells, MMP-2 was more commonly observed in the papillary dermis than in the reticular dermis whereas in junctional nevi, MMP-2 staining was a prominent feature of the dermal-epidermal junction (Fig.5).

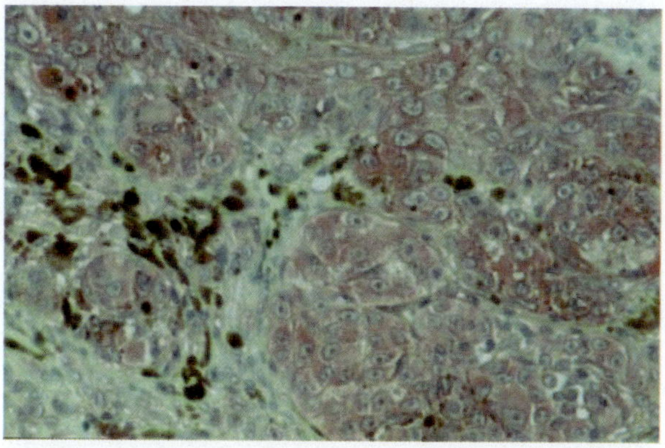

Fig.4. Invasive melanoma: strong vascular endothelial growth factor immunostaining is observed on melanocytic cells (alkaline phosphatase-antialkaline phosphatase technique, x400).

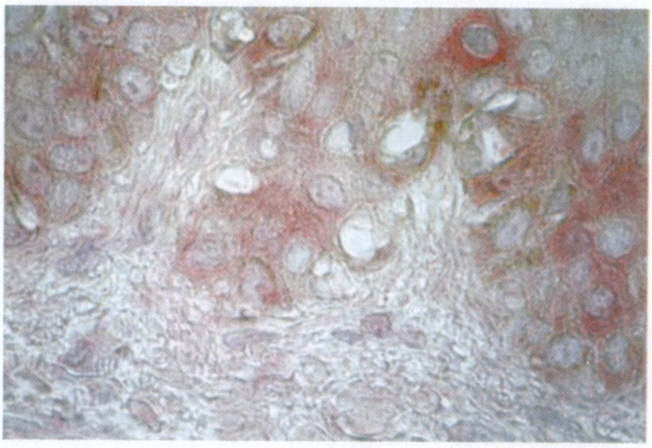

Fig.5. Typical junctional melanocytic nevus: matrix metalloproteinase 2 staining was a prominent feature of the dermal-epidermal junction (alkaline phosphatase-antialkaline phosphatase technique, x 1000).

Each of the Spitz nevi showed immunostaining for MMP-2 varying from moderate to high intensity (Fig.6).

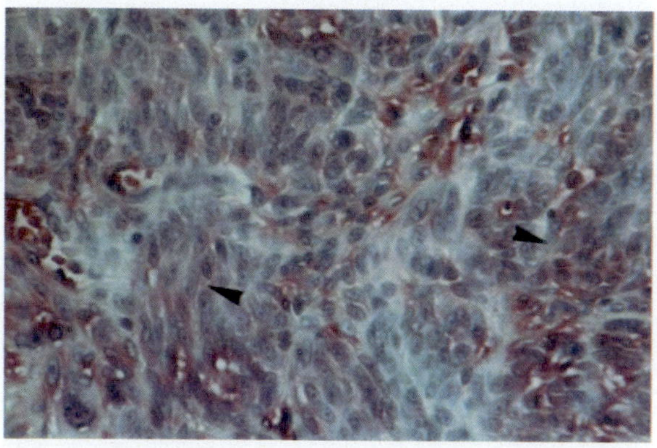

Fig.6. Matrix metalloproteinase 2 immunolocalization is seen on melanocytic cells of Spitz nevi (arrowheads, alkaline phosphatase-antialkaline phosphatase technique, x400).

In atypical melanocytic nevi MMP-2 staining showed a slightly higher expression than ordinary benign melanocytic nevi, especially in atypical compound nevi characterized by severe cellular atypia.

No MMP-9 immunostaining was observed in tissue sections from benign, Spitz (Fig.7) and atypical nevi (Fig.8).

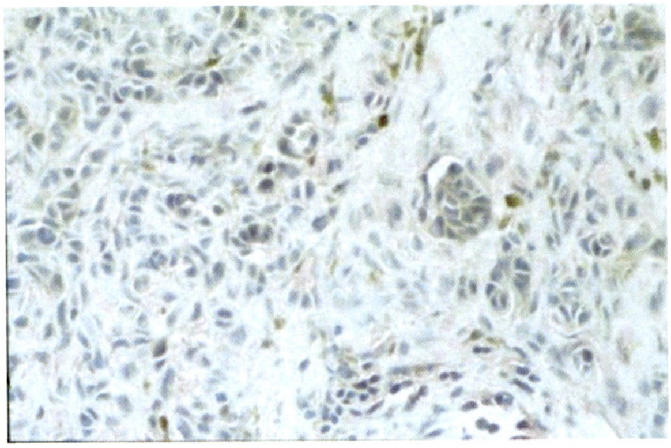

Fig.7. Spitz nevus shows no matrix metalloproteinase 9 immunolocalization (alkaline phosphatase-antialkaline phosphatase technique, x200)

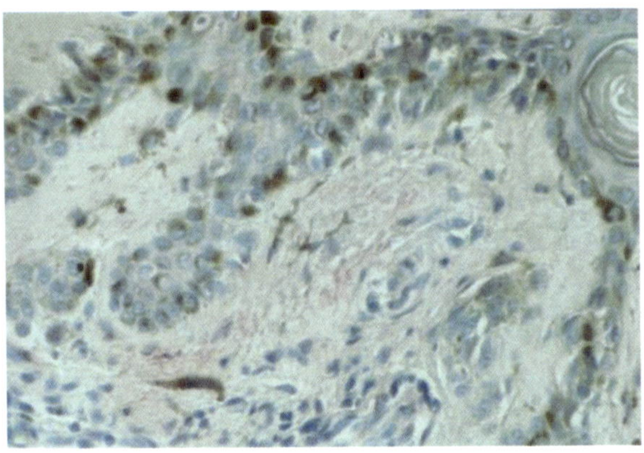

Fig.8. Atypical nevus: no matrix metalloproteinase 9 immunohistochemical expression is observed: alkaline phosphatase- antialkaline phosphatase technique, x400).

Invasive melanomas and in situ melanomas both showed variable immunostaining for MMP-2 and MMP-9. Strong MMP-2 expression was observed in each of the melanomas, with different grades of tumor invasion. In particular high MMP-2 staining was observed in 14 out of 18 invasive melanoma (Fig. 9). Moreover, strong MMP-2 expression was found in 60% of in situ melanoma, whereas the residual 40% showed a moderate level of positivity (Fig. 10). MMP-2 was present in nests of melanoma cells within the epidermis as well as the dermis, but also found in peripheral melanoma cells and in adjacent dermal stroma.

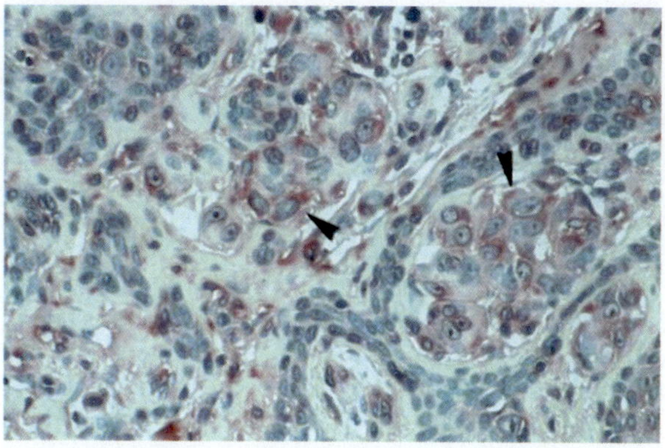

Fig 9. Invasive melanoma: matrix metalloproteinase 2 expression is seen on tumor cells (arrowheads, alkaline phosphatase-antialkaline phosphatase technique, x400).

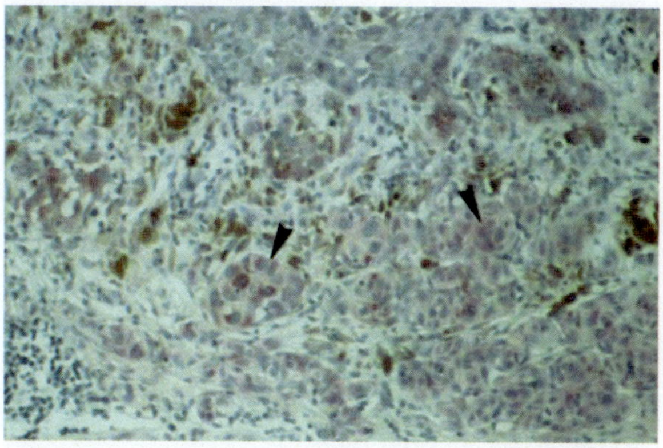

Fig. 10. Melanoma in situ: a moderate expression of matrix metalloproteinase 2 is shown (arrowheads, alkaline phosphatase-antialkaline phosphatase technique, x200).

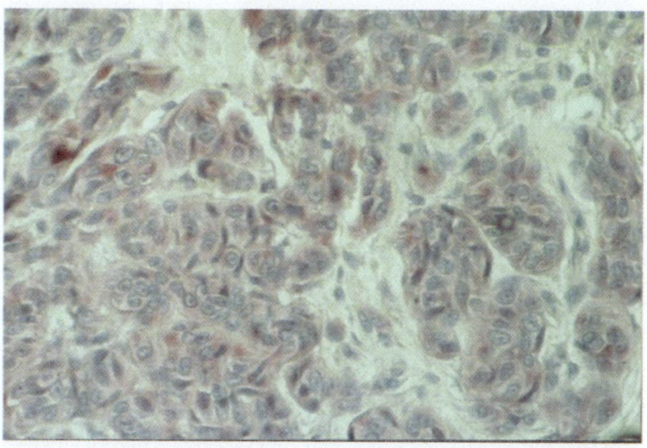

Fig.11. Invasive melanoma: a moderate expression of matrix metalloproteinase 9 is shown (arrowheads, alkaline phosphatase-antialkaline phosphatase technique, x400).

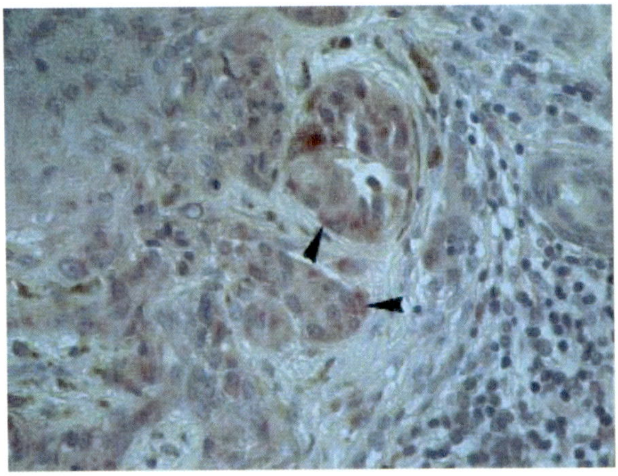

Fig.12. Melanoma in situ: immunostaining of matrix metalloproteinase 9 is shown (arrowheads, alkaline phosphatase-antialkaline phosphatase technique, x400).

13 out of 18 cases at Clark levels IV were positive for MMP-9 immunostaining. In 5 PIMM MMP-9 immunoreactivity occurred in scattered single and nested neoplastic cells in the deeper regions with staining intensity ranging from low to moderate (Fig.11)

6 out of 10 cases of in situ melanoma exhibited positive immunoreactivity to MMP-9 and its distribution within specimens from in situ melanoma showed extensive variations in terms of staining intensity and percentage of tumor cells (Fig.12).

All the results are summarized in Table 1.

Table 1. General summary of immunolocalization data for VEGF, MMP-2 and MMP-9.

	n.	VEGF				MMP-2				MMP-9			
		No	<10	15-30	>40	No	<10	15-30	>40	No	<10	15-30	>40
In situ melanoma	10	-	5	5	-	-	-	4	6	4	1	2	3
Invasive melanoma	18	-	4	-	14	-	1	3	14	5	9	4	-
Spitz nevi	6	6	-	-	-	-	1	3	2	6	-	-	-
Atypical melanocytic nevi	9	9	-	-	-	2	2	5	-	9	-	-	-
Ordinary benign melanocytic nevi	10	10	-	-	-	-	8	2	-	10	-	-	-

n.: number of cases. The value represent the number of positive cases for each antibody gradient staining studied: No: no cellular staining; <10: low staining (1-10% of positive cells); 15-30: moderate staining (15-30% of positive cells); >40: high staining (more than 40% of positive cells).

There was a significant correlation between VEGF immunostaining and MMP-9 index in melanoma samples (r =0.37; P<0.05), (Fig13). In invasive melanomas, this correlation was highly significant (r =0.763; P<0.001).

Discussion

Angiogenesis, the formation of new capillaries, is a crucial component in the growth, invasive progression and metastatic spread of solid tumor. During tumorigenesis, the quiescent vasculature can become activated to grow new capillaries in response to an appropriate stimulus [5-6]. Several potential positive regulators of angiogenesis have been identified [7-9]. The diverse mitogens that initiate the angiogenic response either directly regulate endothelial cell activity or stimulate nonendothelial cells within the vicinity of the target endothelium to produce factors that regulate angiogenesis [47]. Of these factors, VEGF specifically activates endothelial cells to promote proliferation and appears to play a hierarchical role in the regulation of physiological and pathological angiogenesis [7-8, 48]. We assessed the immunohistochemical expression of VEGF in biopsy specimens of malignant melanomas, dysplastic nevi with architectural disorder and cytological atypia of melanocytes, Spitz nevi, and compound or predominantly intradermal ordinary benign melanocytic nevi. In agreement with previous studies [49-50], our results indicated that VEGF expression was greater in invasive malignant melanomas than in situ melanomas, suggesting a correlation between VEGF-induced angiogenesis and aggressiveness of invasive melanomas. In fact we observed strong cytoplasmatic staining for VEGF in melanoma cells in as many as 77% of primary invasive melanomas, whereas only 25% of the in situ melanomas exhibited a detectable immunoreactivity for VEGF. The observation that melanomas in the vertical growth phase produce more VEGF than in the horizontal growth phase is consistent with the hypothesis that a vertical growth phase is necessary for primary melanomas to spread to the regional nodal bed [51-52]. Moreover Salven et al. found VEGF immunoreactivity tumor infiltrating lymphocytes in all melanoma samples, suggesting a possible role for the VEGF-expressing tumor infiltrating inflammatory cells in angiogenesis [53]. Conversely another immunhistochemical analysis [54] showed that the angiogenic factors were mainly localized intracellularly in melanoma cells and not in stromal host cells. We found VEGF-positive tumor infiltrating inflammatory cells in all invasive melanomas, but only few VEGF-positive-tumor-infiltrating host cells were found in situ melanomas.

Interestingly no VEGF immunoreactivity was shown by cells of melanocytic nevi. This included 9 borderline lesions, five of which with severe architectural disorder and cytological atypia of melanocytes. In particular Spitz nevi showed a negative immunoreactivity to VEGF. This finding is of interest because melanomas can be histologically misdiagnosed as Spitz nevi [55]. Moreover there are reports about cases with lesions histologically diagnosed as Spitz nevi which later developed metastases in local nodes and systematically [56]. It is also possible to find recurrent Spitz nevi, caused by previous incomplete excisions, which are difficult to differentiate from melanomas on histologic examination [57].

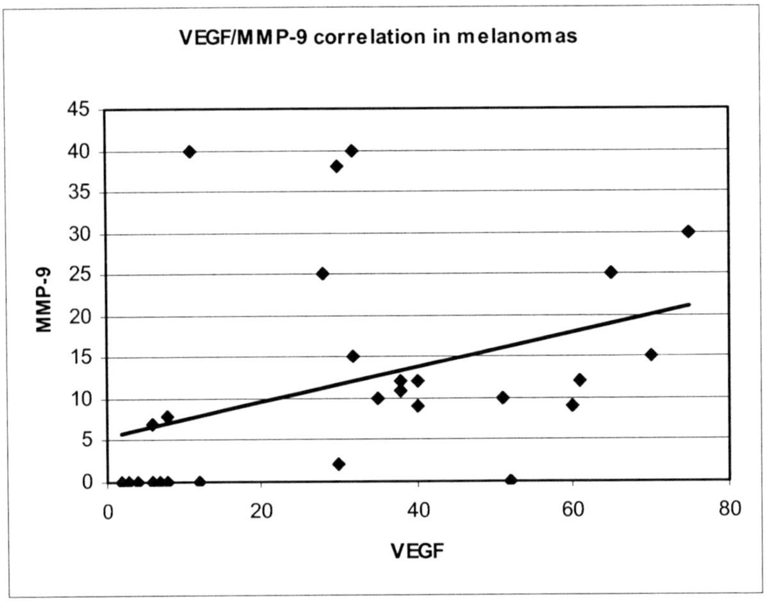

Fig.13. A positive correlation between VEGF and MMP-9 was found in melanomas.

It has been hypothesized that angiogenesis is initiated by a switch turned on during oncogenic transformation [5]. The circumstances leading to angiogenesis in melanomas still remain uncertain, but it is probable that genetic changes occur in the radial growth phase of melanomas with a balance shifting towards angiogenic inducers [5]. The ability to express angiogenic factors is likely to be one of the phenotypic changes that allow melanoma cells to spread and grow in distant sites. Different factors seem to play a critical role in regulating VEGF expression. They include cyclooxygenase 2 (COX-2) [58], heregulin beta1 [59], insulin [60], estrogens and progestins [61-62], epidermal growth factor (EGF) [63-64], N-acetylcysteine [65] as well as basic fibroblast growth factor (bFGF) and fibroblast growth factor-2 (FGF-2) [66]. It has been demonstrated that bFGF might act synergically with VEGF enhancing the vascular permeability for macromolecules, leading to the deposition of fibrin matrix which facilitates the tumor stroma development and angiogenesis [67] Oncogenes are also directly involved in controlling VEGF expression, with a prominent inductive role of the *ras* oncogene and a suppressive function of the p53 tumor suppressor gene [68-69]. Moreover it has been suggested that overexpression of VEGF in melanoma cells could be a consequence of hypoxia [70]. It is well recognized that hypoxia upregulates VEGF expression in a variety of cells in tissues, both in vitro and in vivo [71-72]. Besides it has been observed that transient hypoxia might promote the development of metastases in melanomas [71]. On the contrary, there are also some in vitro data showing overexpression of VEGF in melanoma cells cultured under normal oxygen conditions [73]. Therefore the regulation of the mechanism leading to tumor angiogenesis is complex and depends on multiple and interactive factors. For this reason, inhibition of angiogenesis for therapeutic purpose should preferably not concentrate on a single factor.

Many of the factors inducing angiogenesis are also known as regulators of MMP gene expression (VEGF, TNF alpha, bFGF) [74-75] both in endothelial cells and in other cell types. In particular it has been shown that VEGF specifically induces expression of interstitial collagenase (Matrix Metalloproteinase 1) [26]. It has also been demonstrated that invasion of human melanoma cells through type IV collagen and a reconstituted basement membrane seem to be dependent on MMP-1- expression [76]. Besides VEGF has been shown to increase MMP-2 and TIMP-1 in human ombelical vein endothelial cells, and this change was accompanied by increased activation of MMP-2 [26, 77]. Moreover it upregulated MMP-3 and MMP-9 expression in vascular smooth muscle cells [78]

Metalloproteinases play important roles in neoplastic processes, such as tumor invasion and metastases [31], though conflicting results have been reported regarding the relationship of MMP expression and the invasiveness of melanoma cells both in vitro and in vivo murine models [79-80].

We therefore analyzed the patterns of expression of metalloproteinases MMP-2 and MMP-9 in benign lesions and in different stages of invasive growth of melanomas.

Ordinary benign melanocytic nevi as well as typical junctional melanocytic nevi showed faint MMP-2 expression, suggesting a limited degree of normal connective tissue remodelling. A moderate expression for MMP-2 was also detected in atypical melanocytic naevi. These findings are in agreement with other studies presenting a weak distribution of MMP-2 in the junctional nest of most benign nevi [81]. Moreover Spitz nevi showed moderate to strong labelling for MMP-2. However, MMP-2 is unique among the MMPs in that its expression is constitutive and its activation can be achieved in a membrane-associated manner as has been shown for fibroblasts, for endothelial cells and for tumor cells [82]. Conversely MMP-9 is not normally expressed in developed tissue, yet it is highly expressed in many cancers [83]. According with other studies [84], negative MMP-9 immunostaining was observed in all tissue sections from benign, Spitz and atypical nevi.

Invasive melanomas and in situ melanomas displayed co-expression of MMP-2 and MMP-9, although to a variable extent. In particular high MMP-2 staining was observed in 14 out of 18 invasive melanomas and in 6 out of 10 cases of in situ melanomas. Our results confirmed previous observations, demonstrating a variable production of this enzyme both in situ and invasive melanomas [85]. In previous studies MMP-2 expression was observed both in benign and in malignant melanocytic lesions, and increased MMP-2 expression was correlated with architectural disorder, atypia, progression to melanoma and hematogenous metastasis [81]. In another study [86] a positive correlation between high levels of MMP-2 protein expression and increased malignancies was demonstrated. Actually MMP-2 positivity has been observed in highly invasive cell lines, while it appeared absent in non or poorly invasive cell lines . Moreover increased expression of activated MMP-2 correlates with metastatic behaviour [86], corroborating an important role of MMP-2 in human melanoma invasion and metastasis. MMP-2 activity directly modulates melanoma cell adhesion and spreads into extracellular matrix components, suggesting that MMP-2 may facilitate cell migration and invasion [87]. Even though the biochemical events related to the metastatic cascade are complicated it is more likely that several factors contribute to the development of metastases. Metalloproteinases have indeed been localized by in situ hybridization both in cancer cells themselves and in mesenchymal cells adjacent to the invading tumor front [88]. Other studies on human carcinomas have demonstrated that MMPs were predominantly expressed by stromal cells, and not by carcinoma cells [89-90]. In agreement with other reports [40, 91], our results showed that MMP-2 was present in melanoma cells as well as in tumor-surrounding stromal and/or host cells. Conversely other authors immunolocalized

MMP-2 to malignant melanocytic cells [92]. Our findings indicate that the production of this protesase is not confined to malignant cells, and that fibroblasts may play a role in the degradation of basal membrane. Moreover the observations that MMP-2 is localized both in peritumor stroma cells and in melanoma cells strongly suggest that there is an interaction between tumor and stroma regarding the production of MMP-2. This statement has been supported by identification of a tumor-cell derived factor that stimulates collagenase production in fibroblasts [93].

In this study, positive immunoreactivity for MMP-9 was present in six out of ten cases of in situ melanomas and the staining patterns were similar to those observed in invasive melanoma, although a minor percentage of tumor cells seem to express the MMP-9 antibody (13 of 18 cases). Some authors found that MMP-9 was variably expressed in the radial growth phase of primary melanoma, indicating that MMP-9 expression correlates with early invasion of melanoma [84].On the contrary other immunohistochemical studies revealed that MMP-9 expression was present in an advanced stage of melanoma, but not in the early stage [94]. It was also observed that a number of aggressive cancers, when examined for expression in situ, showed tumor cell associated expression of MMP-9 [88, 95-96], suggesting that this molecule might be an important determinant of aggressive behaviour in some cancers. It follows that the role of MMP-9 in melanoma progression is puzzling and not well defined and one can speculate that variable MMP-9 expression might be related to the presence of different clones in melanoma. Proteinases, such as MMP-9 have been shown to play an essential role in cell migration and tissue remodeling, which occur in many biological processes. They, in fact, degrade extracellular matrix components, a prerequisite for endothelial, smooth muscle, inflammatory or cancerous cells to migrate to distant sites and activate cytokines. MMP-9 has been implicated in wound healing, tumor invasion and metastasis [97-98]. It has recently been reported that a relationship exists between the tumor cell angiogenic protein VEGF and MMP-9 and that the switch from vascular quiescence to angiogenesis involves MMP-9, which is upregulated in angiogenic islets and tumours, rendering VEGF more available to its receptors [43]. Our data support the concept of a relationship between the VEGF and MMP-9 expression in malignant melanocytic lesions. We found a direct correlation between VEGF immunostaining and MMP-9 index ($r = 0.37$; $P<0.05$) which, particularly in invasive melanomas, was highly significant ($p<0.001$). Moreover it is interesting to note that all benign and dysplastic lesions showed neither VEGF nor MMP-9 expression. These findings highlight the relevance of MMP-9 in angiogenesis, stimulating VEGF production. Recently, another intriguing possibility has been postulated suggesting that MMP-9 expression in tumor might simply be an effort to inhibit increased angiogenesis. MMP-9 in fact is implicated in the generation of molecules with antiangionetic activity, converting plasminogen into angiostatin [99]. Interestingly, it has been reported that tissue levels of MMP-9 increased in α_1-integrin-null mice and that these mice showed augmented circulating levels of angiostatin associated with decreased tumor growth [100]

In conclusion our data showed that malignant melanocytic tumors displayed a strong VEGF expression, whereas benign melanocytic proliferations showed no immunoreactivity for VEGF. In particular Spitz nevi, whose biological nature and diagnostic distinction from, or relationship to, melanoma remains a dilemma faced by even the most experienced dermopathologists [101] , showed a negative immunoreactivity to VEGF. On the basis of our data, VEGF showed a high specificity, therefore it could also be used as a discriminating factor between malignant melanoma and uncertain lesions. In addition MMP-2 was variably expressed in Spitz nevi as well as in melanoma, characterizing all infiltrating lesions, while MMP-9 was absent in all benign and dysplastic melanocytic lesions. Furthermore the positive correlation VEGF/MMP-9 found in invasive melanomas suggests a key role of this metalloproteinase in melanoma angiogenesis and that VEGF and MMP-9 both contribute to tumor progression.

Author Note

We thank Mrs Monica Glebocki for expert technical assistance.

References

[1] Koh HK. Cutaneous melanoma. *N.Engl J Med* 325: 1991, 171-182.

[2] Albino AP, Reed JA, McNutt NS. Molecular biology of cutaneous malignant melanoma. In : De Vita Jr. VT, Hellman S, Rosemberg SA, eds. Cancer. Priciples & practice of oncology. *New York: Lippincott-Raven*, 1997, p. 1935.

[3] Clark W, Elder DE, Guerry D, Epstein MN, Greene MH, Van-Horn M. A study of tumor progression: the precursor lesions of superficial spreading and nodular melanoma. *Hum Pathol* 1984, 15: 1147-65.

[4] Herlin M, Clark WH, Rodeck U, Mancianti ML, Jambrosic J, Koprowski H. Biology of disease: Biology of tumor progression in human melanocytes. *Lab Invest* 1987, 56: 461-74.

[5] Hanahan D, Folkmann J. Patterns and emerging mechanism of the angiogenic switch during tumorigenesis. *Cell* 1996, 86: 353-64.

[6] Folkman J. Clinical applications of research on angiogenesis. *N Engl J Med* 1995, 333: 1757.

[7] Detmar M. Tumor angiogenesis. *J Invest Dermatol Symposium Proceedings* 2000, 5:20-23

[8] Ferrara N, Houk K, Jakeman L, Leung DW. Molecular and biological properties of the vascular endothelial growth factor family of proteins. Endocrinol Rev 1992, 13: 18-32.

[9] Ferrara N. Vascular endothelial growth factor and the regulation of angiogenesis. *Recent Prog Horm Res* 2000, 55: 15-35.

[10] Weistat-Slatow DL, Zabrenetzky VS, Van Houtte K, Frazier WA, Roberts DD, Steeg PS. Transfection of trhrombospondin 1 complementary DNA into a human breast carcinoma cell line reduces primary tumor growth, metastatic potential and angiogenesis. *Cancer Res* 1994, 54:6504-511.

[11] Streit M, Riccardi L, Velasco P, Brown LF, Hawigorst T, Bornstein P, Detmar M. Thrombospondin 2: a potent endogenous inhibitor of tumor growth and angiogenesis. *Proc Natl Acad Sci USA* 1999, 96: 14888-893.

[12] Barnhill RL, Fandrey K, Levy MA, Mihm MC jr, Hyman B. Angiogenesis and tumor progression of melanoma. Quantification of vascularity in melanocytic nevi and cutaneous malignant melanoma. *Lab Invest* 1992, 67: 331- 37 .

[13] Graham CH, Rivers J, Kerbel RS, Stankiewicz KS, White WL. Extent of vascularization as a prognostic indicator in thin (< 0.76 mm) malignant melanomas. *Am J Pathol* 1994,145 (3): 510-14.

[14] Luca MR, Bar-Eli M. Molecular changes in human melanoma metastasis. *Hist Histopathol* 1998, 13: 1225-31

[15] Lazar-Molnar E, Hegyesi H, Toth S, Falus A. Autocrine and paracrine regulation by cytokines and growth factors in melanoma. *Cytokine* 2000, 12:547-54.

[16] Singh RK, Gutman M, Radinski R, Bucana CD, Fidler IJ. Expression of interleukin 8 correlates with the metastatic potential of human melanoma cells in nude mice. *Cancer* Res 1994, 54:3242-47.

[17] Asgari MM, Haggerty JG, McNiff JM, Milstone LM, Schwartz PM. Expression and localization of thimidine phosphorylase/platelet-derived endothelial cell growth factor in skin and cutaneous tumor. *J Cutan Pathol* 1999, 26:287-94.

[18] Reed JA, McNutt NS, Albino AP. Differential expression of basic fibroblast growth factor (bFGF) in melanocytic lesions demonstrated by in situ hybridization: Implications for tumor progress. *Am J Pathol* 1994, 144: 329-36.

[19] Potgens AJ, Lubsen NH, Van Altena MC, Schoenmakers JGG, Ruiter DJ, Waal RMW. Vascular permeability factor expression influences tumor angiogenesis in human melanoma lines xenografted to nude mice. *Am J Pathol* 1995, 46: 197- 209.

[20] Neufeld G, Cohen T, Gengrinovitch S, Poltorak Z. Vascular endothelial growth factor (VEGF) and its receptor. *FASEB J* 1999, 13: 9-22.

[21] Lei J, Jiang A, Pei D. Identification and characterization of a new splicing variant of VEGF. VEGF 183. *Biochem Biophys Acta* 1998, 1443: 400-406.

[22] Dvorak HF, Brown LF, Detmar M, Dvorak A. Vascular permeability factor/ vascular endothelial growth factor, microvascular hyperpermeability,and angiogenesis. *Am J Pathol* 1995, 146: 1029-1039.

[23] De-Vries C, Escobedo JA, Ueno H, Houk K, Ferrara N, Williams LT. The fms-like tyrosine kinase, a receptor for vascular endothelial growth factor. *Science* 1992, 255: 989-991.

[24] Termann BJ, Dougher-Vermazen M, Carrion ME, Dimitrov DC, Armellino D, Gospodarowicz D, Bohlen P. Identification of the KDR tyrosine kinase as a receptor for vascular endothelial growth factor. *Biochem Biophys Res Commun* 1992, 187: 1579-86.

[25] Post MJ Angiogenesis: initiation and maintenance.Ann NY Acad Sci 2002, 961: 249-50

[26] Unemori EN, Ferrara N, Bauer EA, Amento EP. Vascular endothelial growth factor induces interstitial collagenase expression in human endothelial cells. *J Cell Physiol* 1992, 153: 557-562.

[27] Pepper MS, Ferrara N, Orci L, Montesano R. Vascular endothelial growth factor (VEGF) induces plasminogen activators and plasminogen activator inhibitor-1 in microvascularendothelial cells. *Biochem Biophys Res Commun* 1991, 181: 902-906.

[28] Blei F, Wilson L, Magnatti P, Rifkin D. Mechanism of action of angiostatic steroid:suppression of plasminogen activator activity via stimulation of plasminogen activator inhibitor synthesis. *J Cell Physiol* 1993, 155: 568-78.

[29] van Hinsbergh VW, koolwijk P, Hanemaayer R. Role of fibrin and plasminogen activation in repair -associated angiogenesis: in vitro studies with human endothelial *cells. EXS* 1997, 79:391-411.

[30] Moscatelli D, Rifkin DB. Membrane and matrix localization of proteinases: a common theme in tumor cell invasion and angiogenesis. *Biochem Biophys Acta* 1998, 948: 67-85.

[31] Stetler-Stevenson W, Liotta, Kleiner D. Extracellular matrix Role of matrix metalloproteinases in tumor invasion and metastasis. *FASEB J* 1993, 7:1434-1441.

[32] Matrisian LM. Metalloproteinases and their inhibitors in matrix remodelling. *Trends Genet* 1990, 6: 121-125.

[33] Fridman R, Toth M, Pena D, Mobashery S. Activation of progelatinase B (MMP-9) by gelatinase A (MMP-2). *Can Res* 1995, 55: 2548-2555.

[34] Testa JE, Quigley JP. The role of urokinase-type plasminogen activator in aggressive tumor cell behaviour. *Cancer Metastasis Rev* 1990, 9: 353-367.

[35] Liotta LA, Rao CN, Wewer UM. Biochemical interactions of tumor cells with the basement membrane. *Ann Rev Biochem* 1986, 55: 1037-57.

[36] Liotta LA, Tryggvason K, Garbisa S, Hart I, Foltz CH, Shafie S. Metastatic potential correlates with enzymatic degradation of basement membrane collagen. *Nature* 1980, 284: 67-68.

[37] Curran S, Murray GI. Matrix metalloproteinases in tumor invasion and metastasis. *J Pathol* 1999, 189: 300-308.

[38] WoessnerJF,\The matrix metalloproteinases family. In: WC Parks, RP Mecham, eds Matrix metalloproteinases. *New York: Academic Press* 1998, pp 1-14.

[39] Saarialho-Kere UK, Crouch E, Parks WC. The matrix metalloproteinase matrilysin is constitutively expressed in adult human exocrine epithelium. *J Invest Dermatol* 1995, 105: 190-6.

[40] Birkedal-Hansen H, Moore WGI, Bodden MK, Windsor LJ, Birkedal-Hansen B, De Carlo A, Engler JA. Matrix metalloproteinases. *A review. Crit Rev Oral Biol Med* 1993, 4:197-250.

[41] Chang C, Werb Z. The many faces of the metalloproteinases: cell growth, invasion, angiogenesis and metastasis. *Trends Cell Biol* 2001, 11:S37-S43.

[42] Vu TH, Shipley JM, Bergers G, Berger JE, Helms JA, Hanahan D, Shapiro SD, Senior RM, Werb Z. MMP-9/gelatinase B is a key regulator of growth plate angiogenesis and apoptosis of hypertrophic chondrocytes. *Cell* 1998, 93: 411-22.

[43] Bergers G, Brekken R, McMahon G et al. Matrix metalloproteinase-9 triggers the angiogenic swith during carcinogenesis. *Nat Cell Biol* 2000, 2: 737-44.

[44] Rodriguez-Monzaneque J, Lane T, Ortega M, Hynes R et al. Trombospondin-1 suppresses spontaneous tumor growth and inhibit activation of matrix metalloproteinase-9 and mobilization of vascular endothelial growth factor. *Proc Natl Acad Sci USA* 2001, 98:12485-490.

[45] Lever WF, Schaumburg-Lever G . In: Histopathology of the Skin. 7th edn.Philadelphia: J.B.Lippincott, 1990; 756-805.

[46] Cordell JL, Falini B, Erber WN. Immunoenzymatic labelling of monoclonal antibodies using immune complexes of alkaline phosphatase and monoclonal anti-alkaline phosphatase. *J Histochem Cytochem* 1984; 32: 219-229

[47] Lamoreaux WJ, Fitzgerald MEC, Reiner A, Hasty KA, Charles ST. Vascular endothelial growth factor increases release of gelatinase A and decrease release of tissue inhibitor of metalloproteina-ses by microvascular endothelial cells in vitro. *Microvascular Research* 1998, 55: 29-42.

[48] Vincenti V, Cassano C, Rocchi M, Persico G. Assignment of the vascular endothelial growth factor gene to human chromosome 6p21.3. *Circulation* 1996, 93: 1493-95.

[49] Bayer-Garner IB, Hough AJ, Smoller BR. Vascular endothelial growth factor expression in malignant melanoma: prognostic versus diagnostic usefulness. *Mod Pathol* 1999, 12: 770-74.

[50] Marcoval J, Moreno A, Graells J, Vidal A, Escribà JM, Garcia-Ramirez M, Fabra A. Angiogenesis and malignant melanoma. Angiogenesis is related to the development of vertical (tumorigenic) growth phase. *J Cutan Pathol* 1997, 24: 212-18.

[51] Erhard H, Rietveld FJ, van Altena MC, Brocker EB, Ruiter DJ, de Waal RM. Transition of horizontal to vertical growth phase melanoma is accompanied by induction of vascular endothelil growth factor expressionj and angiogenesis. *Melanoma Res* 1997; 7(suppl 2): S19-S26.

[52] Gorski DH, Leal AD, Goydos JS. Differential expression of vascular endothelial growth factor-A isoform at different stages of melanoma progression. *J Am Coll Surg* 2003; 197: 408-18.

[53] Salven P, Heikkla P, Joensuu H. Enhanced expression of vascular endothelial growth factor in metastatic melanoma. *Br J Cancer* 1997, 76: 930-4.

[54] Rofstad EK, HalsørEF. Vascular endothelial growth factor, Interleukin 8, Platelet-derived endothelial growth factor, and Basic fibroblast growth factor promote angiogenesis and metastasis in human melanoma xenografts. *Can Res* 2000, 60:4932-38.

[55] Helm KF., Schwartz RA, Janniger CK. Juvenile melanoma (Spitz nevus). *Cutis* 1996; 58: 35-9

[56] Barnhill RL, Flotte TH, Fleshli M, Perez-Atayde A. Cutaneous melanoma and atypical Spitz tumors in childwood. *Cancer* 1995; 76: 1833-45

[57] Casso EM, Grin-Jorgensen CM, Grant-Kels JM. Spitz nevi. *J Am Acad Dermatol* 1992; 27: 901-13

[58] Gately S. The contribution of cyclooxygenase-2 to tumor angiogenesis. *Cancer Metastasis Rev* 2000, 19:19-27.

[59] Xiong S, Grijalva R, Zhang L, Nguyen NT, Pisters PW, Pollock RE, Yu...Up-regulation of vascular endothelial growth factor in breast cancer by the heregulin-beta 1 activated p38 signalling pathway enhance endothelial cell migration. *Cancer Res* 2001,15: 1727-32.

[60] Bermont L, Lamielle F, Lorchel F, Fauconnet S, Esumi H, Weisz A, Adessi GL. Insulin up-regulates vascular endothelial growth factor and stabilizers its messengers in endometrial adenocarcinoma cells. *J Clin Endocrinol Metab* 2001, 86 (1): 363-8.

[61] Mueller MD, Vigne JL, Minchenko A, Lebovic DI, Leitman DC and Taylor RN. Regulation of vascular endothelial growth factor (VEGF) gene transcription by estrogen receptors α and β. *Proc Natl Acad Sci, USA* 2000, 97: 10972-77.

[62] Hyder SM, Huang JC, Nawaz Z, Boettger- Tong H, Makela S, Chiappetti GM. Regulation of vascular endothelial growth factor expression by estrogens and progestins. *Environ Health Perspect* 2000, 108 S5: 785-90.

[63] Maity A, Pore N, Lee J, Solomon D, O'Rourke DM. Epidermal growth factor receptor transcriptionally up-regulate endothelial growth factor expression in human glioblastoma cell pathway involving phosphatidylinositol 3'-kinase and distinct. induced by hypoxia. *Cancer Res* 2000, 60 (20): 5879-86.

[64] Danielsen T, Rofstad EK. VEGF, bFGF and EGF in the angiogenesis of human melanoma xenograft. *Int J Cancer* 1998, 76 (6): 836-41.

[65] Redondo P, Bandres E, Solano T, Okroujnov I, Garcia-Foncillas J. Vascular endothelial growth factor (VEGF) and melanoma. N-acetylcysteine downregulates VEGF production in vitro. *Cytokine* 2000, 12: 374-8.

[66] Claffey KP, Abrams K, Shih SC, Brown LF, Mullen A, Keough M. Fibroblast growth factor 2 activation of stromal cell vascular endothelial growth factor expression and angiogenesis. *Lab Invest* 2001, 81 (1): 61-75.

[67] Pepper MS, Vassalli JD, Orci L, Montesano R. Potent synergism between vascular endothelial factor and basic fibroblast growth factor in induction of angiogenesis in vitro. *Biochem Biophys Res Comm* 1992: 189, 824.

[68] Grugel S, Finkenzeller G, Weindel K, Barleon B, Marme D. Both v-Ha-ras and v-raf stimulate expression of the vascular endothelial growth factor in NIH 3T3 cells. *J Biol Chem* 1995, 270: 25915-19.

[69] Kieser A, Weich HA, Brandner G, Marme D, Kolch W. Mutant p53 potentiates protein kinase C induction of vascular endothelial growth factor expression. *Oncogene* 1994, 9: 963-69.

[70] Claffey KP, Brown LF, del Aguila LF, Tognazzi K, Yeo KT, Manseau EJ, Dvorak HF. Expression of vascular permeability factor/vascular endothelial growth factor by melanoma cells increases tumor growth, angiogenesis and experimental metastasis. *Cancer Res* 1996, 56: 172-181.

[71] Rofstad EK, Danielsen T. Hypoxia-induced angiogenesis and vascular endothelial growth factor secretion in human melanoma. *Br J Cancer* 1998, 77 (6), 897-902.

[72] Li J, Brown LF, Hibberd MG, Grossman JD, Morgan JP, Simons M. VEGF, flk-1, and flt-1 expression in a rat myocardial infarction model of angiogenesis. *Am J Physiol* 1996, 270 (Heart Circ Physiol 39): H1803-H1811.

[73] Graeven U, Fiedler W, Karpinski S, Ergun S, Kilic N, Rodeck U, Scmiegel W, Hossfeld DK. Melanoma-associated expression of vascular endothelial growth factor and its receptors FLT-1 and KDR. *J Cancer Res Clin Oncol* 1999, 125: 621-29.

[74] Cornelius LA, Nehring LC, Roby JD, Parks WC, Welgus HG. Human dermal microvascular endothelial cells produce matrix metalloproteinases in response to angiogenic factors and migration. *J Invest Dermatol* 1995, 105: 170-76.

[75] Qin H, Moellinger JD, Wells A, Windsor LJ, Sun Y, Benveniste EN. Transcriptional regulation of matrix metalloproteinse-2 expression in human astroglioma cells by TNF-alpha and IFN-gamma. *J Immunol* 1998,161: 6664-673.

[76] Durko M, Navab R, Shibata HR, Brodt P. Suppression of basement membrane type IV collagen degradation and cell invasion in human melanoma cells expressing an antisense RNA for MMP-1. *Biochim Biophys Acta* 1997, 1356: 271-280.

[77] Zucher S, Mirza H, Conner CE, Lorenz AF, Drews MH, Bahou WF, Jesty J. Vascular endothelial growth factor induces tissue factor and Matrix Metalloproteinase production in endothelial cells: conversion of prothrombin to thrombin results in progelatinase A activation and cell proliferation. *Int J Cancer* 1998, 75, 780-86.

[78] Wang HE, Keiser JA. Vascular endothelial growth factor upregulates the expression of matrix metalloproteinases in vascular smooth muscle cells. *Circ Res* 1998, 83: 832-840.

[79] Huijzer JC, Uhlenkott CE, Meadows GG. Differences in expression of metalloproteinases and plasminogen activators in murine melanocytes and B16

melanoma variants. Lack of association with in vitro invasion. *Int J Cancer* 1995, 63: 92-99.

[80] Montgomery AM, Mueller BM, Reisfeld RA, Taylor SM, DeClerk YA. Effect of tissue inhibitor of the matrix metalloproteinase 2 expression on the growth and spontaneous metastasis of a human melanoma cell line. *Cancer Res* 1994, 54: 5467-73.

[81] Väisänen A, Tuominen H, Kallioinen M, Turpeenniemi-Hujanen T. Matrix-metalloproteinase 2 (72 kD type IV collagenase) expression occurs in the early stage of human melanocytic tumor progression and may have prognostic value. *J Pathol*, 1996, 180:283-289.

[82] Kurschat P, Zigrino P, Nischt R, Breitkopf K, Steurer P, Klein CE, Mauch C. Tissue inhibitor of matrix metalloproteinase-2 regulates matrix metalloproteinase-2 activation by modulation of membrane-type 1 matrix metalloproteinase activity in high and low invasive cell lines. *J Biol Chem* 1999, 274: 21056-62.

[83] Han Y-P, Nien Y-D, Garner WL. Tumor necrosis factor-α-induced proteolytic activation of pro-matrix metalloproteinase-9 by human skin is controlled by down-regulation tissue inhibitor of metalloproteinase-1 and mediated by tissue-associated chymotrypsin-like proteinase. *J Biol Chem* 2002, 277: 27319-27.

[84] Van den Oord JJ, Paemen L, Opdenakker G, de-Wolf-Paemen C. Expression of gelatinase B and extracellular matrix metalloproteinase inducer EMMPRIM in benign and malignant pigment cell lesions of the skin *Am J Pathol* 1997, 151:665-70.

[85] Walker R A, Wooley DE. Immunolocalisation studies of matrix metalloproteinases-1,-2, and -3 in human melanoma. *Virchows Arch* 1999, 435, 574-579.

[86] Hoffmann UB, Westphal JR, Waas ET, Zendman AJW, Cornelissen IMHA, Ruiter DJ, van Muijen GNP. Matrix metalloproteinases in human melanoma cell lines and xenograft: increased expression of activated matrix metalloproteinases-2 (MMP-2) correltates with melanoma progression. *Br J Cancer* 1999, 81: 774-82.

[87] Raj GM, Stetler-Stevenson WG. Gelatinase A activity directly modulates melanoma cell adhesion and spreading. *EMBO J* 1995, 14: 908-14.

[88] Pyke C, Ralfkiaer E, Huhtala P, Hurskainen T, Dano K, Tryggvason K. Localization of messenger RNA for M 72000 and 92000 type IV collagenases in human skin cancers by in situ hybridization. *Cancer Res* 1992, 52: 1336-41.

[89] Basset P, Okada A, Chenard MP, Kannan R, Stoll I, Anglard P, Bellocq JP, Rio MC. Matrix metalloproteinases as stromal effectors of human carcinoma progression: therapeutic implications. *Matrix Biol* 1997, 15: 535-41.

[90] Heppner KJ, Matrisian LM, Jensen RA, Rodgers WH. Expression of most matrix metalloproteinases family members in breast cancer represents a tumor-induced host response. *Am J Pathol* 1996, 149: 273-82.

[91] Schaumburg-Lever G, Lever I, Fehrenbacher B, Möller H, Bischoff B, Kaiserling E, Garbe C, Rassner G. Melanocytes in nevi and melanomas synthesize basement membrane and basement membrane-like material. An immunohistochemical and electron microscopic study including immunoelectron microscopy. *J Cutan Pathol* 2000, 27: 67-75.

[92] Väisänen A, Kallioinen M, Taskinen PJ, Turpeenniemi-Hujanen T. Prognostic value of MMP-2 immunoreactivity protein (72 kD type IV collagenase) in primary skin melanoma. *J Pathol*, 1998, 186:51-58.

[93] Nabeshima K, Lane WS, Biswas C. Partial sequencing and characterization of the tumor cell derived collagenase stimulatory factor. *Arch Biochim Biophys* 1991, 285: 90-96.

[94] MacDougall JR, Bani MR, Lin Y, Muschel RJ, Kerbel RS. Proteolytic switching: opposite patterns of regulation of gelatinase B and its inhibitor TIMP-1 during human melanoma progression and consequences of gelatinase B expression. *Br J Cancer* 1999, 80: 504-512.

[95] Rao JS, Yamamoto M, Mohaman S, Gokaslan ZL, Fuller GN, Stetler-Stevenson WG, Rao VH, Liotta LA, Nicolson GL, Sawaya RE. Expression and localization of 92 kDa type IV collagenase gelatinase B (MMP-9) in human gliomas. *Clin Exp Metastasis* 1996, 14: 12-18.

[96] Ueda Y, Imai K, Tsuchiya H, Fujimoto N, Nakanishi I, Katsuda S, Seiki M, Okada Y. Matrix metalloproteinase 9 (gelatinase B) is expressed in multinucleated giant cells of human Giant Cell Tumor of bone and is associated with vascular invasion. *Am J Pathol* 1996, 148: 611-22.

[97] Raj GM, Stetler-Stevenson WG. The role of of matrix metalloproteinases and their inhibitors in tumor invasion, metastasis and agiogenesis. *Eur Respir* 1994, 7: 2062-72.

[98] Chambers AF, Matrisian LM. Changing views of the role of matrix metalloproteinases in metastasis. *J Natl Cancer Inst* 1997, 89: 1260-70.

[99] Pozzi A, Levine W, Gardner H. Low plasma levels of matrix metalloproteinase 9 permit increased tumor angiogenesis. *Oncogene* 2002, 21: 272-281.

[100] Pozzi A, Moberg PE, Miles LA, Wagner S, Soloway P, Gardner HA. Elevate matrix metalloproteinase and angiostatin levels in integrin α_1 knockout mice cause reduced tumor vascularization. *Proc Natl Acad Sci USA* 2000, 97: 2202-07.

[101] Barhnill RL, Argenyi ZB, From L, Glass LF, Maize JC, Mihm MC et al. Atypical Spitz nevi/tumors: lack of consensus for diagnosis, discrimination from melanoma, and prediction of outcome. *Hum Pathol* 1999, 30: 513-20

In: New Angiogenesis Research
Editor: Roberta V. Zubar, pp. 219-234
ISBN 1-59454-239-2

Chapter XII

The Role of the Nitric Oxide Pathway in Controlling Angiogenesis in Head and Neck Cancer

Alessandro Franchi[1,*] ***and Oreste Gallo***[2]
[1]Deapartment of Human Pathology and Oncology, University of Florence, Italy
[2]Department of Oto-Neuro-Ophtalmologic Surgical Sciences,
University of Florence, Italy

Abstract

Nitric oxide (NO) is a potent biological mediator which plays a key role in physiological as well as pathological processes including inflammation and cancer. The role of NO in tumor biology remains incompletely understood, although several studies indicate that this molecule plays an important role in neoplastic growth, being involved in tumor cell invasiveness, promotion of tumor angiogenesis and suppression of host anti-tumor defense. Studies performed on tumors of different origin, including head and neck squamous cell carcinoma (HNSCC), have demonstrated that NO levels are significantly increased in tumor tissues in comparison with normal tissues, and this event appears to be crucial for invasion and angiogenesis. In this chapter we review the clinical relevance of the NO pathway in HNSCC, focusing on its role as angiogenic factor. We discuss the correlation of the NO pathway with other factors implicated in tumor angiogenesis, such prostaglandins, vascular endothelial growth factor, matrix metalloproteinases, and p53 gene status, as well as its role and potential as a therapeutic target in HNSCC.

* Correspondence concerning this article should be addressed to Dr. Alessandro Franchi, Deapartment of Human Pathology and Oncology, University of Florence Viale G.B. Morgagni 85; 50134 Firenze Italy; Phone +39 055 4478102; Fax +39 055 4379868; E-mail: franchi@unifi.it.

Introduction

Head and neck squamous cell carcinoma (HNSCC) develops in the mucosal membranes of the upper aero-digestive tract, including the oral cavity, pharynx, hypopharynx and larynx. According to extensive epidemiological studies, tobacco smoking and alcohol consumption appear to be the main risk factors for the development of these tumors. HNSCC is the fifth most common cancer in men, with an incidence of about 780000 new cases per year worldwide [1]. It comprises about 5% of all newly diagnosed cancer cases in the northern and western European countries and in the United States [2], while in parts of Southeast Asia is the most common malignancy accounting for up to 50% of malignant tumors [3]. The incidence of HNSCC increases with age, with most patients being over the age of 45. The average male to female ratio in the western countries is 3:1, but it differs for the various anatomic locations [3]. Over the last decade the incidence of HNSCC is increasing in females, presumably in relation with increased tobacco smoking.

In general, one third of HNSCC patients presents with early stage disease (I and II), while two thirds present with advanced disease (III and IV) [4]. Early stage tumors can be cured with surgery or radiotherapy alone in the great majority of cases. Patients with advanced stages are mostly treated with combined modalities. Despite significant advances in HNSCC therapy, long term survival of patients with HNSCC has only moderately improved over the last 20 years [5]. An important reason for this lack of progress is the relatively high tumor recurrence rate observed for these patients. Indeed, local recurrence occurs in about 10 to 30% of patients with advanced tumors, while metastatic disease develops in 15-25% of patients [6-8]. Another reason for the lack of improvement in clinical outcome of patients with HNSCC is the development of second primary tumors in the upper aerodigestive tract, an occurrence which is observed with a constant annual rate of 3-7% [9]. Therefore, the identification and characterization of the molecular and genetic changes involved in the development, tumor progression and dissemination, as well as in tumor response to therapy is crucial for understanding the underlying mechanisms of unfavorable outcome, and may be crucial for the development of new rational targeted treatment strategies.

Tumor Angiogenesis in Head and Neck Cancer

Angiogenesis is the process by which new blood vessels are formed. The growth of new blood vessels in normal tissue is a crucial event during morphogenesis, reproduction, wound repair and regeneration. Together with these physiological processes, angiogenesis is a fundamental event in several pathological conditions including tumor growth. In fact, in 1971 Folkman [10] first proposed the concept that "tumor growth is angiogenesis dependent", suggesting that tumor blood supply is essential for the growth and spreading of the tumor since it not only supplies the nutrients and oxygen requirements for the growing malignant cells but also provides the vascular routes for haematogenous spread to distant sites [10].

The assessment of tumor angiogenesis in human tumors can be done by immunohistochemical identification of blood vessels in tissue sections using antibodies directed against vascular endothelium [11]. This is followed by quantification of tumor vessels by counting positive vessel profiles, or by computer aided image analysis systems, which allow the determination of other dimensional parameters of tumor vessels. This approach has a number of intrinsic problems, including the choice of the endothelial marker, the immunohistochemical method used, the subjectivity of the assessment of the staining and its quantification. Nevertheless, based on the assumption that the higher the number of microvessels present in the tumor and their relative area, the higher the probability that tumor cells will enter the vascular system and spread to distant site, several studies have found that intratumoral microvessel density (MVD) determined in the primary tumor is significantly associated with metastasis and prognosis [12].

Considering HNSCC, assessment of MVD has been performed using different protocols and therefore a direct comparison of the studies is precluded. In an early study of 70 patients with locally advanced HNSCC, the intensity of vascularity correlated with the probability of metastasis independently from other features analyzed, including clinical stage [13]. In another cohort of 114 patients with HNSCC, tumor vascularization was correlated with mitotic index, nuclear atypia, presence of tumor emboli within microvessels, and with lymph node metastases [14]. Our group performed an analysis of tumor vascularization in 52 consecutive patients affected by HNSCC using an anti-CD31 antibody, and we found that microvessel density was correlated with tumor grade, stage, and presence of lymph node metastasis [15]. In addition, Cox regression multivariate confirmed that higher tumor vascularization was an independent predictor of disease-free and overall survival in patients with head and neck cancer [15].

However, other studies have not confirmed the correlation between angiogenesis and tumor aggressiveness in HNSCC, probably reflecting the technical difficulties in the assessment and reproducibility of tumor vascularization and other limitations, including differences in patient selection, endpoint of the study and type of statistical analysis used [16-18]. Another relevant aspect that should be considered is that the biologic importance and the prognostic relevance of tumor angiogenesis in HNSCC may be related to the site of the primary tumor, either because of a site dependent phenotypic variability determining different production of angiogenic or anti-angiogenic factors by tumor cells, or for a different response of local pre-existing vessels to angiogenic and anti-angiogenic stimuli. Indeed, studies examining cohorts of patients with laryngeal squamous cell carcinoma more frequently found a positive correlation between increased tumor angiogenesis and tumor aggressiveness, considering T stage, level of invasion, or survival rates [19, 20]. In addition, angiogenesis resulted an independent predictor of disease free-survival and of lymph node metastasis in patients with laryngeal squamous cell carcinoma [21, 22]. Conversely, in squamous cell carcinoma of the oral cavity tumor angiogenesis, as currently measured, was not of value in predicting tumor aggressiveness in most studies, either considering early stage or advanced tumors, although a positive correlation with lymph node metastasis was observed by some authors [23-29]. These contradictory results reflect most of all the complexity of tumor angiogenesis and it is unlikely that an accurate assessment of the angiogenic phenomena occurring in a tumor can be obtained by the analysis of one single aspect. Rather, we believe that the integration of several information derived from the analysis of tumor activated endothelium and from the identification of new markers specific for tumor endothelium, which should substitute pan-endothelial markers employed so far, could improve our capacity to determine the clinical significance of angiogenesis in HNSCC.

Improving the understanding of the angiogenic process may have some other relevant clinical applications beyond its use as prognostic indicator in patients with HNSCC, including its influence on the response to therapy. The important role of angiogenesis as a predictive factor of response to cytotoxic and radiation therapy has been recently raised by several authors [30-36]. Poor tumor oxygenation is a well recognized feature related to radio-resistance. Since the vascular density is linked to the availability of oxygen and drugs to the tumoral stroma, poor density should be a potent marker of reduced blood perfusion and, therefore, hypoxia and low drug intratumoral concentration. On the other hand, high vascular density and angiogenic ability of cancer is not synonymous with high blood flow since the geometry of the vascular/epithelial component distribution, vascular collapse due to increased interstitial blood pressure, or non-functional vasculature due to an immature structure of the vessels may not allow the establishment of an adequate blood flow, which results in tissue hypoxia. Moreover, activation of angiogenic pathways confers a cancer cell proliferation/apoptosis advantage and trigger an angiogenic regeneration process during fractionated radiotherapy or between the courses of chemotherapy, resulting in rapid tumor re-growth and failure of radiotherapy due to reasons independent of hypoxia and blood flow. Therefore, a classification of tumors according to their angiogenic ability, as well as a characterization of the phenotype of tumor endothelial cells before and after treatment, could become a useful tool for the identification of sub-groups of patients that could benefit from specific radiotherapy schedules or combination regimens with cytotoxic and anti-angiogenic compounds [31, 32].

The Emerging Role of Tumour Lymphangiogenesis in HNSCC

In contrast to the extensive molecular and functional characterization of tumour angiogenesis in head and neck cancer, comparatively little is known about the mechanisms through which tumour cells gain entry into the lymphatic system. This route of dissemination is likely to be relevant in this group of tumors, since metastasis to regional lymph node represent the first step of dissemination in head and neck squamous cell carcinoma and serves as a major prognostic indicator for the progression of the disease and to guide therapeutic strategies. It has been suggested that the lymphatic vessels play only a passive role during this process and lymphatic invasion occurs when infiltrating tumour cells happen upon preexisting peritumoural lymphatics. However, recent evidences indicate an active contribution of the formation of tumour associated lymphatic vessels to the metastatic spread of several human cancers, including head and neck squamous cell carcinoma.

Earlier studies have shown that HNSCC cell lines and tumors produce lymphangiogenic factors like VEGF-C and VEGF-D, and VEGF-C appears to be frequently overexpressed in tumor tissue samples in comparison with normal mucosa [37]. In addition, VEGF-C overexpression is strongly correlated with presence of lymph node metastasis in HNSCC patients [37]. Therefore, lymphangiogenic factors produced by tumor cells, may induce proliferation and dilatation of peritumoral lymphatics, as well as proliferation of intratumoral lymphatics, thus favoring the metastatic spread. However, the study of lymphangiogenesis in human tumors has been hampered by the lack of specific markers of lymphatic endothelium. Recently, a number of relatively specific lymphatic endothelial markers have been discovered, including vascular endothelial growth factor receptor-3 (VEGFR-3), LYVE-1, podoplanin, and D2-40 [38-40], allowing the identification of lymphatic vessels in tissue sections of human tumors. Studies conducted on HNSCC have demonstrated the presence of intratumoral and peritumoral lymphatics, which have been quantified with similar approaches used for angiogenesis. In one report a positive correlation was found between intratumoral lymphatic vessel density and lymph node metastasis, but only in the subgroup of oropharyngeal SCCs [41], whereas in another report this correlation was observed in the whole series of 71 carcinomas [42]. In addition, double immunostaining with antibodies to LYVE-1 and the proliferation marker Ki67, showed that a proportion of intratumoral lymphatics present in HNSCC are indeed actively proliferating vessels and therefore it is likely that they are not preexisting vessels entrapped in the tumor growth [41]. In another study employing the PA2.26 marker, presence of intratumoral lymphatics has been related to high risk of locoregional recurrence in early stage oral squamous cell carcinoma, without neck lymph node involvement [43].

In a recent study, we have examined the presence and distribution of lymphatic vessels in a series of 52 HNSCCs, using the lymphatic marker D2-40 [44]. We determined the number of vessels and their relative area both within the tumor mass and in the peritumor area (within 500μm from tumor invasive front), using an image analysis system. Lymphatic vessels were significantly more numerous and larger in the peritumor area than within the tumor, and the number and relative area of intratumor and peritumor lymphatics was significantly higher in HNSCC with lymph node metastasis. In addition, multivariate analysis showed that high peritumor lymphangiogenesis (above the median value) was associated with an increased risk of developing lymph node metastasis. Tumor lymphangiogenesis was not correlated with other parameters, including age, sex, smoking history, alcohol consumption, tumor site, histologic differentiation, tumor inflammatory infiltrate, as well as with disease-free or overall survival.

Taken together the results of these studies support the hypothesis that tumor associated lymphangiogenesis is an active process that plays a clinically relevant role as route for lymphatic dissemination in HNSCC. Tumor lymphangiogenesis and its signaling system, which has been only minimally explored so far, could represent potential new targets for development of anti-cancer-therapeutics.

Nitric Oxide as a Regulator of Tumor Angiogenesis in Head and Neck Cancer

NO is a diatomic free radical molecule which participates in several biologic processes and is generated from the oxidation of one of the terminal quinidine nitrogens of L-arginine [45]. NO mediates diverse functions, including the regulation of vascular tone, neurotransmission [46, 47], inhibition of platelet aggregation, and plays a critical role defending against various pathogens and in tumorigenesis [48-50]. NO is generated by the enzyme nitric oxide synthase (NOS): there are at least three distinct isoforms of NOS encoded by three distinct genes [51]. The endothelial and neuronal NOS (eNOS and nNOS) proteins are constitutively expressed (cNOS). cNOS are primarily regulated by fluctuation of intracellular calcium levels, and generate low levels of NO for brief periods of time. The inducible isoform (iNOS or NOS II) is primarily expressed in activated macrophages in response to several cytokines and generates a large amount of NO for prolonged periods of time. The cellular effects of NO depend on NO-mediated increase in the levels of soluble guanylate cyclase, leading to an increase in cyclic GMP (cGMP) levels [52, 53].

Various studies have shown that all three isoforms of NOS, (iNOS, eNOS and nNOS), are present in tumor cells and tumor associated inflammatory infiltrate. However, the precise function(s) of NO in tumor biology remains unclear, and several lines of research have indicated that NO may have dual effects in cancer. While NO had initially shown to have anti-tumor properties, because NO produced by macrophages was shown to block respiration in tumor cells [52], it was later suggested that NO may be carcinogenic by directly altering DNA and by promoting the genotoxicity of other substances, such as alkylating substances [54]. Moreover, Jenkins et al. [54] first reported that human colon carcinoma cells engineered to generate NO continuously showed increased tumor growth when grown in nude mice. In this model the growth of NO-generating tumors was accompanied by increased neovascularization. The hypothesis that NO has tumor-promoting effects, which are relevantly due to his pro-angiogenic effects, was further supported by the findings of Ambs et al [56], who used an experimental model with recombinant iNOS expressing Calu-6 and HT-29 human carcinoma cell lines containing mutant p53, and demonstrated that an NO-mediated up-regulation of VEGF corresponded with increased vascularization in the xenograft tumours.

In HNSCC, the first evidence of a possible involvement of NO in tumor growth, came from the work of Rosbe et al [57] who localized the activity of nitric oxide synthase in these tumors through immunohistochemical analysis using antibodies to L-citrulline (a byproduct of nitric oxide synthase), to iNOS, and to cNOS. They demonstrated the expression of the inducible enzyme in neoplastic cells and concluded that iNOS may play a significant role in tumor growth. Based on consistent data indicating that NO may have a role in tumor growth and metastasis, particularly through its influence on the process of angiogenesis, we examined a series of HNSCC for the status of the NO pathway [58]. We found that tumor tissue fragments had significantly higher levels of iNOS and associated increased cGMP levels, than normal mucosa, and iNOS activity was particularly higher in the tumor invasive front. In addition, increased NOS activity and cGMP levels were significantly correlated with the presence of lymph node metastases. To assess whether the tumor NOS activity correlated with an increased angiogenic potential, fragments of HNSCC were implanted in the rabbit corneal stroma, where they induced angiogenesis. This effect was strictly linked with NO activity, since it was abolished by treatment with NOS inhibitors, indicating that the NO pathway is involved in the control of neovascularization in HNSCC.

We further examined the NOS pathway and its correlation with angiogenesis and tumor progression in a series of 35 squamous cell carcinomas of the larynx using an immunohistochemical staining for iNOS, and we confirmed the strict correlation between iNOS expression, NO and cGMP levels and angiogenesis in these tumors [59]. iNOS was not only expressed by neoplastic cells, but it was also detected in the inflammatory infiltrate accompanying the neoplastic proliferation. However, angiogenesis was neither correlated with the degree of the inflammatory response, neither with the expression of iNOS by inflammatory cells, suggesting that in laryngeal neoplasia angiogenesis is only marginally affected by the inflammatory host response and is mainly modulated by factors produced by neoplastic cells (Figure 1).

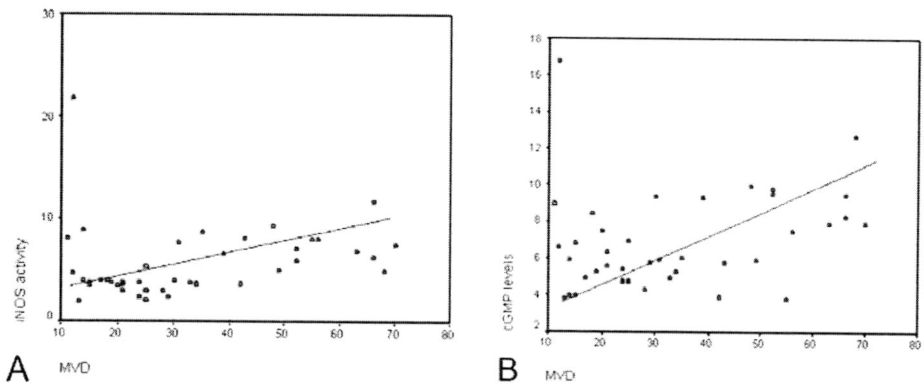

Figure 1. Correlation between microvessel density (MVD) and iNOS activity (A), and cGMP levels in head and neck squamous cell carcinoma. Increased levels of iNOS activity and cGMP are associated with an increase in tumor angiogenesis. For Methods see references 58 and 67.

HNSCC is often preceded by precursor lesions characterized by a progressive disturbance of the maturation of the squamous epithelium, accompanied by the appearance of increasing cellular atypia and mitotic activity. These steps of head and neck carcinogenesis are accompanied by a progressive increase in the number of microvessels associated with the lesion, suggesting that processes like angiogenesis are activated early in the development of HNSCC [59-63]. Interestingly, such increase in microvessel density is accompanied by a significant increase of the expression of the enzyme iNOS by epithelial cells, indicating that the NO pathway may play a relevant role not only in angiogenesis and progression of invasive squamous cell carcinoma of the head and neck region, but it may be also implicated in promoting the angiogenic process that accompanies the development of preneoplastic lesions [59]. These findings have been subsequently confirmed in the oral mucosa, where expression of iNOS was also correlated with the severity of dysplasia [64].

A possible action of NO in tumor growth which is so far unexplored, is its possible influence on the status of lymphatic vasculature. Preliminary observations in our series of HNSCC indicate a direct correlation between iNOS activity and lymphatic area in the peritumor tissue. It can be hypothesized that tumor produced NO could also increase the lymphatic vessel area, thus facilitating the entrance in the lymphatic route by tumor cells.

NO and Tumor Angiogenesis: Controls and Interactions

What are the mechanisms underlying the pro-angiogenic effects of NO in HNSCC and what are its main cellular targets involved in the regulation of angiogenesis? NO may have several important effects on tumor blood flow, by promoting dilation of arteriolar vessels and increasing vascular permeability, but it may actively contribute to the formation of new vessels through the interactions with several other angiogenic factors. In particular, VEGF-induced neovascularization appears to be strictly linked to the NOS pathway [65, 66]. Cancer cells with mutated p53, but not with wild type p53, had accelerated tumor growth associated with increased vascular endothelial growth factor expression and neovascularization [56].

Therefore it is possible that NO generated by NOS (located either within the tumour or in the surrounding stroma) may promote new blood vessel formation by up-regulating VEGF. This neovascularization not only enhances the ability of the tumor to grow, but also increases its invasiveness and metastatic ability.

NO has also important correlations with another metabolic pathway, which is strictly involved in the process of angiogenesis, the COX-2 pathway. We have observed a simultaneous up-regulation of iNOS and COX-2 activity in a series of squamous cell carcinomas of the head and neck region, and the activities of both pathways were strongly correlated with tumor angiogenesis and lymph node metastases [67] (Figure 2). Moreover, *in vitro* studies demonstrated a regulatory contribution of NO on the production of prostanoids in cancer cells with possible implications for tumor angiogenesis *in vivo*. Taken together these data suggest a possible interaction between iNOS and COX-2 pathways *in vivo* and point to iNOS and COX-2 inhibitors as potential anti-tumor drugs, mainly because of a potential anti-angiogenic effect.

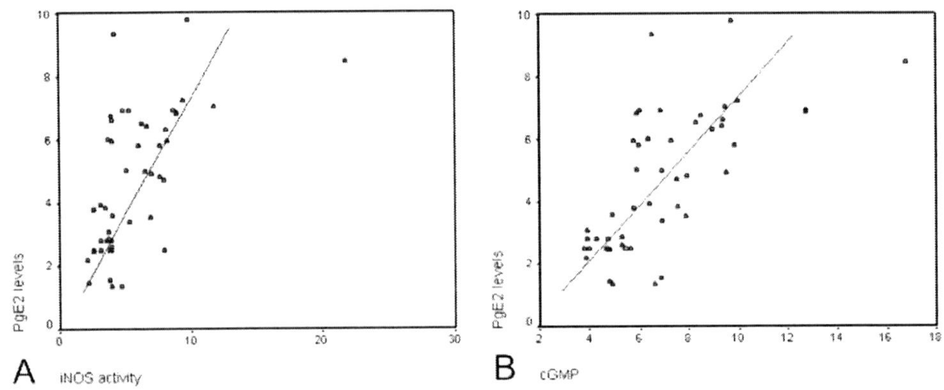

Figure 2. Correlation between prostaglandin levels and iNOS activity (A), and cGMP levels (B) in head and neck squamous cell carcinoma. Increased iNOS activity and cGMP levels are accompanied by an increase in prostaglandin production. For Methods see reference 67.

Finally, NO may be implicated in the control of the expression of matrix metalloproteinases (MMP) and their inhibitors, a group of enzymes involved in the degradation of the extracellular matrix and having a pro-angiogenic activity [68]. Indeed, HNSCCs with MMP-9 overexpression have a significantly higher microvessel density [69, 70], and tumors with higher levels of NO more frequently show overexpression of MMP-9. Therefore, tumour-derived NO also may promote angiogenesis and invasiveness through the up-regulation of MMP production

The mechanisms by which iNOS expression becomes elevated in epithelial cells of head and neck mucosa in the progression from dysplastic changes, to invasive and metastatic carcinoma have been only partially explored. A first relevant aspect to be considered is that hypoxia, a condition which is commonly observed within tumors, can induce iNOS expression by activating the iNOS promoter via a hypoxia-responsive element [71]. Another genetic determinant of the activity of the NOS pathway is the p53 gene. In a series of 43 HNSCCs, p53 mutated carcinomas overexpressed iNOS (Figure 3) and released the highest levels of nitrite/nitrate, in accordance with the hypothesis that p53 mutation has a key role in the HNSCC up-regulation of the NOS pathway [72]. This hypothesis was confirmed by *in vitro* studies demonstrating that in a p53-mutated squamous carcinoma cell line the forced expression of wild-type p53 results in down-regulation of iNOS expression as well as of its products, indicating that iNOS is p53 target gene subjected to p53 repression in HNSCC [72].

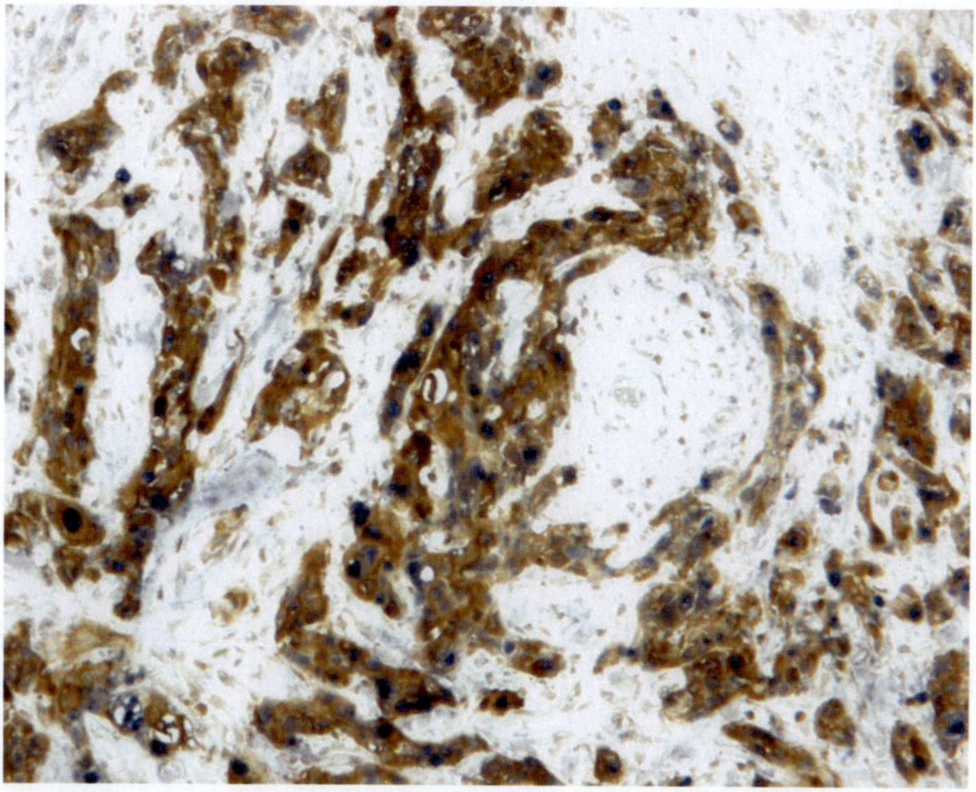

Figure 3. p53 mutated squamous cell carcinoma of the tongue, with double immunostaining for p53 and iNOS. Neoplastic cells show diffuse nuclear positivity for p53 (dark blue staining) and cytoplasmic positivity for iNOS (brown staining). p53 status was determined as described in reference 72.

Moreover, in preneoplastic conditions of the head and neck mucosa, we observed a similar trend, with iNOS overexpression more frequently found in lesions with p53 mutations than in lesions with wild type p53 [73]. Based on these data, our hypothesis is that the loss of p53 wild type function or the expression of mutant p53 in HNSCC cells, frequently due to the mutagenic effect of tobacco/alcohol carcinogens, would activate several key genes in transformed cells with an up-regulation of iNOS. This scenario appears to be different from that hypothesized for the development of other malignancies, like colon cancer. In colon carcinogenesis, considering the genotoxic effect of NO and its capacity to induce mutations, NO predominantly produced by inflammatory cells could be primarily responsible for the occurrence of p53 mutations in the transition from adenoma to carcinoma [74].

Potential Therapeutic Implications of NO Blockage

According to all data reported above, it is conceivable that iNOS activity and NO have a key role in the pathogenesis of several malignancies, including HNSCC. Potential strategies for preventing and treating several human malignancies, as well as HNSCC, thus , may involve iNOS targeting. Relatively few studies have examined the direct impact of iNOS inhibition on carcinogenesis in animal models of human cancer and to date no studies have been done in humans. The strategies to reduce NO production in tumor and non tumor tissues could be different and might include direct and indirect approaches. The potential effectiveness of iNOS inhibition in carcinogenesis is outlined by genetic model of iNOS knokout mice, first generated in 1995 (75). This model showing a central role of NO products in the control of inflammatory responses, has confirmed the potential implication of NO also in carcinogenesis in a study by Konopka et al. (76) describing fewer tumors and lower VEGF expression in iNOS knock out mice injected with B16-F1 melanoma cells.

Further direct evidence of a central role of NO in carcinogenesis comes from the administration of iNOS and NO inhibitors in these models. In fact, inhibition of NO synthesis has been shown to reduce adenoma development in APC (Min/+) mice (77). Rao et al (78) examined the impact of iNOS inhibitors alone or in combination with COX-2 inhibitors on the development of azoxymethane-induced colonic aberrant crypt foci, a precursor of colonic cancer. Doi et al. (79) described a moderate suppression of experimental solid tumor (AH136 hepatoma) cell growth by using a iNOS inhibitor, L-NAME. Moreover, Thomsen et al. (80), showed that the novel iNOS inhibitor 1400W, significantly reduces tumor growth of ENT6 murine mammary adenocarcinomas and human tumor xenografts (colon carcinoma DLD-1) genetically engineered to expresss iNOS constitutively.

Despite the multiple biological effects of NO in human cells, the administration of NO and iNOS inhibithors seems to affect tumor growth and spreading mainly by controlling tumor blood flow and neo-angiogenesis. Tozer et al. (81) showed that co-administration of a tubulin destabilizing agent with N8-omega)-nitroL-arginina methyl ester is able to markedly reduce the tumor established vasculature.

Another way to target iNOS for cancer therapy and prevention is through the targeting of the NF-kappaB pathway, because this pathway is central to iNOS induction. The therapeutic potential of NF-kappa B pathway inhibition in the treatment of cancer has been recently reviewed by Yamamoto and Gaynor (82). In fact, several groups described that NF kappa B sites in the promoter region of iNOS are required for transcriptional activity. Thus, it is not surprising that several drugs targeting NF kappa B also block iNOS gene expression and NO production, and it is likely that their anti-cancer effects could be at least in part due to NO blockage, suggesting their use as anti-cancer drugs. More recently, others have reported a central role of NO release by endothelial and stromal reactive cells after irradiation in HNSCC, treated by curative radiotherapy. In this study, it is reported that iNOS activity has a central role in determining neo-vascularization responsible for tumor failure in HNSCC relapsed after primary irradiation (83), thus suggesting the possibility that iNOS inhibition might increase tumor killing by apoptotic stimuli of gamma-radiation by reducing vascular support in irradiated tumor bed.

In contrast to the above reported studies, others (for review see reference 84) have shown no effect or even an increased cancer risk development and growth by iNOS an NO inhibition, suggesting that some of these effects could be different according to different models and tumor site of growth.

All together, these studies have contributed to better understand potential response of normal and pathological tissues to NO-targeted treatments, suggesting new future anticancer therapeutic strategies based on the control of NO pathway. Nevertheless, it is evident that these potential therapeutic approaches need additional studies to identify new molecules with low or no toxicity specifically targeting iNOS activity and to test the efficacy and mechanisms of current and new iNOS inhibitors in different human cancers, including HNSCC.

References

[1] Sankaranarayanan R, Masuyer E, Swaminathan R, Ferlay J, Whelan S. Head and neck cancer: a global perspective on epidemiology and prognosis. *Anticancer Res* 1998, 18, 4779-86.

[2] Muir C, Weiland R. Upper aerodigestive tract cancers. *Cancer* 1995, 75:147-53.

[3] Parkin DM, Pisani P, Ferlay J. Estimates of the worldwide incidence of 25 major cancers in 1990. *Int J Cancer* 1999; 80:827-41.

[4] Vernham GA, Crowther JA. Head and neck carcinoma-Stage at presentation. *Clin Otolaryngol* 1994; 19:120-4.

[5] Vokes EE, Weichselbaum RR, Lippman SM, Hong WK. Head and neck cancer. *New Engl J Med* 1993; 328:184-94.

[6] Leemans CR, Tiwari R, Nauta JJ, van der Waal, Snow GB. Regional lymph node involvement and its significance in the development of distant metastases in head and neck carcinoma. *Cancer* 1993;71:452-6.

[7] Leemans CR, Tiwari R, Nauta JJ, van der Waal, Snow GB. Recurrence at the primary site in head and neck cancer and the significance of neck lymph node metastases as a prognostic factor. *Cancer* 1994, 73:187-90.

[8] Genden EM, Ferlito A, Bradley PJ, Rinaldo A, Scully C. Neck disease and distant metastases. *Oral Oncol* 2003, 39:207-12.

[9] Leon X, Ferlito A, Myer III CM, Saffiotti U, Shaha AR, Bradley PJ, Brandwein MS, Anniko M, Elluru RG, Rinaldo A. Second primary tumors in head and neck cancer patients. *Acta Otolaryngol* 2002;122:765-78.

[10] Folkman J. Tumor angiogenesis: therapeutic implications. *N Engl J Med* 1971; 285:1182-6.

[11] Weidner N, Semple JP, Welch WR, Folkman J. Tumor angiogenesis and metastasis—correlation in invasive breast carcinoma. *N Engl J Med* 1991; 324:1–8.

[12] Weidner N. Intramural microvessel density as a prognostic factor in cancer. *Am J Pathol* 1995;147:9–19.

[13] Gasparini G, Weidner N, Maluta S, Pozza F, Boracchi P, Mezzetti M, Testolin A, Bevilacqua P. Intratumoral microvessel density and p53 protein: correlation with metastasis in head and neck carcinoma. *Int J Cancer*1993;55:739-44.

[14] Klijanienko J, el-Naggar AK, de Braud F, Rodriguez-Peralto JL, Rodriguez R, Itzhaki M, Russo A, Janot F, Luboinski B, Cvitkovic E. Tumor vascularization, mitotic index, histopathologic grade, and DNA ploidy in the assessment of 114 head and neck squamous cell carcinomas. *Cancer* 1995;75:1649-56.

[15] Gallo O, Masini E, Bianchi B, Bruschini L, Paglierani M, Franchi A. Prognostic significance of cyclooxygenase-2 pathway and angiogenesis in head and neck squamous cell carcinoma. *Hum Pathol* 2002;33:708-14.

[16] Carrau RL, Barnes EL, Snyderman CH, Petruzzelli G, Kachman K, Rueger R, D'Amico F, Johnson JT. Tumor angiogenesis as a predictor of tumor aggressiveness and metastatic potential in squamous cell carcinoma of the head and neck. *Invasion Metastasis* 1995;15:197-202.

[17] Dray TG, Hardin NJ, Sofferman RA. Angiogenesis as a prognostic marker in early head and neck cancer. *Ann Otol Rhinol Laryngol* 1995;104:724-9.

[18] Hegde PU, Brenski AC, Caldarelli DD, Hutchinson J, Panje WR, Wood NB, Leurgans S, Preisler HD, Taylor SG 4th, Caldarelli L, Coon JS. Tumor angiogenesis and p53 mutations: prognosis in head and neck cancer. *Arch Otolaryngol Head Neck Surg* 1998;124:80-5.

[19] Kupisz K, Chibowski D, Klatka J, Klonowski S, Stepulak A. Tumor angiogenesis in patients with laryngeal cancer. *Eur Arch Otorhinolaryngol* 1999;256:303-5.

[20] Sion-Vardy N, Fliss DM, Prinsloo I, Shoham-Vardi I, Benharroch D. Neoangiogenesis in squamous cell carcinoma of the larynx - biological and prognostic associations. *Pathol Res Pract* 2001;197:1-5.

[21] Murray JD, Carlson GW, McLaughlin K, Pennington M, Lynn M, DeRose PB, Williams JK, Cohen C. Tumor angiogenesis as a prognostic factor in laryngeal cancer. *Am J Surg* 1997;174:523-6.

[22] Beatrice F, Cammarota R, Giordano C, Corrado S, Ragona R, Sartoris A, Bussolino F, Valente G. Angiogenesis: prognostic significance in laryngeal cancer. *Anticancer Res* 1998;18:4737-40.

[23] Williams JK, Carlson GW, Cohen C, Derose PB, Hunter S, Jurkiewicz MJ. Tumor angiogenesis as a prognostic factor in oral cavity tumors. Am J Surg 1994;168:373-80.

[24] Gleich LL, Biddinger PW, Pavelic ZP, Gluckman JL. Tumor angiogenesis in T1 oral cavity squamous cell carcinoma: role in predicting tumor aggressiveness. *Head Neck.* 1996;18:343-6.

[25] Shpitzer T, Chaimoff M, Gal R, Stern Y, Feinmesser R, Segal K. Tumor angiogenesis as a prognostic factor in early oral tongue cancer. *Arch Otolaryngol Head Neck Surg* 1996; 122:865-8.

[26] Gleich LL, Biddinger PW, Duperier FD, Gluckman JL. Tumor angiogenesis as a prognostic indicator in T2-T4 oral cavity squamous cell carcinoma: a clinical-pathologic correlation. *Head Neck* 1997;19:276-80.

[27] Hogmo A, Kuylenstierna R, Lindholm J, Munck-Wikland E. Predictive value of malignancy grading systems, DNA content, p53, and angiogenesis for stage I tongue carcinomas. *J Clin Pathol.* 1999;52:35-40.

[28] Lopez-Graniel CM, Tamez de Leon D, Meneses-Garcia A, Gomez-Ruiz C, Frias-Mendivil M, Granados-Garcia M, Barrera-Franco JL. Tumor angiogenesis as a prognostic factor in oral cavity carcinomas. *J Exp Clin Cancer Res* 2001;20:463-8.

[29] Forootan SS, Jones AS, Helliwell TR. Neoangiogenesis and squamous cell carcinoma of the tongue. *Cancer Detect Prev* 1999;23:137-46.

[30] Zatterstrom UK, Brun E, Willen R, Kjellen E, Wennerberg J. Tumor angiogenesis and prognosis in squamous cell carcinoma of the head and neck. *Head Neck* 1995;17:312-8.

[31] Giatromanolaki A, Koukourakis MI, Georgoulias V, Gatter KC, Harris AL, Fountzilas G. Angiogenesis vs. response after combined chemoradiotherapy of squamous cell head and neck cancer. *Int J Cancer* 1999;80:810-7.

[32] Koukourakis MI, Giatromanolaki A, Fountzilas G, Sivridis E, Gatter KC, Harris AL. Angiogenesis, thymidine phosphorylase, and resistance of squamous cell head and neck cancer to cytotoxic and radiation therapy. *Clin Cancer Res* 2000;6:381-9.

[33] Koukourakis MI, Giatromanolaki A, Sivridis E, Simopoulos K, Pissakas G, Gatter KC, Harris AL. Squamous cell head and neck cancer: evidence of angiogenic regeneration during radiotherapy. *Anticancer Res* 2001;21:4301-9.

[34] Hast J, Schiffer IB, Neugebauer B, Teichman E, Schreiber W, Brieger J, Kim DW, Gebhard S, Born CJ, Strugala M, Sagemuller J, Brenner W, Mann WJ, Oesch F, Thelen M, Hengstler JG. Angiogenesis and fibroblast proliferation precede formation of recurrent tumors after radiation therapy in nude mice. *Anticancer Res* 2002;22:677-688.

[35] Taylor AP, Osorio L, Craig R, Raleigh JA, Ying Z, Goldemberg DM, Blumenthal RD. Tumor-specific up-regulation of angiogenic growth factors and their receptors during recovery from cytotoxic therapy. *Clin Cancer Res* 2002;8:1233-22.

[36] Teknos TN, Cox C, Barrios MA, Chepeha DB, Bradford CR, Fisher SG, Wolf GT. Tumor angiogenesis as a predictive marker for organ preservation in patients with advanced laryngeal carcinoma. *Laryngoscope* 2002;112:844-51.

[37] O-charoenrat P, Rhys-Evans P, Eccles SA. Expression of vascular endothelial growth factor family members in head and neck squamous cell carcinoma correlates with lymph node metastasis. *Cancer* 2001;92:556-568.

[38] Partanen TA, Arola J, Saaristo A, Jussila L, Ora A, Miettinen M, Stacker SA, Achen MG, Alitalo K. VEGF-C and VEGF-D expression in neuroendocrine cells and their receptor, VEGFR-3, in fenestrated blood vessels in human tissues. *FASEB J* 2000;14:2087-96.

[39] Sleeman JP, Krishnan J, Kirkin V, Baumann P. Markers for the lymphatic endothelium: in search of the holy grail? *Microsc Res Tech* 2001;55:61-9.

[40] Kahn HJ, Marks A. A new monoclonal antibody, D2-40, for detection of lymphatic invasion in primary tumors. *Lab Invest*. 2002; 82: 1255-7.

[41] Beasley NJ, Prevo R, Banerji S, Leek RD, Moore J, van Trappen P, Cox G, HarrisAL, Jackson DG. Intratumoral lymphangiogenesis and lymph node metastasis in head and neck cancer. *Cancer Res*. 2002; 62: 1315-20.

[42] Maula SM, Luukkaa M, Grenman R, Jackson D, Jalkanen S, Ristamaki R. Intratumoral lymphatics are essential for the metastatic spread and prognosis in squamous cell carcinomas of the head and neck region. *Cancer Res*. 2003;63: 1920-6.

[43] Munoz-Guerra MF, Marazuela EG, Martin-Villar E, Quintanilla M, Gamallo C. Prognostic significance of intratumoral lymphangiogenesis in squamous cell carcinoma of the oral cavity. A study of the early stages. *Cancer* 2004;100:553-60.

[44] Franchi A, Gallo O, Massi D, Baroni G, Santucci M. Tumor lymphangiogenesis in head and neck squamous cell carcinoma. A morphometric study with clinical correlations. *Cancer*, 2004, in press.

[45] Nathan C. Nitric oxide as a secretory product of mammalian cells. *FASEB J* 1992;6:3051–64.
[46] Ignarro LJ, Buga GM, Wood KS, Byrns RE, Chaudhuri G. Endothelial-derived relaxing factor produced and released from artery and vein is nitric oxide. *Proc. Natl. Acad. Sci. USA* 1987;84:9265–9.
[47] Jaffrey SR, Snyder SH. Nitric oxide: a neural messenger. *Annu Rev Cell Dev Biol* 1995;11: 417–40.
[48] Hibbs JB, Taintor RR, Vavrin Z. Macrophage cytotoxicity: role for L-arginine deiminase activity and amino nitrogen to nitrate. *Science* 1987;235:473–6.
[49] Dong Z, O'Brian CA Fidler IJ. Activation of tumoricidal properties in macrophages by lipopolysaccharide requires protein-tyrosine kinase activity. *J Leukoc Bio.* 1993;53:53–60.
[50] Graziewicz M, Wink DA, Laval F. Nitric oxide inhibits DNA ligase activity: potential mechanisms for NO-mediated DNA damage. *Carcinogenesis* 1996;17:2501-5.
[51] Nathan C, Xie Q. Regulation of biosynthesis of nitric oxide *J Biol Chem* 1994. 269:13725-8.
[52] Stuehr DJ, Nathan CF. A macrophage product responsible for cytostasis and respiratory inhibition in tumor target cells. *J Exp Med* 1989;169:1543-55.
[53] Moncada S, Palmer RMJ, Higgs A. Nitric oxide: physiology, pathophysiology, and pharmacology. *Pharmacol Rev* 1991;43:109-42.
[54] Cook JA, Krishna MC, Pacelli R, DeGraff W, Liebmann J, Russo A, Mitchell JB, Wink DA. Nitric oxide enhancement of melphalan-induced cytotoxicity. *Br J Cancer* 1997;76:325-34.
[55] Jenkins DC, Charles IG, Thomsen LL, Moss DW, Holmes LS, Baylis SA, Rhodes P, Westmore K, Emson PC, Moncada S. Roles of nitric oxide in tumor growth. *Proc Natl Acad Sci U S A* 1995;92:4392-6.
[56] Ambs S, Merriam WG, Ogunfusika MO, Bennett WP, Ishibe N, Hussain SP, Tzeng EE, Geller DA, Billiar TR, Harris CC. p53 and vascular endothelial growth factor regulate tumor growth of NOS2-expressing human carcinoma cells. *Nat Med* 1998;4:1371-6.
[57] Rosbe KW, Prazma J, Petrusz P, Mims W, Ball SS, Weissler MC. Immunohistochemical characterization of nitric oxide synthase activity in squamous cell carcinoma of the head and neck. *Otolaryngol Head Neck Surg* 1995;113:541-9.
[58] Gallo O, Masini E, Morbidelli L, Franchi A, Fini-Storchi I, Vergari WA, Ziche M. Role of nitric oxide in angiogenesis and tumor progression in head and neck cancer. *J Natl Cancer Inst* 1998;90:587-96.
[59] Franchi A, Gallo O, Paglierani M, Sardi I, Magnelli L, Masini M, Santucci M. Inducible nitric oxide synthase expression in laryngeal neoplasia: correlation with angiogenesis. *Head Neck* 2002; 24:16-23.
[60] Macluskey M, Chandrachud LM, Pazouki S, Green M, Chisholm DM, Ogden GR, Schor SL, Schor AM. Apoptosis, proliferation, and angiogenesis in oral tissues. Possible relevance to tumour progression. *J Pathol.* 2000;191:368-75.
[61] Sunaga H, Fujieda S, Tsuzuki H, Asamoto K, Fukuda M, Saito H. Expression of granulocyte colony-stimulating factor receptor and platelet-derived endothelial cell growth factor in oral and oropharyngeal precancerous lesions. *Anticancer Res* 2001;21:2901-6

[62] Carlile J, Harada K, Baillie R, Macluskey M, Chisholm DM, Ogden GR, Schor SL, Schor AM. Vascular endothelial growth factor (VEGF) expression in oral tissues: possible relevance to angiogenesis, tumour progression and field cancerisation. *J Oral Pathol Med* 2001;30:449-57.

[63] Laitakari J, Nayha V, Stenback F. Size, shape, structure, and direction of angiogenesis in laryngeal tumour development. *J Clin Pathol* 2004;57:394-401.

[64] Brennan PA, Umar T, Wilson AW, Mellor TK. Expression of type 2 nitric oxide synthase and vascular endothelial growth factor in oral dysplasia. *J Oral Maxillofac Surg* 2002;60:1455-60.

[65] Zhang HT, Craft P, Scott PA, Ziche M, Weich HA, Harris AL, Bicknell R. Enhancement of tumor growth and vascular density by transfection of vascular endothelial cell growth factor into MCF-7 human breast carcinoma cells. *J Natl Cancer Inst* 1995;87:213-9.

[66] Ziche M, Morbidelli L, Choudhuri R, Zhang HT, Donnini S, Granger HJ, Bicknell R. Nitric oxide synthase lies downstream from vascular endothelial growth factor-induced but not basic fibroblast growth factor-induced angiogenesis. *J Clin Invest* 1997;99:2625-34.

[67] Gallo O, Fabbroni V, Sardi I, Magnelli L, Boddi V, Franchi A. Correlation between nitric oxide and cyclooxygenase-2 pathways in head and neck squamous cell carcinomas. *Biochem Biophys Res Commun*. 2002;299:517-24.

[68] Lala PK, Orucevic A. Role of nitric oxide in tumour progression: lessons from experimental tumors. *Cancer Met Rev* 1998;17:91-106.

[69] Riedel F, Gotte K, Schwalb J, Bergler W, Hormann K. Expression of 92-kDa type IV collagenase correlates with angiogenic markers and poor survival in head and neck squamous cell carcinoma. *Int J Oncol* 2000;17:1099-105.

[70] Franchi A, Santucci M, Masini E, Sardi I, Paglierani M, Gallo O. Expression of matrix metalloproteinase 1, matrix metalloproteinase 2, and matrix metalloproteinase 9 in carcinoma of the head and neck. *Cancer*. 2002;95:1902-10.

[71] McLillo G, Musso T, Sica A, Taylor LS, Cox GW, Varesio L. A hypoxia-responsive element mediates a novel pathway of activation of the inducible nitric oxide synthase promoter. *J Exp Med* 1995;182:1683-93.

[72] Gallo O, Schiavone N, Papucci L, Sardi I, Magnelli L, Franchi A, Masini E, Capaccioli S. Down-regulation of nitric oxide synthase-2 and cyclooxygenase-2 pathways by p53 in squamous cell carcinoma. *Am J Pathol* 2003;163:723-32.

[73] Gallo O, Sardi I, Masini M, Franchi A. Re: Relationship between p53 mutations and inducible nitric oxide synthase expression in human colorectal cancer. *J Natl Cancer Inst* 1999;91:1509-11.

[74] Ambs S, Bennett WP, Merriam WG, Ogunfusika MO, Oser SM, Harrington AM, Shields PG, Felley-Bosco E, Hussain SP, Harris CC. Relationship between p53 mutations and inducible nitric oxide synthase expression in human colorectal cancer. *J Natl Cancer Inst* 1999;91:86-8.

[75] MacMicking JD, Nathan C, Hom G, Chartrain N, Fletcher DS Stevens K, Xie Q, Hutchinson N. Altered response to bacterial infection and endotoxic shock in mice lacking inducible nitric oxide synthase. *Cell* 1995; 81:641-50.

[76] Konopka TE, Barker JE, Bamford TL, Guida E, Anderson RL, Stewart AG. Nitric oxide synthase gene II disruption: implications for tumor growth and vascular endothelial growth factor production: *Cancer Res* 2001;61:3182-7.

[77] Ahn B, Oshima H. Suppression of intestinal polyps in APC mice by inhibiting nitric oxide production. *Cancer Res* 2001;61:8357-60.

[78] Rao CV, Kawamori T, Hamid R, Reddy B. Chemoprevention of colonic abberrant crypt foci by an inducible nitric oxide synthase-selective inhibitor. *Carcinogenesis* 1999;20:641-4.

[79] Doi K, Akaike T, Fujiii S, Tanaka S, Ikebe N, Beppu T, Ogawa M, Maeda H. Induction of haem oxygenase –1 nitric oxide and ischaemia in experimental solid tumors and implications for tumor growth. *Br J Cancer* 1999;80:1945-54.

[80] Thomsen LL, Scott JM, Topley P, Knowels RG, Keerie AJ, Frend AJ. Selective inhibition of iNOS inhibits tumor growth in vivo: studies with 1400W, a novel inhibitor. *Cancer Res* 1997;57:3300-4.

[81] Tozer GM, Prise VD, Wilson J, Loke RJ, Vojonovic B, Dennis MF, Chaplin DJ. Combretastatin A-4 phosphate as a tumor vascular targeting agent: early effect in tumors and normal tissues. *Cancer Res* 1999;59:1626-34.

[82] Yamamoto Y and Gaynor RB. Therapeutic potential of inhibition of NF kappa B pathway in the the treatment of inflammation and cancer. *J Clin Invest* 2001;107:135-42.

[83] Sonveaux P, Brouet A, Havaux X, Gregoire V, Dessy C, Balligand JL, Feron O. Irradiation induced angiogenesis through the up-regulation of nitric oxide pathway:implications for tumor radiotherapy. *Cancer Res* 2003;63:1012-9.

[84] Hofset LJ, Hussain PS, Wogan GN, Harris CC. Nitric oxide in cancer and chemoprevention. *Free Radical Biol & Med* 2003; 34:955-68.

In: New Angiogenesis Research
Editor: Roberta V. Zubar, pp. 235-255
ISBN 1-59454-239-2

Chapter XIII

Angiogenesis and Anti-Angioenesis in Neoplastic and Non-Neoplastic Diseases

Hüseyin Abali[1,*] and Gülcan Kuru Abali[2]
[1]Medical Oncology Division, Ministry of Health Numune Research and Education Hospital, Ankara, Turkey
[2]Department of Cardiology, Hacettepe University School of Medicine, Ankara, Turkey

Abstract

Our knowledge on cancerogenesis has increased dramatically. Now, we better know how it survives, grows and metastasizes. We are switching from rather crude therapies like surgery, radiotherapy and chemotherapy to finely engineered, free of side effects and specific ones in the field of oncology. Besides developing cytotoxic agents, new anti-tumoral mechanisms inspired from our knowledge on cancer cell have been engineered. New biological agents targeting some critical steps of cancer cell survival are emerging everyday.

It has been more than 30 years since it was first hypothesized by Folkman that angiogenesis was a must for tumor survival and therefore it had a potential as a target. Angiogenesis, new vessel formation, is normally present in endometrium and wound healing. It is so critical for tumor cells that they can not grow beyond 1-2 mm without developing their own blood vessels. Recently, some agents show promise. For example Bevacizumab, a humanized monoclonal antibody against the major pro-angiogenic factor, has prolonged survival of patients with metastatic colorectal cancer and renal cell carcinoma.

Angiogenesis related therapy is not potentially confined only to cancer, but it may work wherever angiogenesis is operational like diabetic retinopathy or inoperable coronary artery disease. Anti-angiogenic therapies will be in use singly, or in

* Address for Corespondence: Yenibatı Mah. Uygarkent Sitesi, No 52 Batikent / Ankara, Turkiye, Call:+90.312.2559465, E-mail: habali1970@yahoo.com, Fax: +90.312.3113187

combination with cytotoxic agents and other biological agents targeting other critical steps which enable the cancer cell to survive.

Key words: Angiogenesis, cancer, anti-angiogenic therapy, blood vessels

Introduction

War against cancer is very much like the war in reality. Armies need supplies which must be carried by roads, railways, airways and sea for invasion. Without an at least one strategic supply, an army is destined to loose. A good commander, therefore, does not only consider weapons, but also strategic points like as much information as possible about their enemy to attack some vital targets like air bases, planes, bridges, railroads highways and ships.

Unlike war in reality, oncologists' war always has a decent aim: To help people. However, technically they resemble. We doctors must gather as much information as possible on tumor cells to know it better for a more successful battle. Recent developments on cancer biology enabled us to identify many aspects of cancerogenesis and biology of angiogenesis and metastasis, although we are still in need of much more information for ideal successful treatment of cancer. Our information on cancer disclosed many potential strategic targets, the oldest one of which is the transportation means; angiogenesis. Our concept of angiogenesis has been nowadays carried one step further; lymphangiogenesis [1;2], which is another way of transportation.

Angiogenesis is normally needed in development, reproduction, adaptation to exercise and wound healing within the body. Developing collaterals in the vicinity of vascular obstruction like in coronary vessels is also an example of physiological angiogenesis. Under normal circumstances, angiogenesis is under tight control of some suppressor factors [3].

Although it has been over 30 years since Folkman first hypothesized that tumors are dependent upon angiogenesis to maintain their vitality [3;4], observations on tumor angiogenesis date back to as early as 1900's [3]. In a paper in 1939, it was stated that although the newly formed vessels disappeared completely after wound healing in the transparent ear of a rabbit, vessels around the implanted tumor persisted [3]. Debate on tumor angiogenesis continued until Folkman proposed his hypothesis.

Angiogenesis is so vital for a tumor that, without blood supply of its own, it can not grow beyond 1 mm^3 which is thought to be a critical size at which it can no longer derive its nutrients by diffusion [3]. Malignant cells obtain not only oxygen, nutrients and metabolites but also hormones, circulating and endothelial growth factors, pro-invasive and proteolytic activities, escape routes of metastasis, various tumor-modulating influences derived from the coagulation and fibrinolytic system [5]. It was therefore hypothesized originally by Folkman that targeting tumor-induced angiogenesis may be an attractive approach which was confirmed in preclinical studies and it has recently proved true in a randomized phase II trial on patients with colorectal cancer [5].

Cancer is not the sole disease entity which involves neovascularization from a pathophysiological point of view [6]. Diabetic retinopathy, hypertension, wound healing and coronary artery disease involve angiogenesis.

Angiogenesis will certainly be of pivotal role in the management of cancer and other diseases. Some agents have already proved useful in phase I and II trials and phase III trials are underway.

Evidences for Tumor Dependence on Angiogenesis

There were some indirect evidences supporting dependence of tumors on angiogenesis. Two-dimensional flat cultures of malignant cells were observed to indefinitely enlarge horizontally as long as there are fresh and cell free medium [3]. However, three-dimensional droplets of cultures in suspensions of the same cells were unable grow beyond few millimeters [3]. Folkman also stated in his chapter that growth of tumor implants accelerated after angiogenesis. Another observation growth of tumor cells decreased in proportion to the distance from the nearest capillary [3]. It was not until late 1980s and early 1990s that direct evidences emerged for tumor angiogenesis.

Direct evidences came from following group of experiments: 1) Administration of molecules that inhibit angiogenesis selectively, 2) Blockade of tumor derived angiogenic factors, 3) Transfection of dominant-negative receptors for an angiogenic factor into endothelial cells in the tumor bed, 4) transfection of angiogenesis inhibitor proteins into tumor cells, 5) development of spontaneous tumors in transgenic mice [3]. It is beyond the scope of this chapter to mention all the preclinical experiments. We think that the best current evidence is the survival prolongation of patients with metastatic cancer [7]. We will talk about clinical trials later in this chapter in detail.

Not only tumor itself but also its ability to metastasize is dependent upon angiogenesis [3]. One must notice that ability to metastasize requires new vessel formation at the site of origin, destruction of basement membrane of vessels, escape from immune surveillance in the blood circulation, ability to attach the endothelium of the remote vessel, traversing its basement membrane, dissolution of matrix and finally new vessel formation again. Therefore angiogenesis is a must for a tumor to develop clinically detectable metastases [3]. Angiogenesis markers have prognostic value in a variety of cancers [8-12].

Mechanisms

At the time that most tumors become clinically detectable, they have developed angiogenesis. However, they have a pre-angiogenic state for a variable length of time, that is in situ cancer, although there may be some exceptions [3]. Initiation of angiogenesis is dependent upon the net balance of pro- and anti-angiogenic factors (Table 1). In case of an imbalance in favor of pro-angiogenic factors, endothelial cells are activated to start angiogenesis, which is called “angiogenic switching”. Several mechanisms of angiogenic switching have been described: 1) Avascular tumors recruit their own blood supply, 2) circulating endothelial stem cells can incorporate into angiogenic focus, 3) tumors can stimulate host cells and 4) pre-existing tumor cells can be co-opted by tumor cells [3].

It was hypothesized that what opens the way is probably a factor secreted from the tumoral tissue (Figure 1) [13]. As the tumor grows, some tumor cells especially inner ones in the mass become hypoxic. Hypoxia is an important signal for need of blood supply. Hypoxia inducible factors types A and B are factors that are normally found in the body and they provide erythropoietin secretion in response to hypoxia. Apart from hypoxia, they are also activated by a number of growth factors and loss of function of some tumor suppressor genes, too [6]. Hypoxia inducible factors are thought to play a major role in initiating angiogenesis. They are closely co-expressed together with one of the most important pro-angiogenic factors – vascular endothelial growth factor (VEGF) in several kinds of cancer [14]. VEGF is a major growth factor for endothelial cells which makes vascular tubing [3].

Table 1. List of naturally-occurring pro-angiogenic and anti-angiogenic factors. VEGF; *V*ascular *E*ndothelial *G*rowth *F*actor, bFGF; *B*asic *F*ibroblast *G*rowth *F*actor.

Pro-angiogenic Factors	Anti-angiogenic Factors
VEGF	Angiostatin
Angiopoietin	Endostatin
bFGF	Interferon-alpha
Platelet derived growth factor	Interleukins 1, 6 and 12
Hepatocyte growth factor	Platelet factor 4
Matrix metalloproteinases	Prolactin
Placental growth factor	Thrombospondine-1
Angiotropin	Tissue inhibitors of metalloproteinases
Tumor necrosis factor	Placental proliferin related protein
Proliferin	Internal fragment of anti-thrombin III
Granulocyte colony stimulating factor	Troponin I
Interleukin-8 and 18	Inducible protein 10
Leptin	
Transforming growth factor alpha	
Transforming growth factor beta	
Angiotensin II	
Cyclooxygenase 2	
Syndecan-2	
Alternagin	
Agrettin	
Endothelial chemise	

Recently, it was found that the underlying genetic abnormality also contribute to angiogenesis, meaning that new vessel formation may be induced independently from hypoxia [5]. Loss of certain tumor suppressor genes like p53 leads to down regulation of some anti-angiogenic proteins [5]. Up to 20 different such mutations including very well-known ones like ras, c-myc, bcl-2, Her-2 and Epidermal Growth Factor Receptor (EGFR) have pro-angiogenic effects [5]. Therefore, it may not be wrong to say that ability to produce new vessels independently is an innate feature of being malignant. VEGF is also up regulated by oncogenes [5;6].

Ras oncogene abnormalities induce several signal transduction disorders including raf-mitogen activated kinase (MAP) activation (p42/44), phosphoinositol-3 kinase (PI3) activation, nuclear factor kappa beta (NFKκB) activation and generation of reactive oxygen radicals [15]. One other mechanism of VEGF activation is by Inositol 3 phosphate (PI3) activation [15]. It also activates matrix metalloproteinases.

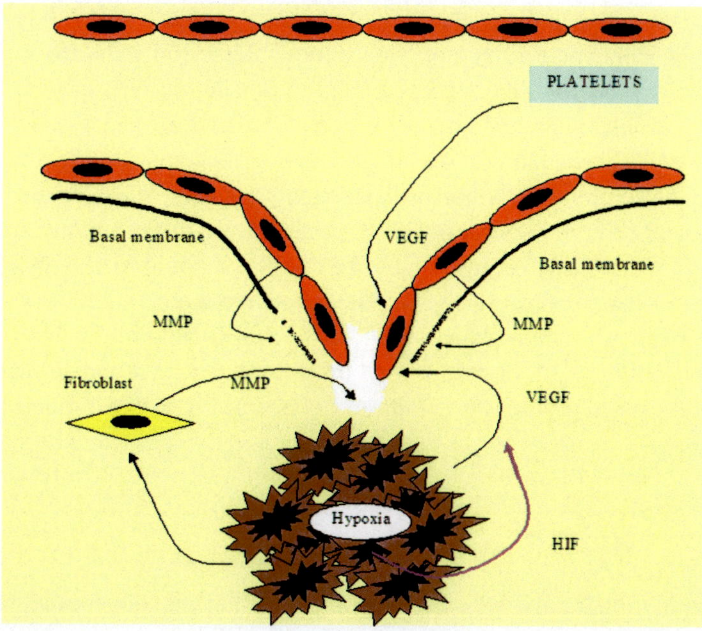

Figure 1. A simplified schematic presentation of angiogenesis. Hypoxic cancerous cells and others secrete VEGF and HIF which activate endothelial cells. Platelets are a good source of VEGF and other pro-angiogenic factors, too. Endothelial cells secrete MMPs to degrade basal membrane. Fibroblasts in the stroma, activated by cancerous cells produce MMPs to degrade matix to create room for endothelial cells form vascular tubes. VEGF; Vascular Endothelial Growth Factor, HIF; Hypoxia Inducible Factor, MMPs; Matrix Metalloproteinase(s). Brownish-yellow background outside the vessel represents the matrix and white area its degradation MMPs.

Angiogenesis is a process closely related to matrix degradation, apoptosis and homeostasis. Matrix degradation to create space is required for new vessel formation, tumor invasion and metastases [16]. They are over 20 different enzymes which can degrade extracellular matrix and dependent upon Zinc^{+2} binding for proteolytic activity [17] and are collectively called matrix metalloproteinases (MMP). Most popular ones are MMP-2 (Gelatinase A) and MMP-9 (Gelatinase B). They play important role in basement membrane turn over. Gelatinase A can degrade Collagen types IV and V, laminin and elastin [18]. They are secreted mostly by stromal cells under the influence of tumor cells, but malignant cells and endothelia may also produce them [3;17]. They can have both a pro-angiogenic role and an anti-angiogenic role, the balance between 2 roles govern the angiogenic switch by matrix metalloproteinases [17]. Extracellular matrix cleaved by these enzymes have pro-angiogenic properties as well [17]. Angiogenesis is a complex process that requires 1) degradation of basement membrane and extracellular matrix around the vessels, 2) chemotaxis of endothelial cells towards an angiogenic stimulus, 3) proliferation of endothelial cells and finally 4) remodeling of basement membrane as the vascular tubing reforms [18].

Apoptosis of microvascular endothelia prevents tumors from growing further [19].

Anti-angiogenic scheduling of chemotherapy, that is at low and frequent doses, causes endothelial cell apoptosis which precedes by 4 days the apoptosis of cancerous cells.

Tumor angiogenesis and homeostasis are also closely linked. Both coagulation and fibrinolysis are activated in cancer-related thrombosis and an increased risks of deep vein thrombosis and pulmonary thromboemboli are accompanying [20]. Almost every component of haemostatic system including platelets, endothelial system, coagulation cascade and fibrinolytic system contribute to tumor angiogenesis [20]. Platelets are a rich source for mainly pro-angiogenic factors like VEGF, FGF and platelet derived growth factor [PDGF], and to a lesser extend anti-angiogenic factors like endostatin, platelet factor 4 and thrombospondin [20]. Thrombin released from tumor causes activation of platelets which in turn secrete VEGF which is the major pro-angiogenic element. Platelets are also blamed on for sheltering tumor cells in the circulation to protect them from immune surveillance [20]. Thrombocyte count and VEGF were found to be correlated and thrombocytosis is an adverse prognostic factor in many cancers [20]. Tissue factor, the major initiator of coagulation, up regulates VEGF expression on endothelium [20]. Anticoagulant therapy have important anti-angiogenic implications [20]. Aspirin and other non-steroidal anti-inflammatory drugs prevent colorectal carcinogenesis [20]. Figure 1 is a simplified illustration of what happens during angiogenesis.

Pro-Angiogenic Factors

There are over 15 naturally-occurring factors which have angiogenesis-promoting effects [3]. However, several other factors were also identified like interleukin 18 [21], Frizzled A [22], Syndecan-2 [23], Agrettin [24], Alternagin-C [25], endothelial chemise [25;26] and anti-adrenomedulline [25-27]. It is not possible to name all the factors which have pro-angiogenic properties, though (Table 1).

VEGF

Endothelial cells are central in producing new vessels regardless of whether or not it is related to malignancy. They proliferate in response to certain stimuli to form vascular tubes or canals. VEGF is the major mitogenic stimulus for endothelial cells, although there are other several other factors like angiopoietin and basic fibroblast growth factor (bFGF) [3] (Table 1). It is also an anti-apoptotic and motility factor for endothelial cells. Apart from above functions it also induces fenestrations in the lining of vascular endothelium to increase vascular permeability, as its previous name implies: Vascular permeability factor (VPF) [3]. Not infrequently, it is even referred to as VPF/VEGF. However, for them to turn into vascular tubes they need extra space in the extracellular matrix. Extracellular matrix must be degraded wherever needed. MMPs do the job [18]. Endothelial cells grow into the tunnel created and vessel is formed.

Fibroblast Growth Factor

FGF was the first angiogenic factor discovered [28]. Unlike VEGF it is not specific for endothelial cells [3] and has a multitude of cellular targets like fibroblasts, smooth muscle cells and neurons. Over 20 different FGF and about 4 types of specific receptors have been described [29]. It has been shown that FGF has significant roles in prognosis, cancerogenesis and invasiveness of many malignancies. It may contribute to the cancerogenesis by several mechanisms: 1) induction angiogenesis, 2) direct mitogenic action for the tumor cells and 3) inhibits apoptosis [29]. Its effect on endothelium is via VEGF.

Angiopoeitins

Angiopoietins are other pro-angiogenic factors. Angiopoietin-1 specifically binds to its tyrosine kinase receptor Tie 2 which is solely found on endothelial cells [3]. Angiopoietins, up to 4 kinds have been identified, act on Tie 2 to from and maintain blood vessels by endothelial cell assembly, cell-to-cell interaction, endothelial cell survival and endothelial cell-extracellular matrix interaction [30]. As for VEGF, hypoxia modulates angiopoietin 1 and 2 expression [30]. Other factors which act on endothelial cells have been less studied.

Anti-Angiogenic Factors

There are a number naturally occurring anti-angiogenic factors. There are also commercially engineered anti-angiogenic factor which either show directly anti-angiogenic activity or show indirect anti-angiogenic effect by antagonizing a pro-angiogenic factor [31]. Angiostatin, endostatin, and an internal fragment of anti-thrombin III [aaAT] are naturally occurring factors [3].

Angiostatin

It is an internal fragment of plasminogen [3]. It is not secreted by the tumor cells, but it is cleaved from plasminogen by a series of enzymes secreted from tumor cells. A tumor derived enzyme, uPA, cleaves plasminogen to form plasmin which is subsequently reduced by a phophoglycerate kinase from hypoxic tumor cells. It is then converted to angiostatin by several metalloproteinases [3]. It has 4 kringles, first one being the most potent [31]. The 5th kringle on the plasminogen molecule potentiates the anti-angiogenic effect of angiostatin 50 folds [31]. It induces apoptosis of endothelial cells, inhibits endothelial migration, and inhibits angiogenesis [3]. Exact mechanism of anti-angiogenesis is not clearly known yet [31].

Endostatin

It is an internal fragment of collagen XVIII and a specific inhibitor of endothelial cell proliferation and migration [32-34]. It is found especially in elastic fibers of aorta and sparse elastic fibers of veins [3]. There are 2 kinds of endostatin based upon their parent collagen XV or XVIII: Endostatin XV and endostatin XVIII [35] with differences in structure, function and localization. It has been shown to suppress tumoral growth [3] and has prognostic value for lung cancer [36].

Other Endogenous Anti-Angiogenesis Inhibitors

Anti-angiogenic conformation of anti-thrombin III, troponin I, interferon beta, platelet factor 4, fibronectin, thrombospondine-1, tissue inhibitors of metalloproteinases, certain angiostatic steroids like tetrahydrocortisol, 2-methoxyestradiol, interleukin-12 and inducible proten-10 are other endogenous angiogenesis inhibitors [3].

Anti-Angiogenic Therapy

As we understand tumor angiogenesis, anti-angiogenic therapy gained popularity over 30 years after its first proposal by Judah Folkman. It may offer some advantages over classical cytotoxic therapies. Anti-angiogenic therapy is less toxic, which may theoretically be confined to toxicity of the agent itself mostly. There may not be a need for break or pause for patient. Sometime later under cytotoxic therapies oncologists have to stop because of the cumulative toxicities. It may be easier to induce apoptosis in vascular endothelial cells since they have a properly working apoptosis machinery, which malfunctions in many cancer. They may be incorporated into cytotoxic therapy either at the same time or afterwards. They may prevent the repopulation of cancerous cells during the intervals between doses of chemotherapy or radiotherapy. Angiogenesis is not only an important role player in cancerogenesis of solid tumors, but interestingly, they also take part in liquid tumorigenesis like leukemia and myeloma [3], which is something surprising at the first glance. Leukemic cells have a tendency to grow nearby vessels and thalidomide induces responses in around 30% of heavily pre-treated myeloma patients [3]. They may even be used for prevention of cancers in future. They may also be used in combination with other biological agents with anti-growth and anti-metastatic features. It is also likely that they will have some roles in the management of non-neoplastic diseases where angiogenesis is a prominent feature like diabetic retinopathy and coronary artery disease.

Many anti-angiogenic molecules have been created by biotechnology and pharmaceutical companies (Table 2). They are produced by 1) identification of a target molecule and development of an antibody or a synthetic inhibitor to counteract (like anti-VEGF antibody), 2) discovery of anti-angiogenic properties of an already existing drug (like thalidomide and interferon) and 3) discovery of a specific endogenous anti-angiogenic molecule [3]. Anti-angiogenic scheduling of chemotherapy is another way of producing anti-angiogenic therapy.

VEGF Targeting

Targeting VEGF has been central in anti-angiogenic therapies since VEGF has a pivotal role in tumor angiogenesis. Either VEGF itself, or its receptors, or the downstream signalling pathway may be a target. It has five different biologically active isoforms; VEGF-A, VEGF-B, VEGF-C and VEGF-D, all of which function through the activation of 3 kinds of receptors (VEGFR-1, VEGFR-2 and VEGFR-3) [31]. The first clue for the anti-angiogenic effect of VEGF related mechanisms came from the experiment in which vessel density of xenograft tumors in nude mice was decreased when they were injected with anti-VEGF antibody [37]. Afterwards several other mechanisms targeting VEGF were explored like anti-HIF, VEGF anti-sense oligonucleotides, VEGF ribosomes, soluble VEGF receptors, expression of a dominant negative mutant of VEGF receptors in target endothelial cells, anti-VEGF receptor antibodies, VEGF receptor mediated downstream signalling pathways and VEGF DNA vaccines [37]. Almost all of these mechanisms worked [37]. At least 10 different compounds were under evaluation.

Table 2. List of some agents with an angiogenesis related mechnaism under evaluation. VEGF; *V*ascular *E*ndothelial *G*rowth *F*actor, FGF; *F*ibroblast *G*rowth *F*actor.

Compound	Mechanism	Company	Trial phase
Bevacizumab	AntiVEGF antibody	Genentech	Phase III
PTK787	VEGF antagonist	Novartis	Phase III
Thalidomide	Several mechanisms		Phase III
ZD6474	VEGF receptor	Astra Zeneca	Phase II
Macugen	AntiVEGF pegylated aptamer	Eyetech Pharmaceuticals	Phase II
phVEGF165	Gene transfer	-	Phase I/II
FGF-1		-	Phase I/II
Angiostatin		-	Phase II
2-Methoxyestradiol-2		-	Phase I
Anakinra	Interleuin 1	-	Phase I
Endostatin		-	Phase I
Topical VEGF	VEGF	Genentech	Phase I
VEGF trap	Clearance of VEGF		Phase I

Anti-VEGF anti-body, bevacizumab (Avastin®) has been tested in several phase I and II trials for different types of cancers [7;38-43]. It was granted by fast tract status for the sake of its potential effectivity in first line treatment of colorectal cancer and was developed by Genentech and Roche [44].

In a phase I/II study by Cobleigh et al, 75 previously treated metastatic breast cancer patients were given bevacizumab at escalated doses ranging from 3 mg/kg to 20 mg/kg every other week [38]. Efficacy was assessed before 6th and 12th doses and safety before every administration. The most frequently encountered side effect was hypertension. The optimal dose was determined as 10 mg/kg every other week. In this single agent trial; stable disease or ongoing response was observed in 16% of patients [38].

In another phase II study by Burstein and co-workers, bevacizumab was combined with vinorelbine for 56 previously treated patients with advanced breast cancer and a response rate of 30% was obtained without significant toxicity [45].

An Eastern Cooperative Oncology Group (ECOG) trial, E200 is comparing paclitaxel 90 mg/m2 weekly (3 weeks, 1 week off) plus bevacizumab 10 mg/kg every other week with paclitaxel at the same dose and schedule alone [40]. A total of 685 patients with metastatic breast cancer will be enrolled to achieve a power of 83% to identify an improvement in the time to progression from 6 months in patients treated with paclitaxel to 8 months in patients receiving paclitaxel plus bevacizumab [40].

Kabinavvar et al demonstrated efficacy of bevacizumab in combination with chemotherapy in the setting of metastatic colorectal cancer [7]. Previously untreated 104 metastatic colorectal cancer patients were randomized to one of the 3 arms by an almost 1/1/1 ratio: 1) Fluorouracil (FU) 500 mg/m^2 plus leucovorin (LV) 500 mg/m^2 alone, or (2) in combination with low dose bevacizumab (5 mg/kg every 2 weeks, and (3) in combination with high dose bevacizumab (10 mg/kg at same intervals). Bevacizumab in combination with chemotherapy produced higher response rates (17% vs. 40 and 24%), longer median time to progression (5.2 vs. 9 and 7.2 months) and longer median overall survival (13.8 vs. 21.5 and 16.1 months). However, thrombosis, hypertension and bleeding were important concerns [7;46]. Authors decided to incorporate low dose warfarin in the next phase III trial [7].

Yang and co-workers applied 3 or 10 mg/kg bevacizumab single agent every other week or placebo to 116 patients with metastatic renal cell carcinoma in randomized phase II study [42]. Time to disease progression and response rates were the primary end points. They experienced minimal side effects mostly hypertension or mild proteinuria. Time to disease progression was significantly prolonged compared to placebo group (hazard ratio 2.55), while the difference between low dose and placebo group was minimal (hazard ratio 1.26). The probability of being progression-free for patients given high-dose antibody, low-dose--antibody, and placebo was 64 percent, 39 percent, and 20 percent, respectively, at four months and 30 percent, 14 percent, and 5 percent at eight months. At the last analysis, there were no significant differences in overall survival among groups.

Cancer and Leukemia Group B is carrying out a phase III trial, which will compare interferon alpha-2b alone with in interferon alpha-2b plus bevacizumab in 700 patients randomized to each arm by a 1:1 ratio.

Bevacizumab has been associated with hemorrhage, thrombosis/embolism, hypertension and proteinuria in clinical trials. Therefore ECOG is monitoring its toxicity in colorectal (E2200 and E3200), breast (E2100), and non-squamous non-small cell lung cancer (E4599) [47]. Of 519 patients treated with bevacizumab, there were only 3 bleeding related deaths. Proteinuria was uncommon and never over grade II. Contribution of bevacizumab to bleeding and hypertension was suggested, but low. Relationship to thrombosis is not supported by the current phase III data [47].

VEGF receptor represents another target in VEGF-related mechanisms. In a study, antibody to VEGFR1 (flt1) was tested in B non-Hodgkin lymphoma cells [48].

VEGF trap is another mechanism. It is a fusion protein consisting of portions of VEGFR1 and VEGFR2 (KDR) extracellular domains fused to the Fc portion of human immunoglobin G1, which acts by binding to VEGF in the circulation and tissues. It has a 100 fold higher affinity for VEGF than monoclonal antibodies and it is fully composed of human proteins in contrast to humanized antibodies [49]. In a phase I study by Dupont and co-workers, VEGF trap is given at 6 weeks intervals subcutaneously to 14 patients at 4 dose levels ranging from 25 mcg/kg to 200 mcg/kg [49]. There were no significant grade III and IV toxicities. Only reversible proteinuria, fatigue and constipation up to grade II were observed.

It is beyond the scope of this chapter to touch on all the clinical data. At least 37 trials are open to test the effectivity of bevacizumab in the treatment of cancer including leukemias. Of them, 6 is phase III study. For those who are interested in ongoing trials, the National Cancer Institute (NCI) web site www.clinicaltrials.govis a good source. With the exception of 2 trials on small cell lung cancer and colorectal cancer which completed accrual, all are recruiting patients. Within several years, they will elucidate the role of bevacizumab more clearly in the treatment of cancer.

Endostatin Targeting

Endostatin targeting is not in the center of trials exploring anti-angiogenic therapies. Therefore expected data to be generated in near future will probably be limited. Preclinical data released clues that endostatin as target of anti-angiogenesis might work [50-53]. A phase I trial which completed accrual of 30 patients to determine the optimal dose and schedule of endostatin is sponsored by NCI. Endostatin will be administered over 20 minutes at 6 dose levels and patients will be followed for dose limiting toxicity for 1 month [54].

Angiostatin Targeting

Clinical research on angiostatin targeting has not gained acceleration as endostatin. Preclinical data indicate that angiostatin targeting may work in clinical studies [50;55-57]. It was shown that a shift in the balance of tumor angiogenesis by gene transfer of a cDNA coding for mouse angiostatin into mouse squamous cell carcinoma NRS-1 and SCC-VII cells suppresses tumor growth in vivo [57]. The inhibition of an angiostatin-transfected tumor was accompanied by a marked reduction in vascularity and the presence of many apoptotic tumor cells without affecting the expression of VEGF and VEGF-R2 in the vascular endothelium [57].

In an interesting phase I trial which made use of in vivo generation angiostatin 4.5 by administrating tissue plasminogen activator (tPA) [58]. Angiostatin 4.5 is an internal fragment of plasminogen. It is converted to angiostatin 4.5 by a 2 step process. It is first converted to plasmin by an activator and then plasmin itself serves as an enzyme and substrate to form angiostatin 4.5 in the presence of a free sulfhydryl donor [58]. Authors hypothesized that administration of tPA with mesna could increase endogenous angiostatin 4.5. With tPA and mesna endogenous angiostain 4.5 level was increased and an angiostatin related protein was generated [58]

Recombinant human angiostatin was tested in the treatment of neuroendocrine tumors in a phase II trial [59]. Forty-one patients with advanced neuroendocrine tumors were treated with subcutaneous angiostatin at a dose of 60 $mg/m^2/d$ at 12 hour intervals for 8 weeks. A median of 24 weeks of treatment was administered. One patient with prior history of coronary artery disease experienced myocardial infarction. Of 37 evaluable patients, 5 (5%) had minor radiological response, 23 (62%) stable disease and 12 (32%) progressive disease. Median time to tumor progression was 39 weeks.

Anti-Angiogenic Scheduling of Chemotherapy

In order for a chemotherapeutic agent to act upon malignant cell, it must traverse endothelial cells. Why not choosing endothelial cells as a target? During classical chemotherapy scheduling endothelial cells are also exposed to cytotoxicity; however they probably recover fast like gastrointestinal and hematopoietic cells. It is logical to expect to pose more cytotoxicity on endothelial cells when chemotherapy is applied at lower doses but more frequently, which is actually what is called anti-angiogenic scheduling of chemotherapy [3]. Preclinical data supported its effectiveness even in chemoresistant tumor cells [3]. Endothelial cells appear to be 10-100 fold more sensitive than tumor cells to taxanes, docetaxel being more potent in this respect [60]. Several phase II studies confirm the effectiveness of this approach.

Other Angiogenesis Inhibitors

Interferon

Interferon alpha has long been known to have anti-angiogenic properties. It acts by inhibiting overproduction of bFGF by tumor cells [3]. Successful treatment of pulmonary hemangiomatosis in a child in 1988 was the first clinical anti-angiogenic therapy [3]. This observation was also confirmed by subsequent case reports. Later on, expression of mRNA of VEGF and bFGF were shown in surgical excision specimens of hemangiomas [61]. Folkman mentions their experience in 74 infants with hemangioma resistant to other therapies, giant cell tumor and angioblastoma [3]. Other investigators also confirm their observation [62;63] and we also treat such hemangiomas with low dose interferon at our hospital. Interferon is also used in the treatment of chronic myelogenous leukemia, multiple myeloma, low grade non-Hodgkin's lymphoma and neuroendocrine tumors. Its action may be partially related to anti-angiogenic effect in above settings. It is important to note that above listed diseases are of low grade proliferative potential.

Thalidomide

It is a sedative and anti-emetic agent originally used for hyperemesis gravidarum but abandoned later on for birth defect it had induced. Its anti-angiogenic effect was discovered afterwards and gained popularity in that respect. Its anti-angiogenic effect is probably related to what it had once caused in intrauterine life [3]. It show anti-angiogenic effect by inhibiting angiogenesis stimulated by bFGF and VEGF, by inhibiting tumor necrosis factor alpha and cyclooxygenase-2, modifying ICAM and extracellular matrix [64]. Its effectiveness was well established in a study on 84 patients with refractory myeloma [65]. Of them, 76 patients had relapsed after high dose chemotherapy with autologous stem cell support. Thalidomide was initiated at 200 mg/day and gradually increased to 800 mg/day. In 32% of patients paraprotein levels decreased with thalidomide therapy by at least 25%. Paraprotein response was associated with a decreased number of plasma cells in bone marrow and increased hemoglobin levels, while microvessel density remained the same [65]. At least 33% of the patients had mild or moderate constipation, weakness or fatigue, or somnolence. After 12 months of follow-up, Kaplan-Meier estimates of the mean (+/-SE) rates of event-free survival and overall survival for all patients were 22(+/-5)% and 58(+/-5)%, respectively. There have been phase II trials exploring its place in the management of prostate cancer and coronary artery.

Cyclooxygenase-2 Inhibitors (Cox2 Inhibitors)

Cyclooxygenase is an enzyme involved in prostaglandin synthesis. Eicosanoid biosynthesis is usually started by the activation of phospholipase A2 and the release of arachidonic acid from membrane phospholipids in response to the interaction of a stimulus with a receptor on the cell surface. Arachidonic acid is subsequently transformed by the enzyme cyclooxygenase (COX) to prostaglandins (PGs) and thromboxane (TX) [66]. Cyclooxygenase is found in 2 distinct forms 1 and 2. Cyclooxygenase-2 (Cox2) is inducible and associated with inflammation [66]. It contributes to cancerogenesis [67]. One mechanism is involvement of angiogenesis [68]. Its expression is well-correlated with that of VEGF and microvessel density in hepatitis B virus induced hepatocellular carcinoma cell [68]. It is also over expressed in many cancers including cervical cancer, lung cancer, colorectal cancer and breast cancer [69-73]. Non-steroidal anti-inflammatory drugs may induce apoptosis by cyclooxygenase independent mechanisms, as well [74].

Large scale retrospective and prospective population-based studies have shown that the use of both non-selective, non-steroidal anti-inflammatory drugs and selective COX-2 inhibitors decreased colorectal cancer incidence and mortality rate [75]. They provide significant risk reductions in prevention of colorectal cancers [76]. In familial adenomatosis poliposis coli, celecoxib 400 mg twice a day resulted in 28% risk reduction in number of colon polyps [77]. In those individuals with colonic adenomas, both 81 mg day and 325 mg day aspirin caused significant risk reductions (19% and 4%, respectively) in overall and 41% and 17% in those with polyps larger than or equal to 1 cm [78]. A study which randomized patients with previous colorectal cancer to receive 325 mg Aspirin a day or placebo found a 35% absolute risk reduction in developing colonic polyps in about a year [79]. Animal studies provide strong evidence that prevention of intestinal tumors is more efficiently accomplished by COX-2 selective inhibition rather than by COX-1 suppression [75].

Cox-2 inhibitors are currently under evaluation combination with radiotherapy and chemotherapy, either concomitantly or sequentially. However, two important member of this family, namely celecoxib and rofecoxib have recently been retracted from the market soon after emerged data indicating that they significantly increased cardiac complications. Their fate in oncology is currently uncertain.

Other Anti-Angiogenic Agents

Squalamine

Derived from the liver of dogfish shark, it is an aminosterol which has a potent anti-angiogenic effect by reducing intracellular pH of endothelial cells, a unique mechanism [64]. It passed phase I trials and a phase II trial completed patient accrual.

Angiotensin Converting Enzyme Inhibitors [ACEI] and Angiotensin-II Type 1 Receptor Antagonists (Sartans)

These agents have long been in use for hypertension, congestive heart failure and reversal of left ventricular hypertrophy. They resulted in significant risk reduction in mortality in above conditions. Compared to agents used in oncology, they are relatively free of side effects and cheap. They act upon renin-angiotensin system, found in many tissues with important functions, which was originally thought to be present only in kidneys [80]. This system is also found in bone marrow microenvironment regulating hematopoiesis [81]. By increasing concentration of a negative hematopoietic regular, goralatide (AcSDKP), they can also protect hematopoietic cells from radiation and chemotherapy, which may enable clinicians to by-pass hematological toxicity [81]. They potentially have anti-angiogenic, anti-metastatic and anti-growth effect on tumors [80].

Bisphosphonates

Bisphosphonates are agents used to prevent pathological bone fractures and bone pain secondary to malignant infiltration in oncology. They are also used in the treatment of osteoporosis. Apart from being an anti-resorptive agent, they have anti-angiogenic, anti-tumoral and pro-apoptotic properties [82;83]. Santini and co-workers studied the effect of single 4 mg zoledronic acid administration on serum levels of VEGF and platelet derived growth factor (PDGF) after 1, 2, 7 and 21 days in 30 consecutive cancer patients [82]. It lowered VEGF by at least 23% for 21 days and PDGF by 25% for 2 days. My colleagues and I also studied the effect of single 4 mg zoledronic acid on serum levels of VEGF and bFGF in 20 consecutive patients with metastatic bone disease or paraneoplastic hypercalcemia [84]. While we did not observe any difference in mean levels of VEGF after 72 hours, we observed a trend for lowering bFGF.

Low Molecular Weight Heparin

Previous in this chapter it was stated that hemostatic system is closely linked to angiogenesis. Anti-coagulation therapy may be an anti-angiogenic therapy as well. It also my prevent tumor cells in the circulation from escaping immune surveillance, since it was thought that they may be coated with coagulum. Icli and co-workers conducted a case control study to compare a low molecular weight heparin in combination with gemcitabine and cisplatin with gemcitabine and cisplatin alone in 17 patients with advanced pancreatic cancer [85]. There are other clinical trials exploring low molecular weight heparins.

Angiogenesis in Non-Malignant Diseases

Diabetes

Retinal angiogenesis is central to pathogenesis of diabetic retinopathy [86]. Suppressed by hypoxia, pigment epithelium derived factor (PEDF) is a major anti-angiogenic factor in retina and changes of PEDG has been shown to induce new vessel formation in hypoxic eye in animal models [86]. Both retinal fluid concentration and immunohistochemical stain for PEDF retinal specimens was found to be lower in diabetic compared to non-diabetics [86]. VEGF and its receptor flt1 is operational in pathogenesis of retinopathy [87]. A common polymorphism in the 5'-untranslated region of the VEGF gene, C(-634)G polymorphism, is associated with diabetic retinopathy in type 2 diabetes [88]. VEGF levels were found to be significantly higher in vitreous of patients with proliferative and nonproliferative retinopathy [89]. Angiotensin-II is another vascular mitogen and it is also operational in diabetic retinopathy generation, additionally it also stimulate migration of retinal pericytes [90;91]. Pre-clinical data support that ACEI and sartans may be useful in preventing diabetic retinopathy [90-92]. Considering underlying pathophysiological mechanisms, anti-angiogenic therapy may improve or at least retard progression. Currently, 2 phase II trials are undergoing on anti-VEGF related mechanism in proliferative retinopathy.

Ischemic Heart Disease

How ischemic myocardium adaptation to ischemia is also related to local angiogenesis together with pre-existing collaterals which open in response [93]. These collaterals turn into arteries through a process called arteriogenesis [93]. Therapeutic angiogenesis is a hot topic in the management of ischemic heart disease. There is a large body of evidence supporting its potential effect [94;95]. Angiogenic treatment is considered a "biological bypass" and early clinical trials of giving pro-angiogenic factors locally showed improvement in angina symptoms and exercise tolerance time together with objective evidences of improved perfusion, left ventricular function and angiographic appearance [96]. The most often utilized pro-angiogenic proteins are VEGF and FGF [97].

In 59 patients with coronary artery disease that was not amenable to mechanical revascularization, effect of increasing doses of intracoronary or intravascular FGF-2 was evaluated by positron emission tomography at baseline, on 29th, 57th and 180th day [98]. Thirty-seven patients had improved resting coronary perfusion.

Conclusion

Angiogenesis is gaining a firm place in the treatment of malignancies. That anti-angiogenic agents are relatively non-toxic in comparison to conventional cytotoxic therapies makes them an attractive treatment modality. Lack of cumulative toxicity enables a patient to take them indefinitely unless their neoplasms become unresponsive. They can be used in conjunction with, before and after conventional cytotoxic therapies and also with other anti-growth and anti-metastatic agents. Genomic medicine will probably enable us to better tailor a cocktail of those agents for a particular type of cancer. We are not yet hoping that our biological agents will cure cancer; however biological therapies will ultimately turn cancer into a chronic disease like diabetes mellitus and hypertension. Think of a patient with inoperable non-small cell lung cancer who is taking an anticancer drug for 20 years. We must not forget that the word "mellitus" literally means lethal, but nobody considers diabetes mellitus lethal no more.

As angiogenesis will be an important crossroads for not only management of malignant diseases but also for non-malignant ones. Wherever angiogenesis has a role, there will be a role for anti- or pro-angiogenic agents, too.

References

[1] Korpelainen EI, Alitalo K. Signaling angiogenesis and lymphangiogenesis. *Curr Opin Cell Biol* 1998;10:159-64.

[2] Plate K. From angiogenesis to lymphangiogenesis. *Nat Med* 2001;7:151-52.

[3] Folkman J. Tumor Angiogenesis. In: Bast RC, Kufe DW, Pollock RE, Weichselbaum RR, Holland JF, Frei E, eds. Cancer Medicine. 5th ed. Hamilton: B.C. Decker Inc; 2000: 132-52.

[4] Folkman J. Anti-angiogenesis: new concept for therapy of solid tumors. *Ann Surg* 1972;175:409-16.

[5] Rak J, Yu JL. Oncogenes and tumor angiogenesis: The question of vascular 'supply' and vascular 'demand'. *Semin Cancer Biol* 2003;14:93-104.

[6] Mukhopadhyay D, Kaustubb Datta. Multiple regulatory pathways of vascular permeability factor/vascular endothelial growth factor (VPF/VEGF) expression in tumors. *Semin Cancer Biol* 2004;14:123-30.

[7] Kabbinavar F, Hurwitz HI, Fehrenbacher L, Meropol NJ, Novotny WF, Lieberman G et al. Phase II, randomized trial comparing bevacizumab plus fluorouracil (FU)/leucovorin (LV) with FU/LV alone in patients with metastatic colorectal cancer. *J Clin Oncol* 2003;21:60-65.

[8] Kato T, Kimura T, Takami N, Miyakawa R, Tanaka S, Muraki H et al. New Prognostic Factors Associated with Long-term Survival in Node-Negative Breast Cancer Patients. *Breast Cancer* 1999;6:370-377.

[9] Toi M, Bando H, Kuroi K. The predictive value of angiogenesis for adjuvant therapy in breast cancer. *Breast Cancer* 2000;7:311-14.

[10] Cox G, Jones JL, Walker RA, Steward WP, O'Byrne KJ. Angiogenesis and non-small cell lung cancer. *Lung Cancer* 2000;27:81-100.

[11] Cox G, Walker RA, Andi A, Steward WP, O'Byrne KJ. Prognostic significance of platelet and microvessel counts in operable non-small cell lung cancer. *Lung Cancer* 2000;29:169-77.

[12] Buchler P, Reber HA, Buchler MW, Friess H, Hines OJ. VEGF-RII influences the prognosis of pancreatic cancer. *Ann Surg* 2002;236:738-49.

[13] Folkman J, Merler E, Abernathy C, Williams G. Isolation of a tumor factor responsible or angiogenesis. *J Exp Med* 1971;133:275-88.

[14] Harris AL. Hypoxia--a key regulatory factor in tumour growth. *Nat Rev Cancer* 2002;2:38-47.

[15] Arbiser ZK. Molecular regulation of angiogenesis and tumorigenesis by signal transduction pathways: evidence of predictable and reproducible patterns of synergy in diverse neoplasms. *Semin Cancer Biol* 2004;14:81-91.

[16] Yoon SO, Park SJ, Yun CH, Chung AS. Roles of matrix metalloproteinases in tumor metastasis and angiogenesis. *J Biochem Mol Biol* 2003;36:128-37.

[17] Chang C, Werb Z. The many faces of metalloproteases: cell growth, invasion, angiogenesis and metastasis. *Trends in Cell Biology* 2001;11:37-43.

[18] Foda HD, Zucker S. Matrix metalloproteinases in cancer invasion, metastasis and angiogenesis. *Drug Discov Today* 2001;6:478-82.

[19] Folkman J. Angiogenesis and apoptosis. Semin Cancer Biol 2003;13:159-67.

[20] Nash GF, Walsh DC, Kakkar AK. The role of the coagulation system in tumour angiogenesis. *Lancet Oncol* 2001;2:608-13.

[21] Alexandrakis MG, Passam FH, Sfiridaki K, Moschandrea J, Pappa C, Liapi D et al. Interleukin-18 in multiple myeloma patients: serum levels in relation to response to treatment and survival. *Leuk Res* 2004;28:259-66.

[22] Barandon L, Couffinhal T, Dufourcq P, Ezan J, Costet P, Daret D et al. Frizzled A, a novel angiogenic factor: promises for cardiac repair. *Eur J Cardiothorac Surg* 2004;25:76-83.

[23] Chen E, Hermanson S, Ekker SC. Syndecan-2 is essential for angiogenic sprouting during zebrafish development. *Blood* 2004;103:1710-1719.

[24] Chung CH, Wu WB, Huang TF. Aggretin, a snake venom-derived endothelial integrin {alpha}2{beta}1 agonist, induces angiogenesis via expression of vascular endothelial growth factor. *Blood* 2004;103:2105-13.

[25] Cominetti MR, Terruggi CH, Ramos OH, Fox JW, Mariano-Oliveira A, De Freitas MS et al. Alternagin-C, a disintegrin-like protein, induces vascular endothelial cell growth factor (VEGF) expression and endothelial cell proliferation in vitro. *J Biol Chem* 2004;279:18247-55.

[26] Doggrell SA, Wanstall JC. Vascular chymase: pathophysiological role and therapeutic potential of inhibition. *Cardiovasc Res* 2004;61:653-62.

[27] Fernandez-Sauze S, Delfino C, Mabrouk K, Dussert C, Chinot O, Martin PM et al. Effects of adrenomedullin on endothelial cells in the multistep process of angiogenesis: involvement of CRLR/RAMP2 and CRLR/RAMP3 receptors. *Int J Cancer* 2004;108:797-804.

[28] Shing Y, Folkman J, Sullivan R, Butterfield C, Murray J, Klagsbrun M. Heparin affinity: purification of a tumor-derived capillary endothelial cell growth factor. *Science* 1984;223:1296-99.

[29] Cronauer MV, Schulz WA, Seifert HH, Ackermann R, Burchardt M. Fibroblast growth factors and their receptors in urological cancers: basic research and clinical implications. *Eur Urol* 2003;43:309-19.

[30] Loughna S, Sato T. Angiopoietin and Tie receptor in vascular development. Matrix *Biology*. 2001;319-25.

[31] Cao Y. Anti-angiogenic cancer therapy. *Semin Cancer Biol* 2004;14:139-45.

[32] Rehn M, Veikkola T, Kukk-Valdre E, Nakamura H, Ilmonen M, Lombardo C et al. Interaction of endostatin with integrins implicated in angiogenesis. *Proc Natl Acad Sci U S A* 2001;98:1024-29.

[33] Saarela J, Ylikarppa R, Rehn M, Purmonen S, Pihlajaniemi T. Complete primary structure of two variant forms of human type XVIII collagen and tissue-specific differences in the expression of the corresponding transcripts. *Matrix Biol.* 1998;16:319-28.

[34] Hohenester E, Sasaki T, Olsen BR, Timpl R. Crystal structure of the angiogenesis inhibitor endostatin at 1.5 A resolution. *EMBO J* 1998;17:1656-64.

[35] Sasaki T, Larsson H, Tisi D, Claesson-Welsh L, Hohenester E, Timpl R. Endostatins derived from collagens XV and XVIII differ in structural and binding properties, tissue distribution and anti-angiogenic activity. *J Mol Biol* 2000;301:1179-90.

[36] Suzuki M, Lizasa T, Ko E, Baba M, Saitoh Y, Shibuya K et al. Serum endostatin correlates with progression and prognosis of non-small cell lung cancer. *Lung Cancer* 2002;35:29-34.

[37] Kim KJ, Li B, Winer J, Armanini M, Gillett N, Phillips HS et al. Inhibition of vascular endothelial growth factor-induced angiogenesis suppresses tumour growth in vivo. *Nature* 1993;362:841-44.

[38] Cobleigh MA, Langmuir VK, Sledge GW, Miller KD, Haney L, Novotny WF et al. A phase I/II dose-escalation trial of bevacizumab in previously treated metastatic breast cancer. *Semin Oncol* 2003;30:117-24.

[39] Fernando NH, Hurwitz HI. Inhibition of vascular endothelial growth factor in the treatment of colorectal cancer. *Semin Oncol* 2003;30:39-50.

[40] Miller KD. E2100: a phase III trial of paclitaxel versus paclitaxel/bevacizumab for metastatic breast cancer. *Clin Breast Cancer* 2003;3:421-22.
[41] Sonpavde G. Bevacizumab in renal-cell cancer. *N Engl J Med* 2003;349:1674.
[42] Yang JC, Haworth L, Sherry RM, Hwu P, Schwartzentruber DJ, Topalian SL et al. A randomized trial of bevacizumab, an anti-vascular endothelial growth factor antibody, for metastatic renal cancer. *N Engl J Med* 2003;349:427-34.
[43] Willett CG, Boucher Y, di Tomaso E, Duda DG, Munn LL, Tong RT et al. Direct evidence that the VEGF-specific antibody bevacizumab has antivascular effects in human rectal cancer. *Nat Med.* 2004;10:145-47.
[44] Salgaller ML. Technology evaluation: bevacizumab, Genentech/Roche. *Curr Opin Mol Ther* 2003;5:657-67.
[45] Burstein H, Parker L, SJea. Phase II trial of the anti-VEGF antibody bevacizumab in combination with vinorelbine for refractory advanced breast cancer. *Breast Cancer Res Treat* 2002;76:115.
[46] Kilickap S, Abali H, Celik I. Bevacizumab, bleeding, thrombosis, and warfarin. *J Clin Oncol* 2003;21:3542.
[47] Gray R, Giantonio BJ, O'Dwyer PJ, Sandler A, Miller K, Comis, RL. The safety of adding angiogenesis inhibition into treatment for colorectal, breast, lung cancer: The Eastern Cooperative Oncology Group's [ECOG] experience with bevacizumab (anti-VEGF). *Proc Am Soc Clin Oncol* 22, 206. 2003 (abstract).
[48] Wang ES, Zang K, Teruya-Feldstein J, Zhu D, Hicklin D, Witte L et al. Anti-VEGF receptor antibodies inhibit the growth of non-hodgkin's lymphoma and enhance the effects of chemotherapy or rituximab in lymphoma xenograft mouse model. *Proc Am Soc Clin Oncol 22*, 210. 2003 (abstract).
[49] Dupont J, Camastra MS, Gordon MS, Mendelson J, Murren J, Hsu A et al. Phase I study of VEGF Trap in patients with solid tumors and lymphoma. *Proc Am Soc Clin Oncol 22*, 194. 2003 (abstract).
[50] Ponnazhagan S, Mahendra G, Kumar S, Shaw DR, Stockard CR, Grizzle WE et al. Adeno-associated virus 2-mediated anti-angiogenic cancer gene therapy: long-term efficacy of a vector encoding angiostatin and endostatin over vectors encoding a single factor. *Cancer Res* 2004;64:1781-87.
[51] Tee D, Di Stefano J. Simulation of tumor-induced angiogenesis and its response to anti-angiogenic drug treatment: mode of drug delivery and clearance rate dependencies. *J Cancer Res Clin Oncol* 2004;130:15-24.
[52] Bjerkvig R, Read TA, Vajkoczy P, Aebischer P, Pralong W, Platt S et al. Cell therapy using encapsulated cells producing endostatin. *Acta Neurochir Suppl* 2003;88:137-41.
[53] Chen W, Fu J, Liu Q, Ruan C, Xiao S. Retroviral endostatin gene transfer inhibits human colon cancer cell growth in vivo. *Chin Med J (Engl)* 2003;116:1582-84.
[54] Endostatin in Treating Patients With Advanced Solid Tumors. http://clinicaltrials.gov/ct/gui/search?term=endostatin&submit=Search . 2004.
[55] Chen YH, Wu HL, Chen CK, Huang YH, Yang BC, Wu LW. Angiostatin antagonizes the action of VEGF-A in human endothelial cells via two distinct pathways. *Biochem Biophys Res Commun* 2003;310:804-10.
[56] Hari D, Beckett MA, Sukhatme VP, Dhanabal M, Nodzenski E, Lu H et al. Angiostatin induces mitotic cell death of proliferating endothelial cells. *Mol Cell Biol Res Commun* 2000;3:277-82.

[57] Matsumoto G, Ohmi Y, Shindo J. Angiostatin gene therapy inhibits the growth of murine squamous cell carcinoma in vivo. *Oral Oncol* 2001;37:369-78.

[58] Kuzel T, Martone B, Avram M, Rademaker A, Benson A, Soff G. In vivo generation of angiostatin4.5 (AS4.5)-phase I trial of tissue plasminogen activator (tPA) plus mesna. *Proc Am Soc Clin Oncol* 2003;22:219 (abstract).

[59] Kulke M, Bergsland E, Ryan DP, Clark JW, Enzinger PC, Michellini A et al. A phase II, open label, safety, pharmacokinetic and efficacy study of recombinant human endostatin in patients with advanced neuroendocrine tumors. *Proc Am Soc Clin Oncol* 2003;22:239 (abstract).

[60] Grant DS, Williams TL, Zahaczewsky M, Dicker AP. Comparison of antiangiogenic activities using paclitaxel (taxol) and docetaxel (taxotere). *Int J Cancer* 2003;104:121-29.

[61] Chang J, Most D, Bresnick S, Mehrara B, Steinbrech DS, Reinisch J et al. Proliferative hemangiomas: analysis of cytokine gene expression and angiogenesis. *Plast Reconstr Surg* 1999;103:1-9.

[62] Kaban LB, Mulliken JB, Ezekowitz RA, Ebb D, Smith PS, Folkman J. Antiangiogenic therapy of a recurrent giant cell tumor of the mandible with interferon alfa-2a. *Pediatrics* 1999;103:1145-49.

[63] Powell J. Update on hemangiomas and vascular malformations. *Curr Opin Pediatr* 1999;11:457-63.

[64] Sridhar SS, Shepherd FA. Targeting angiogenesis: a review of angiogenesis inhibitors in the treatment of lung cancer. *Lung Cancer* 2003;42 (Suppl 1):81-91.

[65] Singhal S, Mehta J, Desikan R, Ayers D, Roberson P, Eddlemon P et al. Antitumor activity of thalidomide in refractory multiple myeloma. *N Engl J Med* 1999;341:1565-71.

[66] Claria J. Cyclooxygenase-2 biology. *Curr Pharm Des* 2003;9:2177-90.

[67] Sato T, Yoshinaga K, Okabe S, Okawa T, Enomoto M, Takizawa T et al. Cyclooxygenase-2 expression in colorectal adenomas. *Dis Colon Rectum* 2003;46:786-92.

[68] Cheng AS, Chan HL, To KF, Leung WK, Chan KK, Liew CT et al. Cyclooxygenase-2 pathway correlates with vascular endothelial growth factor expression and tumor angiogenesis in hepatitis B virus-associated hepatocellular carcinoma. *Int J Oncol* 2004;24:853-60.

[69] Castelao JE, Bart RD, Diperna CA, Sievers EM, Bremner RM. Lung cancer and cyclooxygenase-2. *Ann Thorac Surg* 2003;76:1327-35.

[70] Chan TA. Cyclooxygenase inhibition and mechanisms of colorectal cancer prevention. *Curr Cancer Drug Targets* 2003;3:455-63.

[71] Chen YJ, Wang LS, Wang PH, Lai CR, Yen MS, Ng HT et al. High cyclooxygenase-2 expression in cervical adenocarcinomas. *Gynecol Oncol* 2003;88:379-85.

[72] Cianchi F, Cortesini C, Fantappie O, Messerini L, Sardi I, Lasagna N et al. Cyclooxygenase-2 activation mediates the proangiogenic effect of nitric oxide in colorectal cancer. *Clin Cancer Res* 2004;10:2694-704.

[73] Denkert C, Winzer KJ, Hauptmann S. Prognostic impact of cyclooxygenase-2 in breast cancer. *Clin Breast Cancer* 2004;4:428-33.

[74] Babbar N, Ignatenko NA, Casero RA, Gerner EW. Cyclooxygenase-independent induction of apoptosis by sulindac sulfone is mediated by polyamines in colon cancer. *J Biol Chem* 2003;278:47762-75.

[75] Stoehlmacher J, Lenz HJ. Cyclooxygenase-2 inhibitors in colorectal cancer. *Semin Oncol* 2003;30:10-16.

[76] Rahme E, Barkun AN, Toubouti Y, Bardou M. The cyclooxygenase-2-selective inhibitors rofecoxib and celecoxib prevent colorectal neoplasia occurrence and recurrence. *Gastroenterology* 2003;125:404-12.

[77] Steinbach G, Lynch P, Phillips RKS, Wallace MH, Hawk E, Gordon G et al. The effect of celecoxib, a cyclooxygenase-2 inhibitor, in familial adenomatous polyposis. *N Engl J Med* 2000;342:1946-52.

[78] Baron JA, Cole BF, Sandler RS, Haile RW, Ahnen D, Bresalier R et al. A randomized trial of aspirin to prevent colorectal adenomas. *N Engl J Med* 2003;348:891-99.

[79] Sandler RS, Halabi S, Baron JA, Budinger S, Paskett E, Keresztes R et al. A randomized trial of aspirin to prevent colorectal adenomas in patients with previous colorectal cancer. *N Engl J Med* 2003;348:883-90.

[80] Abali H, Gullu IH, Engin H, Haznedaroglu IC, Erman M, Tekuzman G. Old antihypertensives as novel antineoplastics: angiotensin-I-converting enzyme inhibitors and angiotensin II type 1 receptor antagonists. *Med Hypotheses* 2002;59:344-48.

[81] Abali H, Haznedaroglu IC, Goker H, Celik I, Ozatli D, Koray Z et al. Circulating and local bone marrow renin-angiotensin system in leukemic hematopoiesis: preliminary evidences. *Hematology* 2002;7:75-82.

[82] Santini D, Vincenzi B, Dicuonzo G, Avvisati G, Massacesi C, Battistoni F et al. Zoledronic acid induces significant and long-lasting modifications of circulating angiogenic factors in cancer patients. *Clin Cancer Res* 2003;9:2893-97.

[83] Tassone P, Tagliaferri P, Viscomi C, Palmieri C, Caraglia M, D'Alessandro A et al. Zoledronic acid induces antiproliferative and apoptotic effects in human pancreatic cancer cells in vitro. *Br J Cancer* 2003;88:1971-78.

[84] Abali H, Altundag MK, Baltali E, Oral D, Canpinar H, Guc D, Celik I, Gullu I, Tekuzman G. Does zoledronic acid decrease serum levels of basic fibroblast growth factor and vascular endothelial growth factor? *Proc Am Soc Clin Oncol* 2003;22:215 (abstract).

[85] Icli F, Akbulut H, Utkan G, Dincol D, Isikdogan A, Demirkazik A et al. Low molecular weight heparin (LMWH) increases the efficacy of cisplatinum plus gemcitabine combination in advanced pancreatic cancer. *Proc Am Soc Clin Oncol* 2003;22:286 (abstract).

[86] Spranger J, Osterhoff M, Reimann M, Mohlig M, Ristow M, Francis MK et al. Loss of the antiangiogenic pigment epithelium-derived factor in patients with angiogenic eye disease. *Diabetes* 2001;50:2641-45.

[87] Takagi H, King GL, Aiello LP. Identification and characterization of vascular endothelial growth factor receptor (Flt) in bovine retinal pericytes. *Diabetes* 1996;45:1016-23.

[88] Awata T, Inoue K, Kurihara S, Ohkubo T, Watanabe M, Inukai K et al. A common polymorphism in the 5'-untranslated region of the VEGF gene is associated with diabetic retinopathy in type 2 diabetes. *Diabetes* 2002;51:1635-39.

[89] Duh EJ, Yang HS, Haller JA, De Juan E, Humayun MS, Gehlbach P et al. Vitreous levels of pigment epithelium-derived factor and vascular endothelial growth factor: implications for ocular angiogenesis. *Am J Ophthalmol* 2004;137:668-74.

[90] Lonchampt M, Pennel L, Duhault J. Hyperoxia/normoxia-driven retinal angiogenesis in mice: a role for angiotensin II. *Invest Ophthalmol Vis Sci* 2001;42:429-32.

[91] Nadal JA, Scicli GM, Carbini LA, Nussbaum JJ, Scicli AG. Angiotensin II and retinal pericytes migration. *Biochem Biophys Res Commun* 1999;266:382-85.

[92] Walsh DA, Hu DE, Wharton J, Catravas JD, Blake DR, Fan TP. Sequential development of angiotensin receptors and angiotensin I converting enzyme during angiogenesis in the rat subcutaneous sponge granuloma. *Br J Pharmacol* 1997;120:1302-11.

[93] Buschmann I, Schaper W. The pathophysiology of the collateral circulation (arteriogenesis). *J Pathol* 2000;190:338-42.

[94] Freedman SB, Isner JM. Therapeutic angiogenesis for ischemic cardiovascular disease. *J Mol Cell Cardiol* 2001;33:379-93.

[95] Garcia L, Baim DS, Post M, Simons M, Laham RJ. Therapeutic Angiogenesis Using Endocardial Approach to Administration: Techniques and Results. *Curr Interv Cardiol Rep* 1999;1:222-27.

[96] Syed IS, Sanborn TA, Rosengart TK. Therapeutic angiogenesis: a biologic bypass. *Cardiology* 2004;101:131-43.

[97] Post MJ, Laham R, Sellke FW, Simons M. Therapeutic angiogenesis in cardiology using protein formulations. *Cardiovasc Res* 2001;49:522-31.

[98] Udelson JE, Dilsizian V, Laham RJ, Chronos N, Vansant J, Blais M et al. Therapeutic angiogenesis with recombinant fibroblast growth factor-2 improves stress and rest myocardial perfusion abnormalities in patients with severe symptomatic chronic coronary artery disease. *Circulation* 2000;102:1605-10.

In: New Angiogenesis Research
Editor: Roberta V. Zubar, pp. 257-277

ISBN 1-59454-239-2

Chapter XIV

Immunobiology and Regulatory Mechanisms of the Expression of Angiogenic and Angiostatic Factors in Arthritis Inflammation

Tsuyoshi Kasama, Nobuyuki Yajima, Fumitaka Shiozawa and Ryosuke Hanaoka
Division of Rheumatology and Clinical Immunology, First Department of Internal Medicine, Showa University School of Medicine, Tokyo

Abstract

The progression of synovitis in rheumatoid arthritis (RA) is characterized by a pronounced tumor-like expansion of the synovium. Neovascularization, which may play a pivotal role during progression of the disease, is a complex process involving endothelial cell division, selective degradation of vascular basement membranes and the surrounding extracellular matrix, and endothelial cell migration. The involvement of several types of endogenous molecules has been purported based on the ability of these molecules to regulate the proliferation of endothelial cells. Moreover, a number of angiogenic and angiostatic factors may be important in promoting neovascularization which is present around sites of chronic inflammation. These include vascular endothelial growth factor (VEGF), fibroblast growth factor (FGF), transforming growth factor β (TGF-β), angiopoietins and CXC chemokines such as IL-8 and interferon gamma-inducible protein 10 (IP-10). This review will discuss the biology of these angiogenic and angiostatic factors, and their expression and regulation in the context of chronic inflammatory arthritis such as RA and experimental arthritis such as collagen-induced arthritis.

Introduction

The progression of rheumatoid arthritis (RA) is characterized by development of the inflammatory pannus. This tumor-like expansion of the synovium, which is primarily the result of an over-proliferation of synoviocytes, is the histologic hallmark of RA [1, 2]. Its formation is associated with infiltration of inflammatory and immune cells and with subsequent tissue destruction. Numerous mediators, including inflammatory cytokines and adhesion molecules, have been implicated in this process [3-5], and it is well known that neovascularization plays a pivotal role during the evolution of synovitis.

Neovascularization is a complex process involving endothelial cell (EC) division, selective degradation of vascular basement membranes and the surrounding extracellular matrix, and endothelial cell migration. Several polypeptide mediators have been identified based on their ability to stimulate proliferation of endothelial cells [6], some of which may act as angiogenic factors which are important for the neovascularization found in the RA joint. These include tumor necrosis factor (TNF)-α, fibroblast growth factor (FGF), interleukin (IL)-8 and transforming growth factor (TGF)-β [7, 8]. Another important mediator of neovascularization is vascular endothelial growth factor (VEGF), a heparin-binding, homodimeric glycoprotein secreted by several cell types, with a number of protein variants resulting from alternative mRNA splicing [9, 10].. In this review, we will focus upon the immunobiology of these angiogenic and angiostatic mediators and their expression and regulation during the evolution of arthritis inflammation, including RA and experimental arthritis.

Immunobiology of Mediators Regulating Angiogenesis

In this section, major angiomodulating mediators and their expressional regulation are discussed.

1. Angiogenic Factors

VEGF

VEGF is an endothelial cell-specific, heparin-binding mitogen *in vitro* and an angiogenic growth factor *in vivo* [9, 10]. VEGF was originally thought to be an endothelial cell-derived, angiogenic, autocrine factor, with several alternative splice variants, such as $VEGF_{121}$, $VEGF_{145}$, $VEGF_{165}$, $VEGF_{189}$ and $VEGF_{206}$ [9]. VEGF has been implicated in the stimulation of both normal physiological angiogenesis involved in wound healing, and pathological angiogenesis that underlies proliferative diabetic retinopathy and tumor growth [7, 11]. In addition to stimulating endothelial cell proliferation and chemotaxis, VEGF increases vascular permeability, hence its alternative name of vascular permeability factor, and induces the secretion of matrix metalloprotease (MMP)-1 [12, 13]. Both of these features may be relevant to the actions of VEGF in some pathological conditions such as tumor growth or RA, in that changes in vascular permeability may enhance tissue swelling, whereas stimulation of

MMP activity may be important in both tumor metastasis and cartilage destruction in RA [14]. Although the major cellular sources of VEGF were thought to be endothelial cells, recent reports have shown that fibroblasts [15-17], macrophages [18, 19], alveolar epithelial cells [20], vascular smooth muscle cells [21], polymorphonuclear neutrophils (PMNs) [22, 23] and even chondrocytes [24] also express significant amounts of VEGF. Expression of VEGF is known to be regulated by other mediators, including platelet-derived growth factor [25], TGF-β [26], IL-1 [17], oxygen radicals and nitric oxide [19, 27-29], and hypoxia [21, 28, 30].

Endothelial cells express two homologous VEGF receptors, VEGF-R1 [Fms-like tyrosine kinase 1(flt-1)] and VEGF-R2 [kinase domain region (KDR) or fetal liver kinase 1 (flk-1)], that can be activated by all VEGF isoforms. VEGF-R1 and VEGF-R2 belong to the platelet-derived growth factor receptor (PDGF-R) family of tyrosine kinase receptors and share a high structural similarity, having seven immunoglobulin-like domains [31]. VEGF-R1 and VEGF-R2 are expressed at low levels in endothelial cells under normal conditions, but are upregulated at sites where there is a concomitant upregulation of VEGF [32]. Activation of VEGF-R1 by VEGF does not efficiently induce migration of endothelial cells without simultaneous VEGF-R2 activation [31]. Nevertheless, a recent report showed that activated monocytes and even dendritic cells, which are antigen-presenting cells present at sites of inflammation, expressed only VEGF-R1 and not VEGF-R2 [33-35]. VEGF may thus induce monocyte activation and migration via VEGF-R1 [33, 36]..

FGF

The fibroblast growth factors (FGFs) are also potent angiogenic factors in vivo and in vitro (reviewed in ref. [37]). The two prototype factors are FGF-1, or acidic FGF, which is usually isolated in a 16–18 kDa form depending upon proteolysis, and FGF-2 or basic FGF, which generally has a molecular mass of 18 kDa but may exist in larger forms up to 24 kDa. FGF-2 was in effect the first purified growth factor shown to have angiogenic activity [38]. FGF-2 belongs to a multigene family with important roles in physiologic conditions as well as angiogenesis and wound repair in the mature organism. In contrast to VEGF, FGF-2 is a potent mitogen for many cell types, including fibroblasts, endothelial cells and smooth muscle cells, all of which express FGF receptors. The action of FGF-2 in the vessel wall is therefore not cell-type specific. FGF stimulates endothelial cell proliferation in vitro and angiogenesis in vivo. Furthermore, the combination of VEGF and FGF-2 in vitro represents the most potent angiogenic stimulus currently known. In addition, FGF-2 was found to upregulate the expression of VEGF [39], while the synergy demonstrated between hypoxia and FGF-2 suggests that multiple diverse stimuli may interact via the upregulation of VEGF expression in vascular smooth muscle cells to amplify the angiogenic response [40]. These results suggest that FGF-2 may promote angiogenesis both by a direct effect on endothelial cells and also indirectly by the upregulation of VEGF in certain cells.

TGF-β

TGF-β is a 25-kDa dimeric protein that functions as a potent growth differentiation regulatory cytokine involved in diverse tissue remodeling processes such as wound healing, tissue morphogenesis, tumor development, and angiogenesis [41]. It also possesses pleiotropic properties [42]; in addition to its effects on the immune system, it has the capacity to affect many other cell types in a variety of ways. TGF-β is produced in a latent form by virtually all cell types and must be activated in order to interact with its specific receptors, the transmembrane serine/threonine kinases, and subsequently to elicit a biological response.

The mechanism of the angiogenic effects of TGF-β *in vivo* are, however, controversial since TGF-β is a potent inhibitor of cultured endothelial cell proliferation in some circumstances [43, 44], but it promoted the growth of cells that formed cords [45]. Furthermore, TGF-β down-regulates the expression of bovine endothelial cell VEGF-R2, the major signal-transducing tyrosine kinase receptor for VEGF [46], giving rise to the inhibition (at nanogram/ml concentrations) of VEGF-induced angiogenesis *in vitro*. The observation that TGF-β is both a potent inducer and a potent inhibitor of angiogenesis has given rise to the concept that TGF-β may have either direct or indirect effects on promoting angiogenesis. Support for this concept of indirect angiogenesis is provided by the fact that TGF-β increases VEGF production *in vitro* in human smooth muscle cells, mouse fibroblasts, human lung adenocarcinoma cells, and human histiocytic lymphoma cells [41]. Moreover, hypoxia and TGF-β cooperate in the induction of the promoter activity of VEGF in endothelial cells, demonstrating that both TGF-β and hypoxia signaling pathways can act in synergy in the regulation of VEGF gene expression at the transcriptional level, in association with Sma- and Mad-related protein 3 (Smad3) [47].

The central importance of these growth factors in humans is underscored by the fact that many disease processes are associated with aberrant TGF-β function. Loss of normal TGF-β function has been implicated in the pathogenesis of cancer, atherosclerosis, and autoimmune and inflammatory diseases, while excessive TGF-β production has been implicated in fibroproliferative disorders, immunosuppression, successful parasite infection, and metastasis.

Angiopoietins

Angiopoietin-1 (Ang-1) is a more recently identified cytokine that stimulates neovascularization. The angiogenic peptides Ang-1 and 2, and their specific receptors Tie1 and Tie2, are involved in angiogenic processes occurring subsequent to the actions of VEGF and its receptors [48, 49]. Ang-1 regulates processes at a later stage of angiogenesis than does VEGF, which generates immature blood vessels and increases vessel wall permeability. Although Ang-2 modulates Ang-1-mediated vessel stabilization by competitively inhibiting the binding of Ang-1 to Tie2, resulting in an angiostatic factor, recent studies clearly demonstrate that Ang-2 may induce angiogenesis and subsequent tumor growth via interaction with VEGF-dependent pathways [50, 51]. Numerous studies have shown that Ang-1 activation of Tie2 results in EC migration ultimately leading to EC sprouting and tubule formation, and stabilization of the basement membrane [52, 53]. Although the Tie2 ligands Ang-1 and Ang-2 do not produce a mitogenic response in cultured ECs, they were shown to modulate VEGF-induced postnatal neovascularization. Regulation of Ang-2 and Tie-2 expression on ECs has been demonstrated by several groups, with an increased expression of Ang-2 transcripts seen in cultured human endometrial ECs stimulated by either VEGF or FGF, or under hypoxic conditions [54-56].

In contrast with Ang-2 expression, the literature contains conflicting reports regarding the effect of hypoxia on Tie-2 regulation. Willam et al. clearly demonstrated that hypoxia led to a time-dependent significant rise of Tie2 protein levels in human coronary microvascular ECs and dermal microvascular ECs (3.2- and 2.5-fold, respectively, within 24 hours), and induced a less-marked increase in human umbilical vein ECs (1.7-fold) [57]. On the other hand, Oh et al. did not observe any effect of hypoxia on Tie2 mRNA expression in bovine retinal or aortic ECs [55]. Moreover, Mandriota et al. described a downregulation of Tie2 mRNA (to 62% of control) in bovine adrenal microvascular ECs exposed to hypoxia [54]. These findings suggest that the hypoxia-induced stimulation of Tie-2 expression may be dependent on the origin of the ECs.

Further to the above, Yabkowitz et al. reported that TNF-α and VEGF stimulated the release of soluble Tie-1 from endothelial cells, and that the release of soluble Tie-1 was inhibited by the metalloprotease inhibitor; BB-24 [58]. The orphan tyrosine kinase receptor Tie-1 is thought to be important in vascular development where it appears to have roles in promoting vessel integrity and stability by modulating Tie-2 signaling [59, 60]. These results demonstrated that inflammatory cytokines and VEGF regulate Tie-1 expression on endothelial cells through the activation of a membrane-associated metalloprotease that releases soluble Tie from the cell surface.

In conclusion, enhanced regulation of Ang-2/Tie expression on ECs is modulated by hypoxia, VEGF, proinflammatory cytokines that include IL-1β and TNF-α, and PMA, suggesting their contribution to the angiogenic response in ischemic tissues and inflamed lesions.

IL-8

Chemokines belong to a gene superfamily of chemotactic cytokines that a share substantial homology of four conserved cysteine amino acid residues [61-63]. The CXC family of chemokines [e.g., IL-8, GRO and ENA-78], in which the first two cysteines are separated by a different amino acid residue, is chemotactic for neutrophils and T-cells, whereas the CC chemokine family (e.g., macrophage inflammatory protein-1, macrophage chemoattractant protein-1, and RANTES), in which the first two cysteine residues are juxtaposed, is chemotactic for monocytes and subpopulations of T-cells. Members of the CXC chemokine family are known to play an important role in the control of angiogenesis, which has been related to the Glu-Leu-Arg (ELR) sequence motif at their NH2 extremity [64].. In general, ELR-chemokines (IL-8, GRO, ENA-78) bind to neutrophils and act as angiogenetic factors, whereas non-ELR-chemokines [interferon gamma-inducible protein 10 (IP-10), monokine induced by IFN-γ (Mig), and IFN-inducible T-cell alpha chemoattractant (I-TAC)], which bind to lymphocytes, act as angiostatic factors [61, 65].

IL-8 has been widely investigated as a prototypic angiogenic chemokine. Significant expression of IL-8 by endothelial cells themselves and the ability of IL-8 to promote enhanced endothelial cell survival and proliferation have been substantiated in several studies [66, 67]. Evidence of directed endothelial cell migration *in vitro* in response to varying concentrations of IL-8 and of induced neovascularization in the rat cornea *in vivo*, supports the direct role that ELR-containing CXC chemokines play in mediating angiogenic activity [68, 69]. In contrast, CXC chemokines lacking the ELR motif, such as platelet factor (PF)-4, IP-10 and Mig, behave as potent angiostatic regulators of neovascularization, inhibiting not only the angiogenic activity of ELR-CXC chemokines, but also the structurally unrelated angiogenic factor, FGF-2. Thus, the ELR motif appears to be essential for dictating the angiogenic activity of the CXC chemokines.

2. Angiostatic Factors

IP-10

IP-10 is expressed and secreted by monocytes, fibroblasts and endothelial cells after stimulation with IFN-γ [61, 70], and plays an important role in the chemotaxis of activated T cells via interactions with a specific receptor, CXCR3 [64]. IP-10 also furthers the regression of angiogenesis, in contrast to IL-8 [71-74], as mentioned above. The angiostatic effects of IP-10 have been demonstrated in vitro and in vivo by numerous investigations. For example, a potent inhibitory effect of IP-10 on endothelial cell proliferation was previously shown by Luster, et al. [75], while it has been demonstrated that IP-10 inhibits endothelial cell differentiation into "tube-like" structures which constitutes a critical commitment stage in the formation of new blood vessels [76]. More recently, Romagnani and colleagues clearly demonstrated that CXCR3 is expressed on human endothelium, and that IP-10, Mig and I-TAC attenuate endothelial cell proliferation in a CXCR3-dependent manner [77]. In this latter study, it was revealed that alternative splicing of the CXCR3 gene generates two distinct receptors, termed CXCR3A and CXCR3B [77]. In contrast to CXCR3A, CXCR3B inhibited endothelial cell growth and chemotaxis in response to activation by IP-10 or PF-4. Non ELR-CXC chemokines, on the other hand, mediate the migration of CXCR3A-expressing pericytes and their proliferation around nascent vessels [77].. Further understanding of the regulation and differentiation of CXCR3A and CXCR3B may contribute to the development of therapeutic interventions in the treatment of aberrant angiogenesis via the targeting of CXCR3.

Recent evidence relating to the immune/inflammatory responses and pathogenesis of certain diseases indicates a significant correlation in the balance between T helper type 1 (Th1) and Th2 responses [78-80]. A Th1 /Th2 cytokine imbalance with a predominance of Th1 cytokines, including IFN-γ, is suggested to be of pathogenetic importance in autoimmune diseases such as RA and other conditions [81-83], while a predominance of Th2 cytokines, including IL-4, is important in allergic reactions, such as bronchial asthma [84]. Chemokine receptor expression may dictate the spectrum of action of chemokines, as shown for Th1 and Th2 cells. The Th1 phenotype expresses certain chemokine receptors, including CXCR3 and CCR5, whose agonists are IP-10 and MIP-1β, respectively [85, 86], while the Th2 phenotype expresses CCR4 and CCR8, agonists of which are thymus and activation-regulated chemokine (TARC), and macrophage derived chemokine (MDC) and MIP-1β, respectively.

In addition to the above, IL-12, which exerts a variety of immunoregulatory activities during inflammatory/immune responses, was reported to promote anti-angiogenic activity [87, 88]. A neutralizing antibody to IP-10 substantially reduced the inhibition of angiogenesis induced by IL-12 [87, 89]. Neutralizing antibodies to IFN-γ removed most of the inhibitory effect of IL-12 on neovascularization in both *in vivo* and *in vitro* experiments failed to demonstrate a direct effect of IL-12 on EC growth. These findings indicated that IL-12 inhibits angiogenesis indirectly through the stimulation of IFN-γ and, at least in part, IP-10.

Taken together, these experimental findings suggest that IP-10 and its specific receptor, CXCR3, not only have a pivotal role in both inflammatory processes and angiogenesis but also provide a coordinated regulation of both processes.

Table 1. summarizes the principal mediators of angiogenesis and the stimuli that give rise to their expression. In particular, the proinflammatory cytokines and hypoxia appear to act as important stimuli for several cell populations. Furthermore, the coordinated production of these angiogenic mediators is likely to be important in the orchestration of the complex process of neovasculalization during inflammatory and immune responses.

Table 1. Angiogenic and angiostatic factors and their regulation in arthritis inflammation[1].

Mediators	Stimulation of mediator expression
Angiogenic factors	
VEGF	PDGF, TGF-β, FGF, IL-1, TNF-α, hypoxia oxygen radicals, nitric oxide, cell-cell interaction, CD40 ligation
FGF	LPS, IL-1, IL-4, TNF, GM-CSF, hypoxia
TGF-β	LPS, SAC[2]
Ang-1	TNF-α, TGF-β
Ang-2	VEGF, FGF, IL-1, TNF-α, PMA, hypoxia
IL-8	LPS, IL-1, TNF, GM-CSF, PMA, IFN-γ[3] hypoxia/reperfusion
Angiostatic factors	
IP-10	LPS, IL-1, TNF-α, IFN-γ, PMA, cell-cell interaction
Angiostatin/ endostatin	matrix metalloproteinase (MMP)

[1]Expression and regulation of mediators are differentially dependent upon specific cell population.
[2] SAC: *Staphylococcus aureus Cowan*
[3] IFN-γ differentially regulates IL-8 expression.

Role Of Angiogenesis and their Regulation During Arthritis Development Seen in RA and Experimental Arthritis

The expression and regulation of angiogenesis in RA and experimental arthritis are discussed in the following section.

VEGF

As described above, VEGF is known to play an important role in normal physiological functioning such as in the female reproductive system, as well as in pathological conditions such as diabetic retinopathy, certain tumors and RA [90-93]. Several investigations have revealed the expression of VEGF protein and its transcript in inflamed joint tissue and synovial fluids of RA [91, 92, 94]. However, it yet to be determined whether or not VEGF is directly involved in the induction and maintenance of chronic synovitis such as in RA. Recently, we demonstrated the involvement of VEGF during the evolution of experimental arthritis in our murine model for collagen-induced arthritis (CIA) [95]. An enhanced expression of VEGF that paralleled the expression of two specific VEGF receptors, Flk-1 and

Flt-1, was observed, and correlated with either the degree of neovascularization or the progression of joint disease. During arthritis development, most of the VEGF-expressing cells in the arthritic joints of CIA mice were macrophage- and fibroblast-like cells and chondrocytes, but not ECs [95]. To clarify the potential contribution of VEGF to the progression of experimental arthritis, cytokine depletion experiments were performed using a specific neutralizing antibody. Administration of rabbit polyclonal anti-VEGF antiserum to CIA mice before the onset of arthritis brought forward the onset and heightened the severity of disease, while administration after the onset of the disease had no effect on disease progression [95]. In addition, a study by Oliver et al. demonstrated that treatment of CIA rats with AGM-1470, an angiogenesis inhibitor, caused a reduction in the severity of the disease in association with a decreased expression of VEGF, but not of TNF-α[96]. Taken together with the findings of other studies [97-99], these results suggest that VEGF plays a crucial role during the early stages of arthritis development, affecting both neovascularization and the progression of experimentally-induced synovitis.

VEGF expression *in vitro* by RA synovial fibroblast-like synoviocytes (FLSs) was promoted by stimulation with IL-1 [17, 100, 101], TGF-β[101], and prostaglandin E [100]. Hypoxia also appears to be a potent inducer of VEGF expression in RA, because vascular insufficiency in the growing pannus results in hypoxia in inflamed joints [17, 30, 101-103]. In addition to these mechanisms, we have recently demonstrated the potential and interesting mechanisms by which the secretion of VEGF and expression of its mRNA can be induced in inflammatory cells involved in the evolution of RA. We have shown significant effects on VEGF expression of cell-cell interactions between synovial FLSs and leukocytes [104]. The interaction of inflammatory, activated leukocytes, including monocytes and PMNs isolated from RA synovial fluid (SF), with FLSs resulted in synergistic increases in VEGF expression and secretion, which contributed to the proliferation of endothelial cells and to *in vitro* endothelial tube formation. The induction of VEGF was mediated via specific adhesion molecules (CD11/CD18), as indicated by the finding that anti-integrin antibodies significantly inhibited this induction. Furthermore, levels of VEGF secretion were correlated with cell surface integrin (CD11b and CD18) expression on both monocytes and PMNs in the SF. In this system, it appears that substantial amounts of biologically active VEGF are also secreted from monocytes and PMNs co-cultured with FLSs. Moreover, Cho et al. recently demonstrated that engaging CD40 on RA FLSs induces VEGF expression [105]. This implies that VEGF secreted by leukocytes interacting with FLSs via specific adhesion molecules within arthritic joints, and presumably within the pannus, is critically involved in the progression of synovitis.

Recently, we demonstrated that freshly isolated rheumatoid SF PMNs contain significant amounts of cell-associated VEGF, compared with PMNs isolated from either normal or RA peripheral blood [23]. Levels of PMN-associated VEGF were correlated with levels of free VEGF in SF, integrin expression on SF PMNs, and RA disease activity. Interestingly, the steady-state transcription of a VEGF mRNA variant, primarily in the $VEGF_{121}$ form, was increased. In addition, in both the presence and absence of TNF-α, freshly isolated PMNs of RA SF secreted greater amounts of VEGF than either healthy or rheumatoid peripheral blood neutrophils. Previous studies have shown that treatment of RA patients with methotrexate or methylprednisolone pulse therapy induced a significant reduction of not only SF neutrophil numbers, but also of CD11b and CD18 expression on SF neutrophils and of the concentration of IL-1β in the SF. These findings were associated with an impressive clinical improvement of RA [106, 107], and shed new light on the possible role played by SF neutrophils in the perpetuation of inflammation in RA. As such, targeting activated neutrophils and neutrophil-derived VEGF in the synovial space may form the basis for a new therapeutic approach.

FGF-2

It has been shown that increased FGF-2 expression, in addition to other cytokines and growth factors, is evident in the rheumatoid synovium. Immunolocalization studies have demonstrated that FGF-2 expression was detected mainly in the synovium-cartilage interface where joint destruction occurred, and in hyperplastic synoviocytes of a subset of cell types in the rheumatoid synovium. Strong cytoplasmic FGF-2 staining was associated mainly with mast cells, synoviocytes and vascular cells. [108, 109]. In *in vitro* studies, FLSs obtained from patients with RA, osteoarthritis, and traumatic joint disease secrete FGF-2 as well as TGF-β[110, 111]. In turn, FGF-2 stimulates osteoclastogenesis, including osteoclast recruitment and differentiation, and bone resorption seen in RA [112]. Moreover, FGF-2 inhibits the production of osteoclastogenesis inhibitory factor (OCIF) by synovial fibroblast-like cells in a dose-dependent manner [113]. As expected, inhibition of endogenous FGF-2 via administration of neutralizing Ab attenuated the disease severity with regard to joint swelling and destruction in the rat model of antigen-induced arthritis (AIA) [114].. Increased FGF-2 in RA and experimental arthritis synovitis may significantly regulate joint inflammation, local bone resorption and remodeling through direct and indirect mechanisms that promote angiogenesis and osteoclastogenesis.

TGF-β

Using immunohistochemical techniques, TGF-β was identified in the synovial tissue and cartilage/pannus junction from patients with RA [115-117]. Furthermore, TGF-β was found predominantly in the thickened synovial lining layer in RA, but also detected in a perivascular pattern in the synovial interstitium as well as in occasional cells in lymphoid aggregates. The cells staining for TGF-β were identified as being from the monocyte/macrophage series as well as type B synovial lining cells [116]. From the results of CIA experiments, TGF-β clearly appears to be protective against the evolution of arthritis in the early phase [118]. A recent demonstration by Chernajovsky et al. indicated that infection of arthritogenic splenocytes with a retrovirus expressing TGF-β not only inhibited the development of CIA arthritis but also reduced the severity and inflammation of already established arthritis [119]. Furthermore, repeated administration of metallothionein, which can act as an antioxidant and as an immunosuppressive agent, induced the development of type II collagen-specific, TGF-producing cells to antagonize the expansion of arthritogenic cells, resulting in a dramatic arrest in overall CIA disease progression [120]. Taken together, these data show that TGF-β may act as an antiinflammatory mediator rather than an angiogenic factor during the development and maintenance of chronic inflammatory arthritis.

Angiogenic (ELR-CXC) and Angiostatic (Non-ELR-CXC) Chemokines

Chemokines are involved in leukocyte chemotaxis and migration through the endothelial barrier into the inflamed synovium. It is evident that a number of chemokines, both CXC and CC, secreted spontaneously from inflammatory cells and synoviocytes as well as upon stimulation by inflammatory agonists, can be detected in the affected joint tissue. CXC chemokines are among the most potent angiomodulating factors that may be involved in the regulation of angiogenesis in rheumatoid synovitis. As molecules for chemotactic activity, the enhanced expression and significant roles of IL-8 have been previously discussed [121-125]. Koch and colleagues found that IL-8 and ENA-78 represent major angiogenic factors in the synovium of rheumatoid arthritis [126]. They observed that both IL-8 and ENA-78 immunopositive macrophages were located in direct proximity to RA synovial blood vessels. In relation to the physiological activities of these molecules, not only IL-8, but also ENA-78 accounted for a large fraction of the chemotactic activity of ECs *in vitro* and the angiogenic activity *in vivo* found in the RA synovial tissue [126].

A recent investigation by Patel and associates demonstrated that the angiostatic CXC chemokine, IP-10, and its specific receptor, CXCR3, were expressed in the synovium in rheumatoid arthritis [127]. Consistent with previous reports, we have recently shown the expression and novel regulatory mechanisms of IP-10 in RA [128]. In this study, we clearly demonstrated that RA SF contains greater amounts of IP-10 compared to that in SF from patients with osteoarthritis. Using immunolocalization analysis, IP-10 expression was found to be associated mainly with infiltrating macrophage- and fibroblast-like cells in the RA synovium. What mechanisms regulate the expression of IP-10 in the RA synovium? To address this, we focused on the effects of interactions of FLSs with inflammatory synovial monocytes and PMNs on the expression of IP-10. Although net angiogenesis activity clearly tended towards augmentation, as described above in the section on VEGF, the interaction of activated leukocytes from RA SF with FLSs resulted in marked increases in IP-10 expression and secretion. Moreover, the induction of IP-10 was mediated via specific adhesion molecules, as indicated by the finding that either anti-integrin (CD11b and CD18) or ICAM-1 antibodies significantly inhibited the induction of IP-10. In addition, to further understand the regulatory mechanisms involved in the process of angiogenesis, IP-10 expression induced by cell-cell interaction between endothelial cells and leukocytes was investigated [129]. We found that the interaction of peripheral blood monocytes with human umbilical vein endothelial cells (HUVECs) resulted in synergistic increases in IP-10 expression and secretion, which consequently inhibited endothelial tube formation *in vitro*. IP-10 induction was mediated via specific cell surface molecules, as indicated by the finding that IP-10 secretion was significantly inhibited by anti-CD40 ligand antibody, and to a lesser extent by anti-CD40 antibody. In contrast to fibroblast-leukocyte interactions, a significant stimulatory or inhibitory effect of anti-β2 integrin (CD18) or anti-ICAM-1 Abs on IP-10 secretion was not seen in this culture system. To determine whether the augmented production of IP-10 was regulated by soluble mediators, we investigated the effect of inflammatory and immune-regulating cytokines, including IFN-γ, IL-10, and IL-1β, to modulate IP-10 secretion through endothelial cell-leukocyte interactions. Addition of IL-1, as well as IFN-γ, stimulated a marked IP-10 secretion by unstimulated monocytes, unstimulated HUVECs, and co-cultures of the two cell types. In contrast, IL-10, recognized as an anti-inflammatory cytokine, significantly inhibited IP-10 secretion by co-cultures. As described previously, IL-10 serves as a potent inhibitor of the expression of other cytokines, including IFN-γ and inflammatory cytokines [130-132], and moreover, recent studies demonstrate that IL-10 inhibits monocyte/macrophage-derived IP-10 expression via suppressing IFN secretion [133, 134], which is consistent with our results [129]. The precise mechanism of IP-10 action on the regulation of arthritis development, however, remains to be determined. As an angiostatic factor, depletion of IP-10 seems to lead to an exacerbation of the induction of experimentally induced arthritis, suggesting a protective property of IP-10. However, Salomon et al. demonstrated a promotory effect of IP-10 on adjuvant arthritis [135] which appears to be dependent upon the chemotactic activity of IP-10 acting toward Th1 polarization. Thus, it seems likely that IP-10 may differentially regulate arthritis inflammation, such as in the predominant phase of inflammatory cell migration or of neovasculalization.

In conclusion, these results suggest that IP-10 expression within inflamed joints appears to be regulated not only by inflammatory cytokines, but also by the physical interaction of activated leukocytes and both FLSs and ECs (Figure 1). Moreover, this chemokine might contribute to the migration of specific subpopulations of T-cells (Th1-type) through CXCR3 from the bloodstream into the synovial joints.

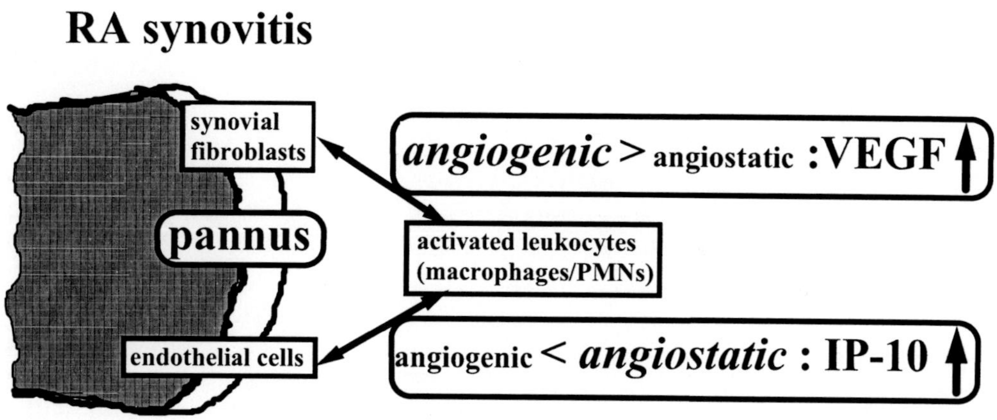

Figure 1. Proposed mechanism for the regulation of angiomodulating cytokine expression in RA synovitis.

Angiostatin and Endostatin

The effects of antagonists against angiogenic factors have been also examined. Angiostatin, a 38 kDa fragment of plasminogen [136], and endostatin, a 20 kDa fragment of the C-terminal part of the collagen XVIII chain [137], are endogenously produced and specifically target ECs, resulting in angiogenesis inhibition. Reduction of the severity of arthritis and bone erosion in CIA was seen when systematic treatment with endostatin was given [138]. In addition, the local production of angiostatin by gene transfer inhibited pannus formation and cartilage erosion, as well as neovascularization [139]. A recent study demonstrated that a regulatory imbalance resulting in the enhanced expression of angiogenic mediators (VEGF and FGF-2) rather than angiostatic mediator (endostatin) expression may contribute to the progressive pannus inflammation in RA [140]. These results suggest that angiogenesis inhibitors may provide a new, effective approach to the treatment of inflammatory arthritis, including CIA and RA.

Conclusion

Although the importance of neovascularization in immune-mediated chronic inflammatory arthritis such as RA and CIA has been clearly shown, the expression and regulation of angiogenic mediators over the course of the disease have not yet been completely resolved. Orchestration of the network between angiogenic mediators and various cytokines may be of crucial importance during the evolution of arthritis. Table 2. summarizes detectable mediators thought to regulate arthritis development. The global profile of angiogenic regulation indicates that each mediator is differentially expressed and regulated at a specific phase and site of arthritis development. Knowledge gained thus far based on the accumulation of information on the biology of angiogenesis will be important in the clinical management and development of new therapeutic strategies for treating RA.

Table II. Expression of Angiogenesis Mediators In RA and Roles In Experimental Arthritis

	Mediators	Expression in RA [Ref]	Effects on experimental arthritis[1]	[Ref]
Angiogenic factors				
	VEGF	[91, 92, 94]	CIA	↑ [95, 97-99]
	FGF	[108-110]	adjuvant-induced arthritis	↑ [114]
	TGF-β	[115-117]	CIA	↓[2] [118, 119]
	IL-8	[121, 122, 126]	antigen-induced arthritis	↑[3] [125]
Angiostatic factors				
	IP-10	[127, 128]	adjuvant-induced arthritis	↑[3] [135]
	Endostatin		CIA	↓ [138]
	Angiostatin		CIA	↓ [139]

[1] Effects of mediators on experimental arthritis are indicated as promotion (↑) or inhibition (↓).

[2] TGF-β may act as an anti-inflammatory mediator on arthritis development.

[3] Evidence for regulation of experimental arthritis may be dependent upon their chemotactic activities.

References

[1] Lee DM, ME Weinblatt. Rheumatoid arthritis. *Lancet*, 2001; 358: 903-911.
[2] Firestein GS. Evolving concepts of rheumatoid arthritis. *Nature*, 2003; 423: 356-361.

[3] Arend WP, JM Dayer. Cytokines and cytokine inhibitors or antagonists in rheumatoid arthritis. *Arthritis Rheum*, 1990; 33: 305-315.

[4] Koch AE, SL Kunkel, RM Strieter. Cytokines in rheumatoid arthritis. *J Investig Med*, 1995; 43: 28-38.

[5] Kunkel SL, NW Lukacs, T Kasama, RM Strieter. The role of chemokines in inflammatory joint disease. *J Leukoc Biol*, 1996; 58: 6-12.

[6] Folkman J, M Klagsbrum. Angiogenic factors. *Science*, 1987; 235: 442-447.

[7] Folkman J. Angiogenesis in cancer, vascular, rheumatoid and other disease. *Nat Med*, 1995; 1: 27-31.

[8] Brenchley PEC. Angiogenesis in inflammatory joint disease: a target for therapeutic intervention. *Clin Exp Immunol*, 2000; 121: 426-429.

[9] Leung DW, G Cachianes, WJ Kuang, DV Goeddel, N Ferrara. Vascular endothelial growth factor is a secreted angiogenic mitogen. *Science*, 1989; 246: 1306-1309.

[10] Keck PJ, SD Hauser, G Krivi et al. Vascular permeability factor, and endothelial cell mitogen related to PDGF. *Science*, 1989; 246: 1309-1312.

[11] Ferrara N, HP Gerber, J LeCouter. The biology of VEGF and its receptors. *Nat Med*, 2003; 9: 669-676.

[12] Zucker S, H Mirza, CE Conner et al. Vascular endothelial growth factor induces tissue factor and matrix metalloproteinase production in endothelial cells: conversion of prothrombin to thrombin results in progelatinase A activation and cell proliferation. *Int J Cancer*, 1998; 75: 780-786.

[13] Wary KK, GD Thakker, JO Humtsoe, J Yang. Analysis of VEGF-responsive Genes Involved in the activation of endothelial cells. *Mol Cancer*, 2003; 2: 25.

[14] Dvorak HF, M Detmar, KP Claffey, JA Nagy, L van de Water, DR Senger. Vascular permeability factor/vascular endothelial growth factor: An important mediator of angiogenesis in malignancy and inflammation. *Int Arch Allergy Immunol*, 1995; 107: 233-235.

[15] Sugihara T, SC Kaul, Y Mitsui, R Wadhwa. Enhanced expression of multiple forms of VEGF is associated with spontaneous immortalization of murine fibroblasts. *Biochim Biophys Acta*, 1994; 1224: 365-370.

[16] Yoshida S, M Ono, T Shono et al. Involvement of interleukin-8, vascular endothelial growth factor, and basic fibroblast growth factor in tumor necrosis factor alpha-dependent angiogenesis. *Mol Cell Biol*, 1997; 17: 4015-4023.

[17] Jackson JR, JAL Minton, ML Ho, N Wei, JD Winkler. Expression of vascular endothelial growth factor in synovial fibroblasts is induced by hypoxia and interleukin 1β. *J Rheumatol*, 1997; 24: 1253-1259.

[18] McLaren J, A Prentice, DS Charnock-Jones et al. Vascular endothelial growth factor is produced by peritoneal fluid macrophages in endometriosis and is regulated by ovarian steroids. *J Clin Invest*, 1996; 98: 482-489.

[19] Xiong M, G Elson, D Legarda, SJ Leibovich. Production of vascular endothelial growth factor by murine macrophages: Regulation by hypoxia, lactate, and the inducible nitric oxide synthase pathway. *Am J Pathol*, 1998; 153: 587-598.

[20] Maniscalco WM, RH Watkins, JN Finkelstein, MH Campbell. Vascular endothelial growth factor mRNA increases in alveolar epithelial cells during recovery from oxygen injury. *Am J Respir Cell Mol Biol*, 1995; 13: 377-386.

[21] Brogi E, T Wu, A Namiki, JM Isner. Indirect angiogenic cytokines upregulate VEGF and bFGF gene expression in vascular smooth muscle cells, whereas hypoxia upregulates VEGF expression only. *Circulation*, 1994; 90: 649-652.

[22] Taichman NS, S Young, AT Cruchley, P Taylor, E Paleolog. Human neutrophils secrete vascular endothelial growth factor. *J Leukoc Biol*, 1997; 62: 397-400.

[23] Kasama T, K Kobayashi, N Yajima et al. Expression of vascular endothelial growth factor by synovial fluid neutrophils in rheumatoid arthritis. *Clin Exp Immunol*, 2000; 121: 533-538.

[24] Gerber H-P, TH Vu, AM Ryan, J Kowalski, Z Werb, N Ferrara. VEGF couples hypertrophic cartilage remodeling, ossification and angiogenesis during endochondral bone formation. *Nat Med*, 1999; 5: 623-628.

[25] Finkenzeller G, D Marme, HA Weich, H Hug. Platelet-derived growth factor-induced transcription of the vascular endothelial growth factor gene is mediated by protein kinese C. *Cancer Res*, 1992; 52: 4821-4823.

[26] Pertovaar L, A Kaipainen, T Mustonen et al. Vascular endothelial growth factor is induced in response to transforming growth factor-beta in fibroblastic and epithelial cells. *J Biol Chem*, 1994; 269: 6271-6274.

[27] Brauchle M, JO Funk, P Kind, S Werner. Ultraviolet B and H2O2 are potent inducers of vascular endothelial growth factor expression in cultured keratinocytes. *J Biol Chem,* 1996; 271: 21793-21797.

[28] Tuder RM, BE Flook, NF Voelkel. Increased gene expression for VEGF and the VEGF receptors KDR/Flk and Flt in lungs exposed to acute or to chronic hypoxia-modulation of gene expression by nitric oxide. *J Clin Invest*, 1995; 95: 1798-1807.

[29] Dembinskakiec A, J Dulak, L Partyka, I Huk, T Mailnski. VEGF-nitric oxide reciprocal regulation. *Nat Med*, 1997; 3: 1177-1177.

[30] Shweiki D, A Itin, D Soffer, E Keshet. Vascular endothelial growth factor induced by hypoxia may mediate hypoxia-initiated angiogenesis. *Nature,* 1992; 359: 843-845.

[31] Neufeld G, T Cohen, S Gengrinovitch, Z Poltorak. Vascular endothelial growth factor (VEGF) and its receptors. *FASEB J*, 1999; 13: 9-22.

[32] Brown LF, B Berse, K Tognazzi et al. Vascular permeability factor mRNA and protein expression in human kidney. *Kidney Int*, 1992; 42: 1457-1461.

[33] Barleon B, S Sozzani, D Zhou, HA Weich, A Mantovani, D Marmé. Migration of human monocytes in response to vascular endothelial growth factor (VEGF) is mediated via VEGF receptor flt-1. *Blood*, 1996; 87: 3336-3343.

[34] Hewett PW, JC Murray. Coexpression of flt-1, flt-4 and KDR in freshly isolated and cultured human endothelial cells. *Biochem Biophys Res Commun*, 1996; 221: 697-702.

[35] Gabrilovich DI, HL Chen, KR Girgis et al. Production of vascular endothelial growth factor by human tumors inhibits the functional maturation of dendritic cells. *Nat Med*, 1996; 2: 1096-1103.

[36] Clauss M, M Gerlach, H Gerlach et al. Vascular permeability factor: A tumor-derived polypeptide that induces endothelial cell and monocyte procoagulant activity, and promotes monocyte migration. *J Exp Med*, 1990; 172: 1535-1545.

[37] Klein S, M Roghani, DB Rifkin. Fibroblast growth factors as angiogenesis factors: new insights into their mechanism of action. *Exs,* 1997; 79: 159-192.

[38] Shing Y, J Folkman, R Sullivan, C Butterfield, J Murray, M Klagsbrun. Heparin affinity: purification of a tumor-derived capillary endothelial cell growth factor. *Science,* 1984; 223: 1296-1299.

[39] Pepper MS, N Ferrara, L Orci, R Montesano. Potent synergism between vascular endothelial growth factor and basic fibroblast growth factor in the induction of angiogenesis in vitro. *Biochem Biophys Res Commun*, 1992; 189: 824-831.

[40] Stavri GT, IC Zachary, PA Baskerville, JF Martin, JD Erusalimsky. Basic fibroblast growth factor upregulates the expression of vascular endothelial growth factor in vascular smooth muscle cells. Synergistic interaction with hypoxia. *Circulation,* 1995; 92: 11-14.

[41] Pepper MS. Transforming growth factor-beta: vasculogenesis, angiogenesis, and vessel wall integrity. *Cytokine Growth Factor Rev*, 1997; 8: 21-43.

[42] Sporn MB, AB Roberts. Transforming growth factor-b: Recent progress and new challenges. *J Cell Biol*, 1992; 119: 1017-1021.

[43] Roberts AB, MB Sporn, RK Assoian et al. Transforming growth factor type beta: rapid induction of fibrosis and angiogenesis in vivo and stimulation of collagen formation in vitro. *Proc Natl Acad Sci U S A*, 1986; 83: 4167-4171.

[44] Merwin JR, W Newman, LD Beall, A Tucker, J Madri. Vascular cells respond differentially to transforming growth factors beta 1 and beta 2 in vitro. *Am J Pathol*, 1991; 138: 37-51.

[45] Iruela-Arispe ML, EH Sage. Endothelial cells exhibiting angiogenesis in vitro proliferate in response to TGF-beta 1. *J Cell Biochem*, 1993; 52: 414-430.

[46] Mandriota SJ, PA Menoud, MS Pepper. Transforming growth factor beta 1 down-regulates vascular endothelial growth factor receptor 2/flk-1 expression in vascular endothelial cells. *J Biol Chem*, 1996; 271: 11500-11505.

[47] Sanchez-Elsner T, LM Botella, B Velasco, A Corbi, L Attisano, C Bernabeu. Synergistic cooperation between hypoxia and transforming growth factor-beta pathways on human vascular endothelial growth factor gene expression. *J Biol Chem*, 2001; 276: 38527-38535.

[48] Hayes AJ, WQ Huang, J Mallah, D Yang, ME Lippman, LY Li. Angiopoietin-1 and its receptor Tie-2 participate in the regulation of capillary-like tubule formation and survival of endothelial cells. *Microvasc Res*, 1999; 58: 224-237.

[49] Polverini PJ. Angiogenesis in health and disease: insights into basic mechanisms and therapeutic opportunities. *J Dent Educ*, 2002; 66: 962-975.

[50] Ahmad SA, W Liu, YD Jung et al. The effects of angiopoietin-1 and -2 on tumor growth and angiogenesis in human colon cancer. *Cancer Res*, 2001; 61: 1255-1259.

[51] Hu B, P Guo, Q Fang et al. Angiopoietin-2 induces human glioma invasion through the activation of matrix metalloprotease-2. *Proc Natl Acad Sci U S A*, 2003; 100: 8904-8909.

[52] Gale NW, GD Yancopoulos. Growth factors acting via endothelial cell-specific receptor tyrosine kinases: VEGFs, angiopoietins, and ephrins in vascular development. *Genes Dev*, 1999; 13: 1055-1066.

[53] Yancopoulos GD, S Davis, NW Gale, JS Rudge, SJ Wiegand, J Holash. Vascular-specific growth factors and blood vessel formation. *Nature,* 2000; 407: 242-248.

[54] Mandriota SJ, MS Pepper. Regulation of angiopoietin-2 mRNA levels in bovine microvascular endothelial cells by cytokines and hypoxia. *Circ Res*, 1998; 83: 852-859.

[55] Oh H, H Takagi, K Suzuma, A Otani, M Matsumura, Y Honda. Hypoxia and Vascular Endothelial Growth Factor Selectively Up-regulate Angiopoietin-2 in Bovine Microvascular Endothelial Cells. *J Biol Chem*, 1999; 274: 15732-15739.

[56] Krikun G, F Schatz, T Finlay et al. Expression of angiopoietin-2 by human endometrial endothelial cells: regulation by hypoxia and inflammation. *Biochem Biophys Res Commun*, 2000; 275: 159-183.

[57] Willam C, P Koehne, JS Jurgensen et al. Tie2 receptor expression is stimulated by hypoxia and proinflammatory cytokines in human endothelial cells. *Circ Res*, 2000; 87: 370-377.

[58] Yabkowitz R, S Meyer, T Black, G Elliott, LA Merewether, HK Yamane. Inflammatory cytokines and vascular endothelial growth factor stimulate the release of soluble Tie receptor from human endothelial cells via metalloprotease activation. *Blood*, 1999; 93: 1969-1979.

[59] Maisonpierre PC, C Suri, PF Jones et al. Angiopoietin-2, a natural antagonist for Tie2 that disrupts in vivo angiogenesis. *Science*, 1997; 277: 55-60.

[60] Marron MB, DP Hughes, MD Edge, CI Forder, NP Brindle. Evidence for heterotypic interaction between the receptor tyrosine kinases TIE-1 and TIE-2. *J Biol Chem*, 2000; 275: 39741-39746.

[61] Luster AD. Chemokines--chemotactic cytokines that mediate inflammation. *N Engl J Med*, 1998; 338: 436-445.

[62] Zlotnik A, J Morales, JA Hedrick. Recent advances in chemokines and chemokine receptors. *Crit Rev Immunol*, 1999; 19: 1-47.

[63] Mackay CR. Chemokines: immunology's high impact factors. *Nat Immunol*, 2001; 2: 95-101.

[64] Romagnani P, L Lasagni, F Annunziato, M Serio, S Romagnani. CXC chemokines: the regulatory link between inflammation and angiogenesis. *Trends Immunol*, 2004; 25: 201-209.

[65] Strieter RM, PJ Polverini, SL Kunkel et al. The functional role of the ELR motif in CXC chemokine-mediated angiogenesis. *J Biol Chem*, 1995; 270: 27348-27357.

[66] Strieter RM, SL Kunkel, HJ Showell et al. Endothelial cell gene expression of a neutrophil chemotactic factor by TNF-α, LPS, and IL-1ß. *Science,* 1989; 243: 1467-1469.

[67] Heidemann J, H Ogawa, MB Dwinell et al. Angiogenic effects of interleukin 8 (CXCL8) in human intestinal microvascular endothelial cells are mediated by CXCR2. *J Biol Chem,* 2003; 278: 8508-8515.

[68] Koch AE, PJ Polverini, SL Kunkel et al. Interleukin-8 as a macrophage-derived mediator of angiogenesis. *Science*, 1992; 258: 1798-1801.

[69] Strieter RM, SL Kunkel, VM Elner et al. Interleukin-8. A corneal factor that induces neovascularization. *Am J Pathol*, 1992; 141: 1279-1284.

[70] Luster AD, JV Ravetch. Biochemical characterization of a g interferon-inducible cytokine (IP-10). *J Exp Med*, 1987; 166: 1084-1097.

[71] Angiolillo AL, C Sgadari, DD Taub et al. Human interferon-inducible protein 10 is a potent inhibitor of angiogenesis in vivo. *J Exp Med*, 1995; 182: 155-162.

[72] Strieter RM, SL Kunkel, DA Arenberg, MD Burdick, PJ Polverini. Interferon gamma-inducible protein 10 (IP-10), a member of the C-X-C chemokine family, is an inhibitor of angiogenesis. *Biochem Biophys Res Commun*, 1995; 210: 51-57.

[73] Arenberg DA, SL Kunkel, PJ Polverini et al. Interferon-gamma-inducible protein 10 (IP-10) is an angiostatic factor that inhibits human non-small cell lung cancer (NSCLC) tumorigenesis and spontaneous metastases. *J Exp Med*, 1996; 184: 981-992.

[74] Tannenbaum CS, R Tubbs, D Armstrong, JH Finke, RM Bukowski, TA Hamilton. The CXC chemokines IP-10 and Mig are necessary for IL-12-mediated regression of the mouse RENCA tumor. *J Immunol*, 1998; 161: 927-932.

[75] Luster AD, SM Greenberg, P Leder. The IP-10 chemokine binds to a specific cell surface heparan sulfate site shared with platelet factor 4 and inhibits endothelial cell proliferation. *J Exp Med*, 1995; 182: 219-231.

[76] Grant DS, KI Tashiro, B Segui-Real, Y Yamada, GR Martin, HK Kleinman. Two different laminin domains mediate the differentiation of human endothelial cells into capillary-like structures. *Cell*, 1989; 58: 933-943.

[77] Lasagni L, M Francalanci, F Annunziato et al. An alternatively spliced variant of CXCR3 mediates the inhibition of endothelial cell growth induced by IP-10, Mig, and I-TAC, and acts as functional receptor for platelet factor 4. *J Exp Med*, 2003; 197: 1537-1549.

[78] Mosmann TR, RL Coffman. TH1 and TH2 cells: Different patterns of lymphokine secretion lead to different functional properties. Annu Rev Immunol, 1989; 7: 145-173.

[79] Gor DO, NR Rose, NS Greenspan. TH1-TH2: a procrustean paradigm. *Nat Immunol*, 2003; 4: 503-505.

[80] Murphy KM, SL Reiner. The lineage decisions of helper T cells. *Nat Rev Immunol*, 2002; 2: 933-944.

[81] Miossec P, W van den Berg. Th1/Th2 cytokine balance in arthritis. *Arthritis Rheum*, 1997; 40: 2105-2115.

[82] Canete JD, SE Martinez, J Farres et al. Differential Th1/Th2 cytokine patterns in chronic arthritis: interferon gamma is highly expressed in synovium of rheumatoid arthritis compared with seronegative spondyloarthropathies. *Ann Rheum Dis*, 2000; 59: 263-268.

[83] Akahoshi M, H Nakashima, Y Tanaka et al. Th1/Th2 balance of peripheral T helper cells in systemic lupus erythematosus. *Arthritis Rheum*, 1999; 42: 1644-1648.

[84] Lukacs NW. Role of chemokines in the pathogenesis of asthma. *Nat Rev Immunol*, 2001; 1: 108-116.

[85] Sallusto F, D Lenig, CR Mackay, A Lanzavecchia. Flexible programs of chemokine receptor expression on human polarized T helper 1 and 2 lymphocytes. *J Exp Med*, 1998; 187: 875-883.

[86] Rossi D, A Zlotnik. The biology of chemokines and their receptors. *Annu Rev Immunol*, 2000; 18: 217-242.

[87] Angiolillo AL, C Sgadari, G Tosato. A role for the interferon-inducible protein 10 in inhibition of angiogenesis by interleukin-12. *Ann N Y Acad Sci*, 1996; 795: 158-167.

[88] Trinchieri G. Interleukin-12: A cytokine at the interface of inflammation and immunity. *Adv Immunol*, 1998; 70: 83-243.

[89] Sgadari C, AL Angiolillo, G Tosato. Inhibition of angiogenesis by interleukin-12 is mediated by the interferon-inducible protein 10. *Blood*, 1996; 87: 3877-3882.

[90] Ferrara N, K Houck, L Jakeman, DW Leung. Molecular and biological properties of vascular endothelial growth factor family of proteins. *Endocr Rev*, 1992; 13: 18-32.

[91] Fava RA, NJ Olsen, G Spencer-Green et al. Vascular permeability factor/endothelial growth factor (VPF/VEGF): Accumulation and expression in human synovial fluids and rheumatoid synovial tissue. *J Exp Med*, 1994; 180: 341-346.

[92] Koch AE, LA Harlow, GK Haines et al. Vascular endothelial growth factor. A cytokine modulating endothelial function in rheumatoid arthritis. *J Immunol*, 1994; 152: 4149-4156.

[93] Dvorak HF, LF Brown, M Detmar, AM Dvorak. Vascular permeability factor/vascular endothelial growth factor, microvascular hyperpermeability, and angiogenesis. *Am J Pathol,* 1995; 146: 1029-1039.

[94] Nagashima M, S Yoshino, T Ishikawa, G Asano. Role of vascular endothelial growth factor in angiogenesis of rheumatoid arthritis. *J Rheumatol*, 1995; 22: 1624-1630.

[95] Lu J, T Kasama, K Kobayashi et al. Vascular endothelial growth factor expression and regulation of murine collagen-induced arthritis. *J Immunol*, 2000; 164: 5922-5927.

[96] Oliver SJ, TP Cheng, ML Banquerigo, E Brahn. Suppression of collagen-induced arthritis by an angiogenesis inhibitor, AGM-1470, in combination with cyclosporin: reduction of vascular endothelial growth factor (VEGF). *Cell Immunol*, 1995; 166: 196-206.

[97] Miotla J, R Maciewicz, J Kendrew, M Feldmann, E Paleolog. Treatment with soluble VEGF receptor reduces disease severity in murine collagen-induced arthritis. *Lab Invest,* 2000; 80: 1195-1205.

[98] Sone H, Y Kawakami, M Sakauchi et al. Neutralization of vascular endothelial growth factor prevents collagen-induced arthritis and ameliorates established disease in mice. *Biochem Biophys Res Commun*, 2001; 281: 562-568.

[99] Etherington PJ, P Winlove, P Taylor, E Paleolog, JM Miotla. VEGF release is associated with reduced oxygen tensions in experimental inflammatory arthritis. *Clin Exp Rheumatol*, 2002; 20: 799-805.

[100] Ben-Av P, LJ Crofford, RL Wilder, T Hla. Induction of vascular endothelial growth factor expression in synovial fibroblasts by prostaglandin E and interleukin-1: a potential mechanism for inflammatory angiogenesis. *FEBS Lett*, 1995; 372: 83-87.

[101] Berse B, JA Hunt, RJ Diegel et al. Hypoxia augments cytokine (transforming growth factor-beta (TGF-beta) and IL-1)-induced vascular endothelial growth factor secretion by human synovial fibroblasts. *Clin Exp Immunol*, 1999; 115: 176-182.

[102] Levick JR. Hypoxia and acidosis in chronic inflammatory arthritis; relation to vascular supply and dynamic effusion pressure. *J Rheumatol*, 1990; 17: 579-582.

[103] Namiki A, E Brogi, M Kearney et al. Hypoxia induces vascular endothelial growth factor in cultured human endothelial cells. *J Biol Chem*, 1995; 270: 31189-31195.

[104] Kasama T, F Shiozawa, K Kobayashi et al. Vascular endothelial growth factor expression by activated synovial leukocytes in rheumatoid arthritis. Critical involvement of the interaction with synovial fibroblasts. *Arthritis Rheum*, 2001; 44: 2512-2524.

[105] Cho C, M Cho, S Min et al. CD40 engagement on synovial fibroblast up-regulates production of vascular endothelial growth factor. *J Immunol*, 2000; 164: 5055-5061.

[106] Thomas R, GJ Carroll. Reduction of leukocyte and interleukin-1β concentrations in the synovial fluid of rheumatoid arthritis patients treated with methotrexate. *Arthritis Rheum,* 1993; 36: 1244-1252.

[107] Youssef P, P Roberts-Thomson, M Ahern, M Smith. Pulse methylprednisolone in rheumatoid arthritis: Effects on peripheral blood and synovial fluid neutrophil surface phenotype. *J Rheumatol*, 1995; 22: 2065-2071.

[108] Nakashima M, K Eguchi, T Aoyagi et al. Expression of basic fibroblast growth factor in synovial tissues from patients with rheumatoid arthritis: detection by immunohistological staining and in situ hybridisation. *Ann Rheum Dis*, 1994; 53: 45-50.

[109] Qu Z, XN Huang, P Ahmadi et al. Expression of basic fibroblast growth factor in synovial tissue from patients with rheumatoid arthritis and degenerative joint disease. *Lab Invest*, 1995; 73: 339-346.

[110] Melnyk VO, GD Shipley, MD Sternfeld, L Sherman, JT Rosenbaum. Synoviocytes synthesize, bind, and respond to basic fibroblast growth factor. *Arthritis Rheum*, 1990; 33: 493-500.

[111] Bucala R, C Ritchlin, R Winchester, A Cerami. Constitutive production of inflammatory and mitogenic cytokines by rheumatoid synovial fibroblasts. *J Exp Med*, 1991; 173: 569-574.

[112] Collin-Osdoby P, L Rothe, S Bekker, F Anderson, Y Huang, P Osdoby. Basic fibroblast growth factor stimulates osteoclast recruitment, development, and bone pit resorption in association with angiogenesis in vivo on the chick chorioallantoic membrane and activates isolated avian osteoclast resorption in vitro. *J Bone Miner Res*, 2002; 17: 1859-1871.

[113] Yano K, N Nakagawa, H Yasuda, E Tsuda, K Higashio. Synovial cells from a patient with rheumatoid arthritis produce osteoclastogenesis inhibitory factor/osteoprotegerin: reciprocal regulation of the production by inflammatory cytokines and basic fibroblast growth factor. *J Bone Miner Metab*, 2001; 19: 365-372.

[114] Yamashita A, Y Yonemitsu, S Okano et al. Fibroblast growth factor-2 determines severity of joint disease in adjuvant-induced arthritis in rats. *J Immunol*, 2002; 168: 450-457.

[115] Miossec P, M Naviliat, AD Dangeac, J Sany, J Banchereau. Low levels of interleukin-4 and high levels of transforming growth factor-beta in rheumatoid synovitis. *Arthritis Rheum,* 1990; 33: 1180-1187.

[116] Chu CQ, M Field, E Abney et al. Transforming growth factor-beta 1 in rheumatoid synovial membrane and cartilage/pannus junction. *Clin Exp Immunol*, 1991; 86: 380-386.

[117] Taketazu F, M Kato, A Gobl et al. Enhanced expression of transforming growth factor-βs and transforming growth factor-β type II receptor in the synovial tissues of patients with rheumatoid arthritis. *Lab Invest*, 1994; 70: 620-630.

[118] Thorbecke GJ, R Shah, CH Leu, AP Kuruvilla, AM Hardison, MA Palladino. Involvement of endogenous tumor necrosis factor alpha and transforming growth factor beta during induction of collagen type II arthritis in mice. *Proc Natl Acad Sci USA,* 1992; 89: 7375-7379.

[119] Chernajovsky Y, G Adams, K Triantaphyllopoulos, MF Ledda, OL Podhajcer. Pathogenic lymphoid cells engineered to express TGF beta 1 ameliorate disease in a collagen-induced arthritis model. *Gene Ther*, 1997; 4: 553-559.

[120] Youn J, SH Hwang, ZY Ryoo et al. Metallothionein suppresses collagen-induced arthritis via induction of TGF-beta and down-regulation of proinflammatory mediators. *Clin Exp Immunol*, 2002; 129: 232-239.

[121] Seitz M, B Dewald, N Gerber, M Baggiolin. Enhanced production of neutrophil-activating peptide-1/interleukin-8 in rheumatoid arthritis. *J Clin Invest*, 1991; 87: 463-469.

[122] Koch AE, SL Kunkel, JC Burrows et al. Synovial tissue macrophage as a source of the chemotactic cytokine IL-8. *J Immunol*, 1991; 147: 2187-2195.

[123] Gerard C, BJ Rollins. Chemokines and disease. *Nat Immunol*, 2001; 2: 108-115.

[124] Bodolay E, AE Koch, J Kim, G Szegedi, Z Szekanecz. Angiogenesis and chemokines in rheumatoid arthritis and other systemic inflammatory rheumatic diseases. *J Cell Mol Med*, 2002; 6: 357-376.

[125] Podolin PL, BJ Bolognese, JJ Foley et al. A potent and selective nonpeptide antagonist of CXCR2 inhibits acute and chronic models of arthritis in the rabbit. *J Immunol*, 2002; 169: 6435-6444.

[126] Koch AE, MV Volin, JM Woods et al. Regulation of angiogenesis by the C-X-C chemokines interleukin-8 and epithelial neutrophil activating peptide 78 in the rheumatoid joint. *Arthritis Rheum*, 2001; 44: 31-40.

[127] Patel DD, JP Zachariah, LP Whichard. CXCR3 and CCR5 ligands in rheumatoid arthritis synovium. *Clin Immunol*, 2001; 98: 39-45.

[128] Hanaoka R, T Kasama, M Muramatsu et al. A novel mechanism for the regulation of interferon-gamma inducible protein 10 (IP-10) expression in rheumatoid arthritis. *Arthritis Res Ther* , 2003; 5: R74-81.

[129] Kasama T, M Muramatsu, K Kobayashi et al. Interaction of monocytes with vascular endothelial cells synergistically induces interferon g-inducible protein 10 expression through activation of specific cell surface molecules and cytokines. *Cell Immunol*, 2002; 219: 131-139.

[130] De Waal Malefyt R, J Abrams, B Bennett, CG Figdor, JE de Vries. Interleukin 10 (IL-10) inhibits cytokine synthesis by human monocytes: An autoregulatory role of IL-10 produced by monocytes. *J Exp Med*, 1991; 174: 1209-1220.

[131] De Waal Malefyt R, H Yssel, M-G Roncarolo, H Spits, JE de Vries. Interleukin-10. *Curr Opinion Immunol*, 1992; 4: 314-320.

[132] Paul WE, RA Seder. Lymphocyte responses and cytokines. *Cell*, 1994; 76: 241-251.

[133] Tebo JM, HS Kim, J Gao, DA Armstrong, TA Hamilton. Interleukin-10 suppresses IP-10 gene transcription by inhibiting the production of class I interferon. *Blood*, 1998; 92: 4742-4749.

[134] Ito S, P Ansari, M Sakatsume et al. Interleukin-10 inhibits expression of both interferon a-and interferon g-induced genes by suppressing tyrosine phospharylation of STAT1. *Blood*, 1999; 93: 1456-1463.

[135] Salomon I, N Netzer, G Wildbaum, S Schif-Zuck, G Maor, N Karin. Targeting the function of IFN-gamma-inducible protein 10 suppresses ongoing adjuvant arthritis. *J Immunol*, 2002; 169: 2685-2693.

[136] O'Reilly MS, L Holmgren, Y Shing et al. Angiostatin: a novel angiogenesis inhibitor that mediates the suppression of metastases by a Lewis lung carcinoma. *Cell,* 1994; 79: 315-328.

[137] O'Reilly MS, T Boehm, Y Shing et al. Endostatin: an endogenous inhibitor of angiogenesis and tumor growth. *Cell*, 1997; 88: 277-285.

[138] Kurosaka D, K Yoshida, J Yasuda et al. Inhibition of arthritis by systemic administration of endostatin in passive murine collagen induced arthritis. *Ann Rheum Dis*, 2003; 62: 677-679.

[139] Kim JM, SH Ho, EJ Park et al. Angiostatin gene transfer as an effective treatment strategy in murine collagen-induced arthritis. *Arthritis Rheum*, 2002; 46: 793-801.

[140] Nagashima M, G Asano, S Yoshino. Imbalance in production between vascular endothelial growth factor and endostatin in patients with rheumatoid arthritis. *J Rheumatol,* 2000; 27: 2339-2342.

Index

A

B

L

M

N

O

P

V

W